GROUP PSYCHOTHERAPIES
FOR CHILDREN

GROUP PSYCHOTHERAPIES
FOR CHILDREN
A Textbook

S. R. Slavson
Mortimer Schiffer

INTERNATIONAL UNIVERSITIES PRESS, INC.
NEW YORK

Library of Congress Cataloging in Publication Data

Slavson, Samuel Richard, 1890-
  Group psychotherapies for children.

  1. Group psychotherapy. 2. Child psychotherapy. I. Schiffer, Mortimer, joint author. II. Title. [DNLM: 1. Psychotherapy, Group—In infancy and childhood. WM430 S631g]
RJ505.G7S55   618.9'28'915   74-23272
ISBN 0-8236-6463-5

Second Printing, 1975

Manufactured in the United States of America

Contents

v

CONTENTS

CONTENTS

CONTENTS

Introduction

The experiences of four decades with many thousands of children in a great number of groups of different modalities and in different situations are described in this volume. When conducted by qualified therapists, group psychotherapy for children has proved almost unfailingly successful in the United States and in many other nations in Europe, Asia, Africa—and to a more limited extent in Australia and New Zealand. Clinical findings indicate that group psychotherapy should be an integral part of all programs of psychological therapy for child patients. Where it is not included, effective treatment of certain diagnostic types of emotional and physical disorders is rendered difficult, if not altogether impossible.

We attempt a detailed presentation of theories and practices, especially the latter, of group psychotherapy with children, giving emphasis to the following aims and characteristics of the various types of treatment groups:

1. Basic principles and concepts and their relation to child psychotherapy generally.

2. Common elements and differences in group therapies of children.

3. Specific criteria concerning diagnoses and choice of treatments as they are related to the psychobiologic nature of child development and its aberrations.

4. The critical elements in group psychotherapy: the proper selection and grouping of patients and group balance, especially in activity group therapy.

5. The significant influences in group treatment of the physical setting and psychological climate.

6. Differences in the therapist's roles and techniques in the various group treatment modalities.

7. Therapeutic group methods in elementary schools and in corrective residential settings, and the unique problems encountered in these settings.

8. Numerous other related elements.

Protocols from actual treatment groups and condensed case histories are presented to illustrate major elements of the various children's groups.

Emotional problems of children vary, and different modalities are therefore essential in dealing with them. The methods of group treatment described in this volume, in their order of presentation, are activity group therapy (AGT), activity-interview group psychotherapy (A-IGP), play group therapy (PGT), the therapeutic play group (TGP) in schools, and transitional groups. The largest portion is devoted to activity group therapy (AGT). Introduced in 1934, it was the first method of group treatment. Used for some years with children and later extended to adolescents and adults, AGT was the forerunner of "group psychotherapy" as it is known today. The basic book of AGT was published many years ago.[1] The present volume sets forth broader formulations based on extended experiences, innumerable studies, and massive research of the dynamics that led to elaborations of theory and experience.

Attention is focused on AGT, not because it was the progenitor of other methods, but for definitive, psychologic considerations that recommended it as the treatment of choice for the largest number of emotional disorders of latency-age children. In primary behavior and character disorders, AGT is specifically indicated as the *exclusive* method. In children with other types of problems AGT is a valuable and often essential adjunctive treatment supplementing individual therapy. AGT has also proved helpful as a preparatory experience for some resistive or intractable children who become accessible to individual therapy through the group experience. In other cases, it is indicated as a tapering-off form before terminating individual therapy to test children as to their ability in human relations and in dealing with freedom constructively.

The avoidance of verbal interpretations in AGT should not be construed as a rejection of the principles of analytical psychology. In fact, AGT, as well as the other methods of group therapy de-

---

[1]*An Introduction to Group Therapy* (Slavson, 1945) can be read with profit in conjunction with this volume.

scribed in this volume, has its roots in the basic Freudian psycho-analytic tenets. AGT differs from the psychoanalytic therapies in methodology, not in its psychologic rationale. The youth of the patients and the nature of their mental structure and emotional problems preclude the use of strictly psychoanalytical procedures. The omission of interpretation in activity groups in no way lessens the analytic therapeutic dynamics, nor does it spare the therapist by simplifying his functions. Rather, despite his essentially *passive* role, it makes it all the more mandatory that he be alert and sensitive to the feeling tones and latent meanings of behavior and remarks of children as well as to his own conscious and sub-liminal feelings.

To facilitate the theoretical formulations of AGT, the authors felt that theoretical statements would be made more tangibly relevant for readers and students without first-hand experience in this type of therapy after they knew what actually transpires in an activity therapy group. The volume therefore opens with the full protocol of a session of a boys' group without comments or interpretations. They are reserved until after the student has established a frame of reference and has understood the rationale for the untrammeled freedom of the patients and the therapist's unvarying, rather unorthodox conduct (Chapters IX and X).

Parts II and III are concerned with analytical methods of group therapy with children, where the therapist actively partici-pates by comment, inquiry, explanation, and interpretation of patients' and groups' handicrafts, play, and verbal productions and behavior.

Part IV concerns the use of a tested group treatment method, the therapeutic play group, with young emotionally disturbed children in public elementary schools. This method has been employed with much success for more than two decades in a considerable number of schools in New York City.

The traditional urban schools are justifiably being exposed to a variety of critical evaluations, not only in terms of their viability as instruments for social and educational changes, but also because of their failure to maintain physical and emotional health of children, especially now when we can no longer rely on community-based voluntary mental health resources alone. In their present state these agencies cannot meet the needs of the extraordinarily large numbers and varieties of youngsters with difficulties.

Hospitals and child guidance agencies of various types, which have been relied upon in the past to deal with problems of families and individuals, barely scratch the surface. There is a burgeoning need for services to provide in a more realistic fashion for the needs of distressingly large numbers of disturbed youngsters who will *otherwise not receive any help whatsoever*. The schools, the locus of the child's world in which he spends much of his life during many of his formative years, are uniquely qualified to diminish, and in many instances correct, malformations in their pupils, increasing their happiness and preventing educational and personality handicaps that work to their detriment and that of the world in which they are to live as adults. Furthermore, the developmental problems of children need to be identified early, and corrective rehabilitative procedures mobilized before puberty and adolescence solidify them into pathological permanence.

In this volume, the authors have laid particular emphasis upon the pragmatic details of practice. Such details as arrangement of and equipment of rooms, safety precautions, and the conduct of therapists have received microscopic attention. Theory, which is extant in the literature, has been employed here only to the degree that it illuminates these details. There is a great discrepancy in the world of science between knowing *what* to do and *how* to do it. This volume is designed to help close the gap.

The dynamics of our group therapies are acceptance of, and respect for, the individuality of the patient; emergence of transference feelings, free verbal and action association, self-reliance, experimentation in social relations, spontaneous behavior modification and varying degrees of derivative or direct insight. Of even greater significance, however, is the climate of freedom of choice and individual decision making.

Decades after the initiation of AGT, various types of "ego therapy" have made their appearance in the treatment of adults. Among these can be included reality therapy, aversive therapy, behavior modification, rational-emotive and a host of other "innovative" techniques generally predicated on reconditioning behavior through reinforcement of desirable and discouragement of negative behavior, i.e., by the application of "learning theory."

The major among these newer techniques for the treatment of both children and adults are subsumed in what are known as encounter groups. Their climate is basically authoritarian insofar as it is planned and controlled: the patients (or educands) are manipulated (and in some instances instructed) to perform certain tasks or to respond in definite ways which, it is assumed, will lead to desirable outcomes. Many of these modalities are implicit in AGT. In AGT they do not, however, abrogate spontaneity in patients' self-generated inner growth and progressive maturation as is the case in the derivative procedures where change cannot help but be temporary and evanescent, analogous to "transference cure" in psychoanalysis. Authoritarian procedures cannot dissolve the pathological structure of the personality or effectively repair the ego. Only self-generating and self-directing participation by patients can yield such outcomes. In such a plan of therapy, free acting out by group members subjects the therapist to considerable strain and frustrations, and his sensibilities are assailed by their intractable aggression, causing him to feel emotionally drained and fatigued, especially during the learning period of his practice.

Though this may not be the therapist's or the educator's conscious intent, the rewards gained via direct conditioning have, to a considerable extent, the characteristics of bribe or punishment, and lack the potentials to effect substantive, lasting improvements in character and personality. The procedures outlined in this volume eschew such mechanical conditioning and all manipulation. Instead, we await the patients' *readiness* and *preferences* in specially designed settings for gradual, automatic internalization of benign feelings, attitudes, values, and conduct.

It is significant that many of the therapeutic dynamics presented in this volume had not been recognized by us at the outset of our work in 1934. They were introduced intuitively and did not surface into cognition until much later—some of them decades later. The perceptive student will recognize the inherent presence of some of these basic assumptions and practices in AGT as well as in the other modalities presented here, and the basics that emerge spontaneously from freedom in behavior and interpersonal interaction. Their effect on personality integration, maturity, and growth are adequately demonstrated in the pages of this volume. In our procedures patients are not manipulated or directed to perform specific tasks or respond in specific patterns that purportedly lead to better mental health, for under these circumstances behavior patterns and social responses cannot be learned as they were initially in early childhood. Above all, effective therapy requires that patients be engaged in the process of deconditioning and reconditioning themselves. They are not animals in training. In humans, unlike other animals, willingness has to be enlisted. And this can best be achieved through freedom and love.

The authors are indebted to those whose words are referred to in the text, to Mrs. Irene Azarian of International Universities Press, for her many fruitful suggestions during the preparation of the manuscript, to Mrs. Susan Sexton for her painstaking editorial work, and to Mrs. Esther Schiffer for her patient and painstaking secretarial assistance in the preparation of this volume.

S. R. Slavson
Mortimer Schiffer

New York
November, 1974

PART I

Activity Group Therapy

I

Protocol of an Activity Group Therapy Session

The following is a protocol record of the fourteenth session of a boys' activity group.[1] It was selected because it is a suitable documentation of a group session characteristic of activity group therapy (AGT) in the early stages. The therapist's function inherent to his *neutral* role and *permissiveness* and some of the major group dynamics, as well as a detailed analysis of the protocol (see Chapter IX), are delineated in detail in following chapters. Here it must be noted, however, that in dealing with the episodes, the therapist carefully discriminates between the therapeutic needs of the individual children and modifies his behavior in keeping with these considerations.

In one instance, for example, he immediately leaves his own work to assist one of the boys. By contrast, he leaves the vicinity of a boy who needlessly seeks his protection and support by settling in his proximity; he persistently avoids interfering in the aggressive play of the boys, though requested to do so by a fearful member. He is, however, seen in a generally helpful role, still maintaining the necessary separation from an overdependent, demanding youngster. With a group member who has a need to defy authority, we see how the therapist skillfully avoids being placed in a vulnerable position.

[1]All children's names here and throughout the rest of this volume are fictitious.

The therapist permits an extraordinary amount of acting out without becoming restrictive. And throughout, the reader gains the distinct impression of the therapist as a giving, sustaining, and supportive person as he sensitively and appropriately uses his understanding of each child and his problems to govern his own responses. The record also depicts the complexity of interpersonal impacts in AGT and the demanding role the therapist is called upon to play.

BRIEF ANAMNESES OF PATIENTS

The group under consideration, composed of seven boys (six are present at this session), has been meeting for about three months, once weekly for the regular two hours. Four of the boys have been treated in exclusive group therapy. Two were in cooperative (individual and group) treatment for a time; but since both were resistive to individual therapy with their respective caseworkers, they were terminated by their caseworkers and continued in exclusive AGT. In fact, the reason for their being referred to group treatment as given in the case summaries was their inaccessibility in a one-to-one relation. Greatly condensed anamneses of each boy at the time of referral for group treatment follow.

Morris, Age Eleven

Morris was nine years old when originally referred to the child guidance clinic. He had had two years of individual treatment with caseworkers. The chief problems were that he resisted going to school, demanding that his mother dress him; had severe temper tantrums, including breaking windows; exhibited marked sibling conflict with a sixteen-year-old sister, who dominated him and ordered him around, and whom he once threatened to kill. Morris's mother had great difficulty controlling him. While he was stubborn and aggressive at home, he was quite fearful of children and polite with teachers and strange adults. The father, to whom the boy had been very close, died when Morris was five years old. The boy "reacted badly" to this death. The mother, a harassed woman, displayed little warmth for her only son.

Since the father's death, Morris had been surrounded entirely by women: his mother and two older sisters, all of whom ordered him about to varying degrees. Morris had been able to speak with his caseworker about some of his difficulties but was usually quite uncommunicative. However, the female caseworker reported that he grew less evasive after a brief time in AGT and revealed his feelings of anger against women more freely. The psychiatric diagnosis was "behavior disorder," but because of anxieties and somatic complaints, it was later changed to "potential psycho-neurosis." It was the psychiatrist who recommended AGT, in addition to individual treatment, for the following reasons: "A boys' group with a male therapist would foster male identification, the boy might become less anxious about discharging aggression which was evidenced only at home and repressed elsewhere, and he would become less insecure were he to gain social acceptance in a group." The psychiatrist's recommendation and his reasons for placing the boy in a group were reviewed by the group therapy department, which concurred with them.

Paul, Age Ten

Paul was referred to the clinic by his school principal because of underachievement, aggressive behavior, and association with "troublemakers." At home he was said to be "nervous and fearful." Also reported were occasional nocturnal enuresis, thumb-sucking since birth, nightmares, and extreme sibling rivalry. His mother said Paul was dependent and close to her, and he often asked her to dress him. The family was intact, with one sibling, a brother several years older than Paul. The mother was an over-anxious and rigid woman who overstressed physical care of both children. The father, on the other hand, was remote from the children, partially because he worked long hours. He tended to be overly lenient and passive.

Paul was inordinately jealous of his brother, who had been receiving more attention from the parents because of a chronic illness. The diagnosis of "primary behavior disorder with neurotic traits" was established, and it was decided to place Paul in an activity group, mostly on an exploratory basis, because of the intensity of aggression which characterized his behavior in school, and because of the extreme degree of sibling rivalry which might

11

have made him an intractable member of the group. Should difficulties arise, he would be tranferred to individual treatment. This did not prove necessary, and Paul was treated exclusively in AGT.

Arthur, Age Eleven

Arthur was referred by the school because he was inattentive, worked below capacity, and would not do assignments in written work. His parents described him as stubborn, with a severe temper, clumsy, and absentminded. He had "nervous" habits: lip biting and eye rolling. Among other things reported were food fads, occasional nocturnal enuresis, rivalry with a younger sister, and some fear of going to sleep. Arthur's relations with peers were poor; he always wanted to "boss" them, which usually ended up in fights, so that he eventually had to play entirely by himself. When his father worked nights, he sometimes slept with his mother. Arthur frequently teased and provoked her to a point where she would beat him.

The father was a tense, defensive man who, in interviews with caseworkers, made contradictory statements about the boy. The mother, a submissive and anxious woman, seemed deeply involved with Arthur, despite her occasional angry flare-ups with him. In a psychiatric conference a tentative diagnosis of "anxiety hysteria" was made, with the possibility of schizoid personality. It was decided to accept Arthur for exclusive AGT, with consideration of the possible need for individual treatment if group treatment failed to reduce his anxiety and daydreaming. The mother was to be seen in individual casework treatment.

Sol, Age Eleven

Sol was referred because of poor schoolwork, although he had the capacity to do better. He had infantile mannerisms and fears of the dark and of being alone, and he played only with younger children, arguing with them constantly. The family situation was pathological. The father was separated from the family when Sol was three years of age, and the boy saw him only rarely. The mother was an extremely dominating and "castrating" woman, who was so disturbed that she could not be involved in treatment. She focused her attention on an older son, sixteen years of age, who acted the role of the father toward Sol.

Sol had been in individual therapy for six months, but continued to be very resistive. He would not talk about his problems with his caseworkers; instead, he spent most of the treatment sessions in playing games. He was then referred for AGT in the hope that he would become more secure in a peer group and acquire masculine identification. Psychiatric diagnosis was "potential psychoneurosis, incipient anxiety hysteria."

Ronald, Age Eleven

Ronald was first referred to the clinic by a school nurse because of "nervousness." He had difficulty in getting along with peers and had few friends. He was fearful, insecure, and anxious, was persistently enuretic nocturnally, had poor eating habits and fears of the dark, of being alone, and of "tough boys." There were also sleep disturbances. Ronald bit his nails, worried about being ill, and used to vomit a good deal. The family was intact. No problem was reported with respect to a younger daughter of two.

Both parents were extremely disturbed and frequently argued. The father was very strict with Ronald, expected instant obedience from him, and often beat the boy. As a result, Ronald was very fearful of his father. His mother, still dominated by her own mother who lived nearby, seemed overwhelmed. She was easily upset by Ronald, and she too hit him occasionally. More often, she yelled at him. Psychiatric diagnosis was "possible psychoneurosis, with anxiety features." Ronald was referred for AGT after an initial attempt to involve him in individual treatment failed.

Robert, Age Eleven

- Robert was referred by his mother, at the school's urging. He was disobedient, moody, and unhappy. He interrupted his teachers and was unable to get along with classmates because he tried to dominate them. Robert was markedly negativistic toward his mother, who complained that he did not respond when she spoke to him. She also complained that he had "terrible personal habits and ate like a pig."

Robert was an unplanned and unwanted child. His mother was nineteen years old when she gave birth to him, and she resented him vigorously because he "interfered with her career as an artist." She was a tense, narcissistic person and did not hesitate to vent her anger on Robert at the slightest provocation.

The father seemed to be "more balanced," but did not see much of Robert because he worked nights and slept during the day hours. Nonetheless, Robert appeared to be close to his father, but because of circumstances, they could spend little time together. At a psychiatric conference, a diagnosis was made of "primary behavior disorder, with indications of anxiety about sexual identification." Robert was recommended for exclusive AGT.

Synopsis of Early Group Sessions

For the first six or seven sessions the boys went through a phase of slow *acclimatization*. Several were frankly suspicious of the therapist. Conversation was limited and had to do mainly with the crafts work. The boys made only fleeting contact with each other; no real affiliations developed between any of them. The therapist pointedly stayed away from activities, allowing the boys to assess the permissive environment and react to it in accordance with their specific personalities. The more dependent ones began to seek him out, mainly for help; some attempted to work in close physical proximity to him. The group, as a whole, seemed to concentrate mainly on work.

By the eighth and ninth sessions increasing signs of spontaneity in behavior began to appear, and as the growing assurance that the therapist was really permissive was demonstrated in various ways, some of the games became increasingly aggressive. Several boys made swords of wood and engaged in "duels," which made Morris manifestly very anxious. Increasing arguments for possession of tools and over sharing of supplies and distribution of food at refreshment time appeared. Rivalry grew more sharply evident, particularly among the boys for whom this rivalry was a problem.

The noise level mounted rapidly; it had been quite moderate

up to this time. By the ninth session distinct subgroup affiliations and *supportive ego* relations made their appearance. These were evidenced in the now aggressive "war games." Play grew rougher; pieces of plasticine and other small objects became the "ammunition" for the games. As these interactions mounted, work projects lagged, except for a few boys, who apparently used them for security against involvement in aggression, which still frightened them.

During the twelfth group session much more open anger and deliberate provocations were displayed among some of the boys: they began to throw and hide each other's coats and locked some of the group members out of the treatment room. Vigorous wrestling on the floor and near fistfights also occurred. This behavior continued to frighten two boys. Transference to the therapist was now fairly well established, and a good deal of unconscious acting out in the transference was observable in the behavior of some of them. It was acted out mostly indirectly: in messing up the room, painting chairs, careless and wasteful use of supplies, and other more subtle forms of defiance. Throughout, the therapist continued his neutral and accepting role and responded to any demands for help made upon him.[2]

SESSION FOURTEEN

When the therapist arrived a few minutes early, Arthur and Paul were wrestling playfully in front of the door. On seeing him, both boys stopped and ran up to greet him. Arthur at once asked what refreshments they were having. The therapist replied, "cake, soda, and milk." He then added that since Arthur had asked at the preceding session for soda and Paul for milk, he had brought both beverages (A). Arthur made a gesture as if to resume the wrestling, but Paul said that they shouldn't, because he already had a slight scratch on his lip.

As the therapist approached the door, Paul offered to help him by holding the packages he was carrying and took them, remark-

[2] This was the tone of the activity group at the time of the fourteenth session, the record of which follows. Comments and interpretations of the events and transactions will be found in Chapter IX, keyed to the letters here.

ing that he had arrived at one o'clock. The therapist listened with interest but made no response (B).

When all three came upstairs, the therapist first unlocked the tools and materials cabinet and then took off his jacket and hung it on a hook (C). The boys, however, threw their coats on chairs, a procedure they had followed at all previous sessions (D). Arthur commented on the fact that several more chairs had been covered with paint (by another group) and read the inscriptions on several of them. He immediately took two jars of paint and a brush out of the closet and, commenting that there was no red paint and that the red paint bottle was mostly water, began to paint one of the stools. He was quite sloppy in his work, so that drops of paint splashed to the floor (E).

Paul took some wood and began to saw on what looked like the outline of a gun. Sol, bundled up with his coat buttoned to the neck, came in a moment or two later. He looked at everybody but did not greet anyone. He stood in front of the supply cabinet for a few moments, stating that he did not know what to do. He wandered over to where Arthur was painting and became critical of him, calling attention to the fact that the paint was dropping to the floor and asking why he had to paint chairs (F).

Paul went over to Arthur, asked if he could help him, and using another brush, did so for a moment or two. Since Arthur kept criticizing him for the way he handled the brush, Paul gave it up and went back to his own project.

In the meantime the therapist had seated himself at the far worktable, away from where the boys had congregated, and worked on his linoleum block. For some time all three boys continued to work quietly. Paul did a little sawing on his "gun"; Sol was very rapidly tracing a picture on drawing paper. Paul now told Sol that he had better move away from the carpentry bench, because he was going to do some hammering on it. Sol did not move but continued with his picture for about ten minutes and then again, seeming lost, stood around watching first Paul and then Arthur at their occupations (G).

Ronald arrived, looking neat and clean. He lisped slightly as he approached the therapist and began to tell him some of the latest sports news. He then narrated a trip he had taken to a sporting exhibit, describing the fencing, the boxing, and the wrestling. He said he liked the judo best and described a fight in which a very small man was able to "throw over" a large one. He displayed much interest and excitement. He then left the therapist, who continued working throughout the narration, and joined Paul (H).

Sol now asked if the therapist had any leather lanyard material. The therapist left his work and went over to the closet and gave him what there was of it. He asked for another color, stating that he wanted to work with two colors. The therapist, after examining the contents of the closet, said this was all there was. While the therapist was looking for the lanyard material for Sol, Arthur asked if he had got the molding set for him. (He had made brief mention of such a set the previous week.) Sol now wanted to know if the therapist had received the boats that he and somebody else had asked for. The therapist replied that he had ordered the boats in a nearby store and had been promised them for the coming week. Arthur now asked if the therapist could get him a boat too. The therapist asked what type he wanted and, having been informed, said that he would. Now Paul also joined in and wanted a boat model, which the therapist promised (I).

Morris arrived, entering in his characteristic energetic fashion, with his face beaming. He immediately came over to the therapist to ask what he was doing. The therapist told him, and Morris wondered if it was difficult. The therapist said it wasn't too difficult. Thereupon Morris asked if the therapist could show him how to cut his initials in a block. The therapist helped him get started, and Morris gradually took over working with the linoleum cutter (gouge). The therapist unobtrusively moved to another table. Several times in the ensuing hour, particularly when the play of the other boys got rather rough, Morris approached the therapist with his linoleum work. Although he was doing a very simple thing—just gouging out his initials—he asked innumerable questions, giving the impression of being far duller than he really was.

A few moments after starting, Morris moved over to where the therapist was and began to work near him. He volunteered that he had missed several "meetings" because of having gone to hockey games. However, he planned to come regularly now. He didn't want the therapist to have to "waste any more postcards" writing to him. Could he still be in "the club" if sometimes in the future he decided to go to a game instead of coming to a "meeting?" The therapist assured him that it would be O.K., if that is what he liked to do. Morris continued to work but kept asking for help from the therapist. He now wanted to know if the "club" could go to a hockey game sometime, and the therapist replied that it could if the boys wanted to. During a lull in the conversation, the therapist again moved to another table where he continued his work, but not before he had busied himself first with returning some tools to the cabinet, as a pretext for leaving the boy (J).

Arthur continued to use the paints sloppily and spilled part of a jar of red paint on the floor. Paul said it was "a stupid thing to do" and he should "clean it up." Arthur continued painting in his usual nonchalant and somewhat detached manner—he had a way of seeming unconcerned about activities going on around him while he worked, until he actually entered into them himself, and then he became more alert.

After a while the therapist fetched a rag and began to wipe some of the paint off the floor. Arthur ignored this, continuing his work. Since a good deal of paint was spilled, the therapist had to make several trips for water. While he was on one such trip, he heard Paul again criticizing Arthur, stating that he should not let the therapist do that. Arthur paid no attention, except to move the chairs away so there would be room for the therapist to do the cleaning. About five minutes after the therapist had finished cleaning and had replaced the cleaning implements, Arthur packed up the paintbrushes and put them back in the closet (this was contrary to his usual practice of leaving things around carelessly) (K).

Robert arrived at this time (about forty minutes late), and greeted everybody. He worked for a few moments smoothing the hull of the boat on which he had been working and which he kept in the storage cabinet. He then went to the closet, took out a large plasticine bar, and asked for still more. The therapist said there was more there, showing him where it was. Robert volunteered that he was going to model a large figure of Frankenstein. After he had unwrapped the plasticine, he came over to where the therapist was and asked if there were any modeling tools. Asked just what he wanted, Robert described a modeling set he had once seen in a friend's home. The therapist said that there were none just like them and gave him some substitute possibilities: a little metal rod, a nail, the back of a brush, and flat piece of wood. Robert accepted these, stating he thought they would do.

Sol had been moving from activity to activity, without remaining at anything very long, and criticizing Arthur and Paul several times for what he considered inadequate performances. He finally attached himself to Robert and watched him work. When Robert took the two available bars of plasticine, Sol began to complain and wrestled with him for them. He complained that Robert used up "too much clay." Robert asserted himself, however. Sol withdrew and again became a spectator. Robert had a talent for modeling and was gradually succeeding in fashioning a Frankensteinlike face.

Sol, in the meantime, played with the piece of "clay" that Robert was not using. With a small stippling hammer (pointed at one end), he pounded two large holes in the plasticine for eyes, another hole for a nose, then a long, slanted mouth. He giggled as he did this and held it up for the therapist to see. Then, as he continued to watch Robert and to deprecate Robert's efforts, Sol smashed the head he had roughly fashioned into little bits and called the therapist's attention to what he had done (L). In the meantime, Ronald had invited Paul to play ping-pong, which they played for about fifteen minutes. Morris continued to ask for the therapist's comments on his linoleum project. Arthur asked if he could make another copper ashtray, and the therapist gave him the material, with which he proceeded to work at the table. Sol, watching Morris, said that he would show him the right way to cut linoleum, but he could not find the kind of "tracing" (carbon) paper he thought he needed in the closet. He described it for the therapist, who also searched for it; but he too could not find any. Sol asked the therapist to get some for him, so that he could make "the right kind of linoleum block" the following week, explaining the "proper" procedure (M).

Robert came to where the therapist was working to show him the plasticine head and asked, "How does it look?" The therapist said it looked good. Robert then asked where he could store it, and the therapist suggested the "club cabinet" (a cubbyhole allotted for each "club" to store work in progress). Robert placed it there, and then, after a moment of watching Ronald and Paul at ping-pong, he began to interfere with their game by grabbing the ball. The two boys stopped the game at once and "ganged up" on Robert. One of the things they did was to throw plasticine pellets at him. Robert at first protested feebly, but then said nothing.

The following episode, involving the "ganging up" against Robert, lasted for forty-five minutes—until refreshment time. At first, Morris and Arthur stayed out of the action. Morris continued to ask for suggestions and help with his linoleum work, even asking the therapist to do "a little" of it for him. As the turmoil among the other boys became more violent, he came to the therapist for help more frequently. Arthur continued hammering on his copper ashtray, then asked if it would be a "good base for a vase" and how he could use it for one. The therapist showed him how to flatten it more (N).

The mood grew increasingly playful as Ronald and Paul chased Robert around the room, pelting him with plasticine pellets. Robert picked some of these up from the floor and flung them back at them. Sol now ran to the door, held it wide open, and suggested to Paul and Ronald that they force Robert outside. This now became the emphasis of the play. Robert refused to be moved in the direction of the open door, and kept retreating before them. Sol then suggested that they just grab him and "throw him out," but the others did not follow this suggestion.

The plasticine battle was now becoming more violent as Robert was losing his good humor. Apparently afraid of his own anger, or growing fearful, he announced that he was "giving up" and that the others should stop. But Sol kept urging Paul and Ronald to throw Robert out of the room, and Paul insisted that the "fight" could not stop unless Robert was outside in the hallway. Robert, equally insistent, said he would not go, and the chase continued. Robert, finally losing his temper, shouted for them to stop and said again he did not want to fight anymore. The others still paid him no heed (O).

Having completed the linoleum block a short time before, the therapist was sawing small squares of wood to make some mounting blocks. As the boys ran by, Robert picked up some of these squares and threatened Paul with them, demanding that he stop throwing "clay" at him, but Paul ignored him. After several threats, Robert threw a wooden block directly at Paul, striking him in the temple. Paul placed his hand to his temple and bent his head down as tears began to fill his eyes. The therapist walked over to him, noted there was no real injury, and left without comment, paying no attention to the others gathered around Paul. The boys were startled by the developments of their game and looked on silently at Paul for a moment or two. Robert exclaimed that he had told them to stop. Ronald said: "Now we'll show you!" Sol added: "Let's really throw him out." (Several times earlier, when Sol had left the door open, the therapist had gone over and closed it, but Sol kept returning to it, holding it open so that the boys could get Robert out). But, instead of trying to shove Robert out, the boys began to throw pellets at each other indiscriminately (P).

Paul's usual good temper seemed to return as he was now calmly throwing the plasticine as though he were taking part in a friendly game rather than a struggle. Because of this, Robert seemed to calm down, too, and was now laughing as the boys chased him from one part of the room to another.

When the three began to pelt him lightly, he climbed onto the little table that held the hotplate and shielded his face with a pot. The others threw the plasticine but did nothing else to arouse his ire. Robert ran to the other end of the room and looked in the closet for some more plasticine, but found pieces of crayon instead. Ronald protested that Robert was not using (the soft) plasticine. Paul called a "truce" and, seeing that Robert had plasticine as well, said Robert was just "holding" the crayons but was really throwing plasticine. It was all right (Q).

The throwing continued and again grew somewhat more violent. Robert was now trapped standing on one of the worktables, and the boys again threw pellets at him. He kept asking them to stop, but they would not. He then jumped off the table and ran into the washroom. Sol said they could lock him in there. Paul refused and said they should force him out of that cubicle. Arthur ran over and began to build a wooden barricade at the end of the passageway leading to the washroom (R).

Robert came running out, ran around the barricade, and took his position at the opposite corner of the room. Arthur, who had refrained from participating up to this point, now joined in the activities. In the corner of the room were two very tall sections of clapboard. Robert began to barricade himself against the barrage of pellets, using these sections. Arthur grabbed a hammer, raised it above his head, and told Robert to stop. Robert ignored the threat. Arthur put the hammer down and began to wrestle with him. While continuing to wrestle, Robert managed to set up the barricade. In the course of this, however, one of the larger boards was broken and the plasticine pellets, the ammunition, spread all about that corner of the room. The other board was partially broken as well (S).

By this time, Morris had come over to the therapist several times suggesting that he stop the ruckus. It was "too much," he said. The therapist listened sympathetically but made no response. Everybody was now arrayed against Robert, except for Morris, who continued to work but also continued to approach the therapist periodically to protest his permitting the uproar to go on. The therapist again made no response, continuing with his own project (T).

Paul had been the directing power behind the "onslaught" on Robert, who was now behind the barricade. Robert, in very good humor and playful mood, hurled back the pellets thrown at him. Paul had fashioned a piece of wood in the shape of a rifle, with which he directed "his men." He now seemed to notice the accumulation of trash from the broken "barricade" in the corner and proclaimed that it was "enough fighting." Obviously relieved, the others at once stopped throwing pellets. Paul, while acting "the general" and proclaiming that "things had to be cleaned up," now appeared in the role of a neutralizer. He directed Arthur to do something about the broken boards as the other boys were gathering up bits of plasticine strewn on the floor. Paul continued to give orders. Robert now also agreed, "That's enough," but Arthur countered, "We have to have a peace treaty." Saying this, he picked up a piece of drawing paper and ran to the refreshment table. The boys dropped what they were doing and sat around him as he began to frame the document.

At this point, since refreshment time was approaching, the therapist proceeded to clean up. He first replaced parts of the broken boards and then swept various sections of the room. He also replaced equipment in the closets prior to locking them. Paul remarked; "Al [the therapist] is cleaning after us." Arthur had written a document which read; "We shall have peace, except in certain times we shall have war." All the boys signed it. Paul said he was the president and was proclaiming peace. Robert said the "club" had never elected a president. Ronald said they needed a president (U).

The group then held an election, with Morris gradually becoming more vociferous. He had kept out of the activity until the group began to frame the peace treaty. Now, as the conversation continued, Morris spoke more and more loudly, calling for a vote, according to "correct constitutional procedure." Arthur supported this, stating that "it had to be democratic." The therapist could not follow the details, since he was cleaning up, but there were nominations and attempts at a voice vote. Arthur called for a "secret ballot." Each boy was given a piece of paper on which he wrote his preference. When the votes were counted, there were four votes for Morris (the frightened pacifist), who was elected president. Morris came over to the therapist at the other end of the room and proudly told him he was president. The therapist smiled at him. The boys repeated this procedure for the election of a vice president. Paul was elected to that office. Arguments now arose about the various other offices that had to be filled, but the boys did not get around to having other elections (V).

In the meantime, the therapist had completed cleaning up, and locking the closets. A moment before, Arthur had come running to him to ask for a nail. He took it and a hammer and nailed the "proclamation" to the wall. The others stood around reading it. Morris once more loudly announced he was the president. Sol, who had participated in the nominations, said Morris was not *his* president, because he was not in the group (fighting). Robert said he was not in it either. Paul came over and began arguing with him. The argument continued for some minutes until Paul finally said, "So we will not have a president." As Ronald tore up the "proclamation" and Arthur the list of officers, Morris comforted himself by saying, "I was president for a little while." Arthur then suggested, "Let's have a battle."

All the boys grabbed chunks of wood that were to be used as "guns." Three boys took up positions behind the barricade Arthur had devised earlier; the other three took positions in various parts of the room and made gun noises. This simulated, unorganized battle lasted about five minutes (W).

As soon as the therapist began to set the table for refreshments, Paul came up to help by putting the cups near the chair the therapist had occupied previously. He pointed out the two seats at either side of the therapist, saying they were reserved for him and Morris. Morris, on the other hand, said he would rather have his usual seat.[3] Paul then called the others to come to the table, and all, with the exception of Arthur, expeditiously took their usual seats even before the table was fully set. Paul poured soda into the cups, the therapist sat down, and the repast began. Arthur came a moment later and poured himself some milk (X).

Throughout the thirty-minute refreshment period, the conversation was animated and friendly. Morris remarked that he had not been president for long. This resulted in questioning who had voted for whom, and how many votes each received. Paul suggested they stop the discussion, that they should "forget it." Robert commented that the refreshments were good, and then said, "Suppose you had a house [home], Al, and invited us all to visit. Then you had refreshments and let us have some. Wouldn't it be nice if we invited you [to their homes] to have some, too?" The therapist listened attentively to Robert, but made no response.

Morris returned to the subject of the elections and said they

---

[3]As is customary in all continuous groups, in AGT groups also, each member usually returns to the seat he occupied at first. This repetitive pattern is a way of economizing on libido; i.e., it spares one from making new adjustments to new neighbors.

were "not complete" because everybody was not there (meaning the absentee boy). Ronald reacted to this with the assertion, "Almost everybody was here." Sol claimed that "it was a majority anyway." Morris asked the therapist where the absentee was, describing him, as he did not remember his name.[4] The therapist said that he had been there last week. Now Morris broached the subject of sports; Ronald and Robert were the loudest and most vociferous participants in the discussion. As each boy had mentioned his favorite team, Morris stood up and very dramatically announced his favorite team in each of the popular sports. He then asked the therapist which teams he favored. The therapist said noncommittally: "I like all the New York teams." As was usual with him, Morris talked most during the refreshment period.

Arthur asked if the therapist recalled the boys had requested frankfurters at the previous session. The therapist said he had remembered, but none were available in the store on the day of the session, and he intended to look elsewhere next week. Sol said, "Maybe we should get them all cooked, since it would take too long to cook them here." Arthur rose, went over to the hotplate nearby, and announced, "It got hot fast." He then asked if the therapist could get some of "that clay that is soft and has to be baked." The therapist said he would order some. The other boys then crowded around Arthur, watching the hotplate as the therapist cleared the table (Y).

While this was going on, Paul and Ronald sneaked away Robert's coat and threw it over the three-quarter partition. As the therapist continued to straighten the room, and a few minutes before the end of the session, the two boys began to put their coats on, pretending that they were ready to leave. The others followed suit. Robert could not find his coat and turned to the therapist, asking him where it was. Though knowing full well where it was, the therapist joined Robert in hunting for it. Paul whispered to the therapist that it was in the same place Arthur's coat had been last week. Robert then looked through the door in

---

[4] One of the striking phenomena we have observed in all our boys' groups is that they do not know each other's names even after two years of membership. This can be explained by the fact that in these groups there is little or no direct interaction requiring them to address each other, nor does the therapist have much opportunity to employ appellations within earshot of the others.

the partition and located his coat. No further effort was made by the others to keep it from him.

Paul, however, still had Robert's cap under his coat. By now, the boys were running around excitedly, pushing one another about. Morris came over to the therapist as he was washing the cups and said, "There is too much fighting in this club. You ought to stop it." The therapist listened to him with interest but made no response. A few minutes later Morris came back and again said, "This isn't the way it was the first few weeks. Everything was quiet then." He repeated that he didn't like it this way. The therapist listened without responding. Morris then added that it was true he had to go to hockey games and miss "meetings," but the fighting, too, was keeping him away. He stayed close to the therapist as the latter finished straightening the room, helping him to arrange things on the kitchen shelves.

Robert returned to ask where his hat was, and the therapist went to look for it with him. Paul, at the foot of the stairs in the hallway, showed Morris that he had his hat, and Robert raced down after him. By the time Morris and the therapist reached the exit door, the boys were racing around the corner. Morris was going to the left; the therapist said that he had to go to the right and said good-bye. As they were walking down the stairs, Morris told the therapist that Sol had fallen down the stairs. The therapist did not see this, but noted that Sol was not running with the others (Z).

It should be added that earlier in the session, prior to the "battle," Morris had cut his finger slightly with the linoleum gouge and had come over and shown this to the therapist. The latter at first ran water over it and then applied iodine. Morris squirmed but otherwise did not demur. He asked for details as to what the therapist was doing as the finger was being bandaged. During refreshments, Morris asked if he could take the bandage off so that he could wash his hands before eating. The therapist said that it was all right for him to do so.

II

Some Basic
Characteristics of Children
and Their Group Therapies

Group pyschotherapy and individual psychotherapy with children are based on the same elements and dynamics: (1) ready transmutation of ideas and feelings into motoric expression, (2) impulsivity and transilience, (3) weak ego organization, (4) inadequate superego formation, (5) the surface nature of a child's unconscious, and (6) the nonverbal or action communication natural for children.

Other characteristics of children are their fluid identifications and the rudimentary state of their defenses. These and other childhood attributes render them malleable in relationships and capable of personality modifications *through experience*. Children *internalize experiences*; i.e., they make psychic adaptations which they incorporate in themselves. Older persons by contrast tend to persist in their idiosyncratic, rigidized defenses, life patterns, and values.

The child, being still in the process of forming and patterning his personality, is in a nascent state with labile emotions and inconsistencies, which we have seen in the preceding chapter. He is experimenting with himself and with his surroundings, and because he is transilient, his concentration span is short. Some of these characteristics result from organic instability due to growth,

27

others are outcomes of congenital temperament, and still others are due to inadequacies of ego control.

The Child's Primitivism, Fantasy and Reality

Of significance to psychotherapy is that the child is in the thrall of primitive impulses and therefore little able to withstand frustration. Because of his still unregulated urges, he is given to rages and tantrums. He is intensely concerned with, and has an impelling need for freedom of movement, action, and play. He is rich in fantasy, and at certain age levels reality and imagination are confluent and reversible. This state of flux is derived from organic changes and psychic evolvement, as well as from emotional resentments and reactions to external actualities.

Education (not schooling) has long recognized the importance of play and activity for the young. For the child, functioning as he does out of primitive impulses with limited cerebration, motility is of fundamental importance. The child has still to discover the *meanings* of realities around him and establish a workable acquaintance with them. Physical activity is therefore very important and has more than education values; it is essential also to mental health, for suitable discharge of impulse through the vasometer system of the body aids physical growth and emotional equilibrium.[1]

Because of these considerations, activity therapy and the various types of play therapy for young children with which this volume deals were introduced.

The Scope of the Concept "Activity"

Activity, in a psychological frame of reference, subsumes more than motoric random action, the sense in which the word is customarily employed. In good education and particularly in therapy, it includes all human processes: physical, intellectual, and emotional. As we shall see later, specially designed settings that differ for each type of therapy are required by children of different ages, with different problems and personalities.

---

[1] See Slavson (1946), especially Chapter 11.

All reality, or rather actuality, imposes demands on the young child, forcing him to make adjustments (or adaptations). Reality's implicit messages to the developing child are *control* and *discipline,* first imposed from without but literally leading to internal controls transforming primitive behavior, self-indulgence, and fulfillment of random impulses, leading to socially acceptable forms and sublimations. The child's stimulations and adjustments in a therapeutically designed milieu necessitate *corrective experiences* in the living situation which still offer essential impulse gratifications.[2]   In its extreme manifestations, corrective activity occurs even in a passive type of adaptation. The child has little choice; to gain approval and acceptance, which are his prime survival necessities, he must eventually give up egocentricity and fantasies of omnipotence.

Groups in Character Development

Social group experience is a continuum and an extension of the child's earlier adaptations in his family. The regulative and modifying strictures imposed by groups affect character development during an individual's formative years as he actively engages first in preconceptual and later in conceptual or cognitive experiential learning associated with early interindividual interactions in the family groups. The learning experiences and the psychological mechanisms that affect character are only partially conscious formulations. Character evolves, in the dimension of time, as the summation of the total responses to ordinary and extraordinary influences and demands, planned and incidental, to which each individual is subjected from birth, and as modern fetology insists, prenatally as well.

The environment, through its influences and controls, acts as an integrating, disciplining force. This is a basic assumption in all types of therapy groups with children. The resultant character is the idiosyncratic aspect of personality which has been modeled by the conditioning forces in the environment and is typified in the expressive behavior and the thought processes of the individual.

[2]Except in the case of psychoses, in which the ego's accommodative capacity has become inoperative and has lost its integrative functions, where the primary process is dominant.

As a gestalt, character is composed of constitutional predisposing and conditioning forces that actively modify and inhibit instinctive, egocentric, narcissistic, and aggressive urges. In the light of this, freedom to *experience* independently is an absolute necessity for effective developmental learning generally and even more so in psychotherapy. Activity which is designed, imposed, or directed robs the child of the opportunity to realize and expand potential capabilities. When such deterrents have impeded development of the ego and deprived the individual of security, individuality, and independence — especially when *excessive* adult surveillance and control have been exercised — measures of freedom are indicated as correctives. For a young child free interaction with, and active exploration of, his environment (which should involve others) constitute *corrective experiences.*

The concept of free activity in varying meanings and concatenations as they relate to and affect the development of personality has been insufficiently recognized. While a clinical approach to the understanding of personality growth takes cognizance of the multiple dynamic processes involved in the social and psychosexual development of children, not enough attention has been directed to the neuromuscular and vasomotor activity needs of the human organism and their effects upon emotional growth. We have only to examine disturbed children and, for that matter also adolescent and in many instances adult patients, to find results of these malforming influences.

For instance, many children, adolescents, and adults find it difficult and in some instances impossible to express feelings in a spontaneous, vigorous, direct manner; others have almost complete inhibition of emotions that normally should be discharged with spontaneity. At another extreme are individuals who readily release feelings and tensions through verbal and motor channels in an exaggerated manner. Thus, behavior ranging from apathy to overassertive, aggressive acting out represents extremes of the expressive spectrum of personality.

As already indicated, verbalization is a minimal vehicle for expression of feelings by young children. When disturbed, their immediate need is to give their feelings active outlet in accordance with their level of development and basic personality.

Tensions, anxieties, fears impel them toward "fight or flight," but mostly the former. Obviously young children would be unable to sit quietly and reflect on their emotional symptoms and their relationship to life experiences as do adults. The communicative process and the discharge of feelings by children occur, in the main, through play, fantasy, and motor activity, which in addition to sloughing off emotional tensions also yield feelings of power and adequacy. It is through the liberation of cathected emotions which may subsequently become elaborated cognitively that alterations in personality are made possible.

REQUIREMENTS FOR CHILD PSYCHOTHERAPY

Motoricity, the natural form of child expression, also serves as a form of communication even in psychoanalytic therapy, but it is the sole medium of catharsis and communication in the non-analytic therapies such as activity group therapy.

To be therapeutically effective, activities must have a functional relation to the clinical needs of the young patients. The physical setting, the materials and games have to be appropriate for their age and sex and lend themselves as vehicles of communication. Materials and equipment need to be potentially suitable for discharge of fantasy and aim-directed work and creativity. (The two latter criteria are not as essential for the analytical therapies.) The physical setting for therapies based on activity must be planned to provide free movement and engaging occupations. All activities must originate with the children themselves free of adult control or direction.

Unrestricted activity in the early stages of group treatment will undoubtedly result in damage to the setting. To maintain the therapeutic intent, this cannot be interdicted in purely activity groups, as demonstrated in the preceding chapter. Instead, *situational restraints* are planfully supplied in advance within the setting itself. These will be described later in this volume, especially in Chapter VIII. Behavior challenging the therapist, however (which hardly ever occurs in a well-constituted group), must be controlled at the outset. Techniques for this, too will be found later in this volume.

THE MATTER OF DIAGNOSIS

While there is a trend in some quarters to reject categorizing patients by diagnostic entities, our extensive work with patients of all ages in a wide spectrum of personality and mental and emotional disorders leads us to the conviction that clinical diagnoses are essential in facilitating understanding of patients and formulating treatment plans. One cannot gainsay the assertion that the therapist needs to be concerned with the *total* personality of his patients, rather than with their pathology alone (a malpractice that is unfortunately extant in medicine as it is in psychotherapy). However, the treatment modality selected for a patient should address itself to the *specific quality of malfunction* presented. In psychotherapy, as in medical practice, explorations leading to clarification of etiology and nosology aid in determining the direction and content of the corrective effort of the healer, whether he labels the complaint or not. But clinical diagnosis, if correct, sets an attitude in the therapist and supplies him with a key to the treatment procedure. Labeling a patient psychoneurotic (which is hardly ever the case with young children) at once suggests the treatment modality to be employed, namely, the resolution of internalized conflicts by the method of verbal catharsis involving a transference reaction with an individual (the therapist) and acquisition of insight.

On the other hand, a patient with a character disorder gives the therapist the cue that he requires a more active and interactive type of treatment, which can best be found in a group. When a group is unavailable, the therapist will be required to serve the role of external reality and of a superego confronting the patient with his deleterious attitudes and conduct (Slavson, 1947). A patient found to be schizophrenic requires in addition to unconditional acceptance, accorded to all patients, also massive ego support and guidance from his therapist and others involved in his daily living. Evoking psychologic insights must be avoided; his psychotherapy should be supportive and based on workaday realities.

The above classifications do not completely apply to children, whose personalities are still in the process of formation and whose characters are still in a nascent state. The beginnings of these later developments, however, are often clearly in evidence even in some young children. Nonetheless, the choice of patients for groups is vastly less rigid, and grouping can be less meticulous than in work with adults and adolescents.

Children who are brought to treatment, usually by a mother, to a child guidance facility (or much less frequently for private therapy) are most often those whose behavior is troublesome to parents or teachers, or both. They most likely fall into the category of "primary behavior disorders" (Van Ophuijsen, 1945).[3] In this classification are included children who react with primary activity impulses to unwise and repressive dealings on the part of parents (most often the mother), who employed discipline at a period when *nurturing* and protection were essential for the child. Such treatment lays the foundation for anxiety and/or rebellion.

PRIMARY BEHAVIOR DISORDERS

When a behavior disorder is reactive to parental authoritarian and punitive treatment, but uncomplicated by strong emotions, it constitutes a simple (or preoedipal) primary behavior disorder, which has been the most common disturbance among children in latency in our culture, but extends now into adolescence. A simple behavior pattern, phenomenologically identical with a primary behavior disorder, may also be a *habit disorder*; i.e., the child carries over behavioral patterns from an earlier stage of development.

Diurnal and nocturnal enuresis and encopresis may be part of a behavior disorder syndrome; it can also be a habit disorder as a result of faulty training or neglect. Enuresis may also be a neurotic by-product in the category of a *neurotic trait*. It is therefore advisable to ascertain these diagnostic facts before or during the early stages of treatment, since that will determine the direction treatment should take. Among other examples of habit disorders are some tics such as eyeblinking or movements of the head or shoulders. These can be part of a neurotic syndrome in

---

[3] The term "primary" is employed to designate that the behavior does not stem from a constitutional source, such as brain damage or schizophrenia. Such behaviors are labeled "secondary" to the somatic condition.

adults, but are seldom as strongly cathected in children and disappear (or are "sloughed off") as the child's anxieties are reduced, his ego strengthened, and his self-image improved during the course of therapy or ordinary growth.

Primary behavior disorders in latency children are of two categories: preoedipal and oedipal. The discernment of these is important for planning treatment.

The basic characteristic of the preoedipal type of behavior disorder is that it involves one of the parents or both as individuals, not as a couple. When harsh treatment is applied by either of the parents but their relation with each other is not involved, the child's resentments and the consequent reactions are directed against the parents as individuals and are usually carried over to, or displaced on, others outside the family circle. But when the parents combine their hostilities against the child, the threat to him and to his security is immeasurably magnified, for he is deprived of all support and affection. This results in heightened fear and anxiety and increases behavioral abreactions. This alone would not be as crucial, however, without the additional element that intensifies the child's anxiety in the oedipal behavior disorder. This is that his infantile sexual strivings toward the parent of the opposite sex are imperiled and the factor of guilt is added to his emotional complex. A primary oedipal behavior disorder may also result when the parent of the same sex as the child fails to shield him against his strivings toward the parent of the opposite sex, generating anxiety.

In a family syndrome where the oedipal feelings of a child are assailed, neurotic reactions or traits beyond mere behavioral manifestations will inevitably arise. Thus, most oedipal behavior disorders require more than mere corrective experiences in action and relationships on the ego level alone, though such experiences may serve as a starting point. In most instances the child needs to *work through,* in fantasy and play, his tensions and anxieties. To do this, we have devised modifications of AGT for such children in latency, and younger, where free activities and interactions in a group serve as precursors to analytic play groups in which verbalization of feelings and rudimentary insight are part of the process. We term these groups activity-interview group psychotherapy for latency children and play groups for preschool children.

SLOUGHING OFF VERSUS WORKING THROUGH

Traditional psychoanalysis and all psychoanalytically derived psychotherapies employ "working through" as the basic dynamic. "Working through" consists of verbal associations by the patient and/or of exploratory processes in which the therapist participates in the unraveling of former experiences and their associated feelings, thereby bringing them into awareness, which diminishes their significance in the child's psychic economy.

Child psychotherapy has recourse to this process only rarely, for the child manifests his difficulties in behavior, fantasy, and the forms his creativity assumes. With the help of an empathic, warm, and understanding adult — the therapist — and/or a group of peers (in which the adult plays a significant role), the child is *relieved* of his oppressive feelings and *sloughs off* (as do also older persons, though temporarily) the malignancies of his character and his malefic conduct. As the anxieties and tension are reduced, neurotic traits, if any, also disappear. Because of the child's malleability, the new life pattern is permanently integrated into his character.[4] This is not the case with adults. The newly found feelings of adequacy and self-regard strengthen the child's budding ego, and the quanta of physical and emotional energies that have been consumed in dealing with tensions are freed for personal expansion and self-control.[5]

In this less encumbered psychological state and enhanced freedom of movement beyond the home, the child's ego can progressively grow and be strengthened through extra-familial opportunities, especially when they favor the orderly development of personality. The inevitable outcome of such a state of being, which therapy groups engender, is that the child no longer requires self-defeating mechanisms to deal with events and exi-

---

[4] This process we designate as the children's capacity to "internalize experiences."

[5] See Slavson (1964), Chapter VIII "The Bio-Quantum Theory of the Ego."

gencies in his life. He has sloughed off the reactive patterns upon which he found it necessary to rely in the past.[6]

---

[6]Actually, even in adult psychotherapy, where "working through" is a major modality, the sloughing off process is also in operation. Here it is a minor concomitant of the major process of working through. Once the nuclear difficulty and some secondary problems are worked through and no longer impel the individual toward neurotic and erratic emotional responses, some of the malignant overt reactions fade out. Thus, character is also affected, to a degree, by psychotherapy, though in psychoneurotics analysis of emotions and their sources are the centers of treatment.

III

Characteristics of Activity Therapy Groups

The Primacy of
"Reactive Behavior" and Corrective Reexperience

Because the primary behavior disorder is a direct reaction to conditions in the home, the child's behavior has been advisedly described as "reactive behavior." This nomenclature suggests that once the environment and the treatment of the child are altered, his behavior will follow suit. Although this logical theorem was not the conscious rationale of AGT at its initiation,[1] as practice with many thousands of latency patients extended and deepened, it led to this conclusion. It became evident that extra-familial influences such as schools, recreation, club work, and the effect of children on each other and on adults in the community replicated invidious climates of homes. Quite accidentally we found that exposure of children to "corrective reexperiences" in a favorable environment and with benign relations *permanently* altered their personalities and attitudes. It became clear that a suitable physical environment and a favorable psychological and social climate counteracted the "psychomalignancies" with which the young patients came to us. The student will find details in Chapter IV. Consideration will be given here to *general* elements that must prevail in such a corrective milieu and the activities that flow from it.

---

[1] See Spotnitz, 1961, pp. 37-41.

Types of Activity and Their Uses

Activity as an instrumentality in therapy has specific character and connotation. Under specific stimuli, patients generally act out, abreact to, or reenact emotional stress. In all mental therapies all three types of activity are present at different times and to different degrees. As we have seen in the preceding chapters, in AGT the children's activities are for a considerable time almost predominantly of the *acting-out* genre. But one can readily discern in them also the element of reenactment as a child reacts toward the therapist as a parent figure or toward other children in the group as if they were his siblings.

As could be expected, reenactment occurs most frequently in early sessions of a group when children respond to the group as they customarily did to their families and in their classrooms. Not infrequently, children manifest tension and irritation upon arrival at a session and *abreact* to them either by hyperactivity, aggression, and destructiveness or by sullen withdrawal. In AGT the therapist must recognize such conduct as the result of some antecedent frustrating or demeaning events prior to coming to the group and overlook it until it automatically dissipates. "Overlooking" in this instance includes meticulous avoidance of looking or even glancing at the "offending" child. Abreaction can be viewed as a process of self-therapy and should be accepted as such.

While in the analytic (interview) group therapies, the therapist would attempt to help even a young patient to become aware of his conduct and attempt to trace it to its cause, the "unconditional acceptance" and "neutrality" of the therapist in AGT preclude such a line of action. Questioning the child not only would signify disapproval and make him self-conscious and guilty but would foster libidinal transference feelings that must be avoided in this type of therapy. The very fact that transient negativism is accepted without notice constitutes a major therapeutic dynamic for patients selected for AGT.

Activity in groups may also be *aggressive, assertive, destructive, playful,* or *constructive,* and the therapist must differentiate among them and their meanings in terms of each patient's condition. Since action, rather than verbal communication, is the sum and substance of AGT, the conduct of each patient needs to be understood. It is this understanding that establishes rapport between the adult and the child and leads to the latter's improvement; it also assures suitable reactions on the part of the therapist.

MEANINGS OF INITIAL RESPONSES

Children reveal through their conduct basic personality traits and their defenses; some require one or more sessions to mobilize courage to draw the curtain of concealment. Still others continue their initial demeanor for a considerable time until they break through the fears that were fostered in their past. These initial reactions are analogous to the "first memories" adult patients communicate at the outset of treatment in analytic-oriented psychotherapy. As treatment proceeds, however, the changes that occur in the behavior of young patients in response to the freedom in a group are a reliable gauge of inner change.

Each of the types of initial response to the new setting of the group reveals the child's basic problems as well as his assets. A child, for example, may act up to test the therapist and the permissiveness of the new situation, or he may withdraw. In time, the assumed manners and facades disappear, to be replaced by more revealing demeanor. Similarly, initial constructive responses to the strange situation by aim-directed work may have a variety of meanings. They may denote internalized rigidity imposed by a child's life situation and well-entrenched submission to the demands and authority of adults. Such an overmature mode may be part of sibling rivalry in which the adultlike behavior arises out of a struggle to defeat a sibling through overconformity to parents. Initial constructive activity may also be only a short-lived stratagem stemming from fear of self-revelation and a testing period before a hilarious and infantile career in the group. Some children may be initially aggressive and destructive as an outcome of a conflictual home and school life by which their character was shaped. Such children may become, and continue to be, disturbing to a group as instigators of aggression and disorder, characterized as *true centers of infection* (see Chapter VI), jeopardizing the *therapeutic climate* of the group.

39

EFFECTS OF VIOLENCE AND DISORDER

Extended violence and disorder cannot be tolerated, and a child driven by such inexorable psychic pressure has to be removed from the group. On the other hand, such behavior may be only temporary, intended as a test of the therapist's tolerance, a competitive maneuver toward the therapist, reenacting a prevalent attitude toward a weak father, or a part of sibling rivalry battle in the home. Unless complicated by more deeply neurotic dynamics, these behavior disorders automatically abate.

It is clear from the above condensed characterization of a variety of personality dynamics that active interaction can generate a myriad of interpersonal impacts that, because of the malleability of children's psyches, have deeply affecting modification potentials. Unrestricted acting out and free interpersonal interactions in AGT release psychic forces for full play so that their impact has maximal effects.

ESSENTIALITY OF MANUAL ACTIVITIES

If young children with various atypicality, and even children who fall within the tenuous category of "normal," were to be gathered in a room with nothing to occupy them, chaos would ultimately arise, with risks of physical injuries and psychological disorientation as inevitable outcomes. In order to prevent unbridled, random acting out and chaos, which ultimately always lead to physical conflicts, the AGT groups are provided with tools and materials appropriate to the sex and age of the young patients who can engage in playful, experimental, or purposeful activity and creative interests. In the analytic therapies, such as play and activity-interview groups, the equipment and materials supplied are designed to *activate* the children's libido. But because AGT groups address themselves solely to patients' egos, the setting is rather *libido-binding;* i.e., it consists of simple, commonplace objects that can lead to aim-directed handiwork within the young patients' capacities and comprehension but will not activate the children's unconscious.

Tools are provided for metalwork, woodwork, painting, plasticine modeling, weaving, and similar simple arts and crafts.

Included also are individual, pair, and group games such as quoits, checkers, handball, and ping-pong.[2] After a period of free undirected work, the children partake of refreshments, which are prepared by the therapist until the children, on their own initiative, take over this responsibility. The atmosphere being permissive, the materials, tools, and total environment may be used in whatever way befits the fancy of each child. He may be destructive or constructive; he may isolate himself or enter into relationships with fellow members; may work or idle, do school homework, read funnies, play or fight, eat with the group or by himself. At appropriate times, later in the life of the group, this simple and attenuated reality is extended and modified by visits to restaurants, by trips, picnics and excursions, selected and planned by the children.

Throughout, five elements in the treatment process remain unchanged. These are:

1. The "knowable" nature of the group.
2. The role of the therapist (see Chapter VIII).
3. The element of social mobility versus social fixity.
4. The levels of identification.
5. The phenomena of nodal and antinodal group behavior.

THE "KNOWABLE" NATURE OF THE GROUP

All groups are threatening to all individuals. One source of fear is the unpredictability of reactions of fellow members and the group as a whole. An individual cannot be certain what the collective response to him will be. Each member sustains a partial ego modification and partial de-egotization. One will submit to a group but may be resistive in individual relations; another is uncontrolled and hilarious in a dyadic situation and quiet and withdrawn in a group; still another abreacts to a feeling of discomfort by humor and volubility; while a fourth who may be gentle in individual contacts becomes overbearing. Even more confusing to the observer or leader, one person may react in different ways at different times to situations or persons in a group and to the total setting. In addition, an integral physi-

[2] For a comprehensive list of materials and equipment, see pages 81-85.

ognomy of the group—its specific group culture—which emerges has to be dealt with quite apart from the individuals composing it.

Groups arouse early family memories and unconscious and suppressed feelings associated with it and with its members. The individual expects to be hurt, rejected, exposed by the group, and he may feel secretive or guilty. As a reaction to these threat complexes, he may evolve defensive amenities and strategies, while others evade or reject groups or attack them. Such reactions to groups are slight and rudimentary in most children but can be dominant in others.

To be therapeutic, a children's group must be free of the threatening characteristics of the pathogenic families from which patients are drawn, and schools must in no way replicate these families. Instead, the group must supply security, status, and acceptance. Such a milieu eliminates blockings to self-revealing expressions and frees the child of his fears of establishing relationships. The elements that make this possible are: (1) the genuine respect by the adult for the individuality of each member and unconditioned acceptance of him; (2) unwavering positive attitude on his part; (3) emphasis upon the constructive rather than negatives in achievement; (4) equalitarian group status; (5) prevention of rejection and prolonged attacks on a member by others through careful choice and groupings of patients; and (6) corrective reexperiences through ego and motoric gratifications.

The knowable nature of a group in AGT requires that no major changes are made throughout its life (usually of two school years). The children's feelings of security are assured by the use of the same room, the same physical arrangement, the same therapist, and for a time the same comembers. All elements of the unexpected and the unpredictable should be avoided. Both the age of the children and, especially, their weak egos render them vulnerable to new adaptations which frighten and disturb them. For at least a year, the young patients must know exactly what they will find upon arrival at the room at each session. Minor changes may be introduced in the second year of treatment when the children have gained in psychic strength and feel less threatened by change.

To assure the essential feelings of security, therapists are required to leave the activity room in *precisely the same order* in which it was originally arranged. This means that every piece of furniture and equipment is replaced in its original location. To prevent distractability and loss of interest in an ongoing activity and avoid confusion and frustration in the already unstable members of these groups, order in the replacement of tools, raw materials, and projects in process is essential. As we shall see later, the children are subjected, near the end of treatment, to a variety of frustrations to test the degree of their tolerance. The findings in these tests determine the readiness of some to be terminated and others to be continued in the same or another form of therapy.

SOCIAL MOBILITY VERSUS SOCIAL FIXITY

The major reason some boys and girls who have failed in ordinary groups can make easier adjustments to a therapy group is the freedom of action and the unrestricted mobility which the therapy group provides. Ordinary human congregates automatically evolve social crystallizations, rigidities, codes, and pressures. Each participant is expected or is required to follow its mores, manners, ideas, programs, and convictions. Divergence from the group norms is tolerated only to the degree to which the group morale and its cohesiveness are not threatened. Pressures against a divergent or dissident individual force him to conform, or his survival as a member of the group grows untenable.

Such groups can be described as groups of *social fixity*, in which, to be accepted, the individual must adapt himself to them, give up or limit his autonomy, and conform to defined or implicit norms. The neurotic or otherwise disturbed individual or one with malformed character finds such conformity difficult and is in conflict with the group.

In no type of *true* therapy group can norms be imposed, and pressures for conformity occur rarely and are tenuous. When a common group goal is involved, such as the choice of a place to visit or purchase food for refreshments, decisions are arrived at by the group. The total climate supports individual autonomy, and cooperation arises spontaneously. Because deviant and disturbing behavior is unconditionally accepted by the adult, members of the group follow his example and grow tolerant of each other. Conversation, cooperation, and subgroups spontaneously arise almost in a desultory manner and are dissolved as they fulfill the transient needs of the particular participants. A child can either remain in isolation or attach himself to another on a basis of a feeling of comfort, mutuality, support, or any other type of emotional need. Such a group is in every sense mobile and may be described as one of *social mobility*.

FIGURE 1

Fixity and Mobility in Groups in Relation to Polarity

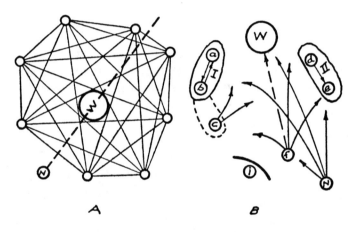

A   B

Reprinted from *A Textbook in Analytic Group Psychotherapy* (Slavson, 1964, p. 54).

Figure 1A illustrates schematically the compactness of a "fixed" group. Lines representing relationships emanate from each one of the members to every other. The therapist (*W*) is in the center. The newcomer (*N*) must cut through—adapt or force through—the maze. It may require considerable flexibility (partial de-egotization), great submission, or inner strength to make his way into the group through adaptation or by domination.

Figure 1B is a schematic representation of a "mobile" group. In configuration I there is a strong (bilateral) relation between the two individuals (*a* and *b*) in the solid ellipse, *c* having a loose and partial relation with *a* and *b*. He also moves about freely, as shown by the arrows, and relates himself to all or some comembers at different times (multilateral relations). II is a configuration of a bilateral relation permitting little or no invasion. I illustrates a *symbiotic* relation where *a* and *b* depend upon each other; II, on the other hand, illustrates an anaclitic or dependent-supportive relation, where *e* is the support of *d*; *f* is a "free-floating" individual who may or may not attach himself to different persons or configurations. He is shown here as having a strong attachment to the therapist, which for therapeutic reasons, he must be helped to solve. *i* is an isolate who works by himself and has little or no contact with the other members of the group. Here *N*, the newcomer, need not cut through fixed *lines of relationships* to attain acceptance and comfort. There are many possibilities for him to establish such relationships. It is this basic dynamic of mobility that makes *therapy through a group* possible.

Levels of Identification

Because of early negative experiences in relationships, the initial capacity to identify is very low in AGT patients. As image distortions and distrust and fear of human relations diminish and are ultimately overcome, capacity to identify is increased. Important is the growing ability of each patient to accept the compresence of others and to work out with them operational patterns of living and working together. It would be an error, however, to lay too much emphasis upon developing strong relationships in an activity therapy group. Rather, what we seek is to develop *capacity* for relationships. In interview analytic group therapy of adolescents, especially in girls, for example, libido manifestations always come to the fore, and selective identifications are frequent. This is not the case in group treatment of children in latency, where we deal predominantly with the nonsexual libido. However, girls in preteen ages also tend to manifest libidinal interest in each other as they share "secrets" and other intimacies or dance with each other.

The majority of patients are selected for activity groups because of faulty "social" adjustment. These maladjustments are largely due to character structure, rather than results of sexual problems. Therefore, as the child's ego is strengthened through the group, and as he grows more secure and gains confidence in himself, i.e., when his self-image is improved, he is able to relate more constructively to other people and identify with them. We designate the instinctive affectual need for human relations as *social hunger*. However, relationships are rarely carried over outside the groups (occasionally among girls, hardly ever among boys). This phenomenon can be understood in part in terms of group cohesiveness, which is entirely absent in therapy groups, and in part in the fact that the members are drawn from different backgrounds and geographical locations and that social identity, on which cohesiveness is based, is therefore not operative. This phenomenon is analogous to adult hospital patients, who may become close and friendly while on the same wards or in semiprivate rooms but hardly ever continue relationships after discharge. What has been said here concerning limits does not mean that the process of relatedness is not occurring in activity groups. On the contrary, it is continually in operation. The very nature of freedom, sharing, and especially the period of repast evoke *capacities* for relatedness in young patients.

The Phenomena of Nodal and Antinodal Group Behavior

The children in an activity therapy group feel strained and act subdued during the early sessions. They concentrate on work with materials or individual play and have little to do with one another. This is the period of *acclimatization*. Previous acquaintance, such as attendance at the same school, though undesirable from the therapeutic point of view, may shorten the initial insecurity; the "warming-up period" is briefer, and release occurs sooner. The presence of outgoing or aggressive children also shortens this initial period.

Groups alternate between stages of equilibrium and disequilibrium. Conflicts, fights, playful hilarity, and destructiveness are regularly followed by periods of quiet and more or less constructive activity. These cycles have a definite rhythm: at first they are more frequent during the eating period, contributed by the anxiety associated with food and the closer physical proximity around the table. Reenactment of habitual behavior similar to that in the home, such as fighting and hilarity, may also be a factor as well as the stimulating effect of food. The period of hyperactivity or group disequilibrium is referred to as *nodal behavior*, and the stages of quiescence and equilibrium as *antinodal* behavior (Figure 2).[3]

FIGURE 2
Periodicity of Nodal and Antinodal Stages in Therapy Groups

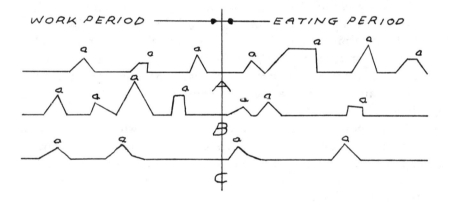

Reprinted from *A Textbook in Analytic Group Psychotherapy* (Slavson, 1964, p. 55).

As the children become more acclimated to the situation, the periodic frequency of hyperactivity (nodal behavior) is reversed; it occurs more frequently during the work period than during the

[3] The phenomena of nodal and antinodal behavior in groups occur in all small gatherings of people of all ages. At home parties, for example, a pall of quiet descends upon the gathering following periods of lively and even vociferous conversation. These alternations occur throughout the gathering's compresence and may be attributed to emotional fatigue.

refreshment period. Even after a boisterous work session, boys and girls bring themselves under control and settle down to a quiet meal, indicative of increased security and greater interest in each other as they strike up a conversation. Gradually the alternations of nodal and antinodal behavior grow less frequent and are equally distributed during the two periods of the session, which indicates general improvement and greater maturity. The food anxieties, with which the children at first approach the refreshments, gradually decrease, and relationships among the children become more marked. The equal distribution of the cycles also indicates a growing poise, which after many months is manifested by complete disappearance of cyclical behavior. The group now functions evenly and quietly.

The therapeutic process occurs at the point where nodal hyperactivity behavior is transformed into a state of equilibrium (antinodal), when self-control, compromise, mutual understanding, and other neutralizing factors that help individuals grow psychologically come into being. The points of transition from the nodal to antinodal states are the growth-producing foci; when integration, maturity, emotional controls, and expansion occur and their frequency and intensity can be considered the barometer of internal changes in the patients.

In a group where eruption of hyperactivity with inadequate or infrequent transition to equilibrium occurs, little therapy can be expected. A group in prolonged turmoil, conflict, and anxiety affects every member negatively. The neurotic child grows more anxious and may withdraw; others either become more entrenched in the undesirable acting out or feel frightened and threatened by it. The child whose infancy has been prolonged finds in the disorder an operational field that meets his preferences only too well, but his needs for growth are not met. On the other hand, in a group where a constant state of equilibrium is maintained, little interpersonal dynamics occur and no intrapsychic changes take place.

A in Figure 2 represents the greater stability of the group during working time than during the refreshment period at the early stages of a group's life. This state is reversed later, as shown by *B*. *C* represents schematically the behavior of a group after prolonged group treatment. The frequency and intensity of nodal behavior are more or less the same in both periods. The a's represent stages of transition from nodal to antinodal behavior, when self-control, conflict resolution, and individual or group restraints become the rule.

Because of the therapeutic dynamics of the nodal-antinodal phenomena, the value of instigators and neutralizers[4] becomes apparent; the former activate the group and the latter help bring it under control. Both instigators and neutralizers, while affecting the complexion of the group, also move toward more balanced personality integration themselves. The overactive child brings himself under control through the group, while the more withdrawn overcomes his fears and diffidence. If for any reason the hyperactive member continues to overstimulate the group to a point from which it cannot make the transition to the quiet (antinodal) state and thus prevents the emergence of the essential therapeutic climate, a reevaluation of his personality problems should be made. When so indicated, he is removed from the group and other therapeutic plans are made for him. While serving an essential function in the group, the neutralizers, as well, should not be so repressive as to *prevent* the needed release in the other members and must themselves have the capacity gradually to overcome their diffidence.

Nodal and antinodal behavior proceed from a number of sources. *Infectiousness* is one of the elements when the mood of the stronger children is taken on by the less self-directed or unautonomous. Present also is the mechanism of *interstimulation* common to all animals as well as man. One child may begin to play boisterously or grow hilarious; soon others who had been working constructively and are ordinarily self-contained lose their self-control. This reacts further upon still others, who in turn, intensify each other's mood. Thus there is a chain of interstimulating behavior which, if continued too long unabated, may reach a point of group hysteria.[5]

[4] See Chapter VI.

[5] See Chapter VI, "Selection and Grouping."

THE PHENOMENON OF SUPERNODALITY

The session of a group selected for presentation in Chapter I is a characteristic example of the height of hyperactivity that a group of male youngsters can reach in, to them, an unaccustomed climate of freedom and in the absence of adult restraint, revealing their "real" selves. When acting out reaches the intensity of that at the session reported, a point of *supernodality* is reached.

The requirements for including youngsters in AGT groups must therefore be such that they *all* have the capacity for autogenic guilt and anxiety, though to different degrees. This was manifested as the group in question progressed.[6] In the fourteenth session the intensity of aggression and scapegoating overstrained the budding superegos in the instigators of the "games." The self-restraint that emerged prevented them even more from going "whole hog" in the future.[7] While a few of the boys did occasionally for some time thereafter regress to "games," the hilarity was moderate and short-lived and never again involved the entire group. The mechanism of carrying a group into deviant behavior beyond its capacity to sustain it, we term *supernodal*.

The threat of the resulting excessive violence is mostly generated in the internalized superegos among the effective group members, such as the leaders, or *instigators*, but it can also be assumed in most or even all of the group members. Should the leadership individuals be aggressively psychopathic, psychotic, acting-out schizoids, or constitutionally defective, the supernodal activity would not automatically terminate and would require the impermissible prohibitive intervention of the adult. This not only would vitiate the group therapeutic climate but might eventually lead to the group's dissolution. *Careful selection and grouping are therefore of supreme importance.*

In many respects, the supernodal mechanism is analogous to the nodal-antinodal phenomenon. As was pointed out, the therapeutic thrust in a group occurs at the point of transition from the nodal to the antinodal phases, that is, where the egos of the

---

[6] This process is well illustrated in the group sessions reported in Chapter X.

[7] See Chapter X, "Evidences of Group and Individual Improvement."

participants enter the complex and displace the primacy of impulse (the id). These repeated swings from one to the other strengthen the ego, and its strength is eventually integrated into the character structure of each participant. This mechanism occurs in the wake of a supernodal episode as well, but instead of only the individual egos being affected, the group ego comes into play and thus becomes a guiding force in the group's life.

Another contrasting element is that of the superego. In the transition from nodal to antinodal behavior, the superego of individual participants is not involved. The transition can be attributed to fatigue and probably also to monotony. In the case of supernodality, however, the members of the group feel guilty at the outrage they inflict by their conduct upon the social norms under which they have been conditioned, upon their own latent individual values, and probably also upon the therapist.

REEDUCATIONAL POTENTIALS OF AGT

Because of the malleability of the child's organism, the group experiences contain reeducational potentials. The patients are referred for treatment because they have manifested behavior troublesome to their environment. In the absence of deep neurotic involvement, gross organicity, or pathology, an environment that favors reconditioning feelings, values, and attitudes—that is, one that supplies corrective reexperiences and reconditioning of responses—is effective. Such an environment is AGT. In this treatment modality alterations occur not only on the psychic level, but also in neuronic and glandular functions. These changes cannot be achieved by the usual didactic methods, teaching and preaching, as is commonly assumed by parents, preachers, and pedagogues. Verbal procedures are ineffectual where feelings and values are implicated. Changes in AGT occur on biological as well as on psychological levels—where accommodations to environment involve conduct and feeling, i.e., the soma as well as the psyche. In this sense, AGT is a reeducational process in which, as we shall see later, the therapist as a model of identification and imitation plays an important role.

THERAPY "IN AND THROUGH" THE GROUP

As already indicated, AGT is primarily an ego-level form of therapy in which outcomes flow without the benefit of verbal interpretation or conscious cerebration. At first, the meaningful psychological interactions within the group are given their momentum by the attitude and conduct of the therapist, who by his demeanor sets the climate that supports and encourages his young patients to begin to *experience ab novo* human relationships.

As we have seen, at the outset, the youthful patients operate as separate individuals seemingly unaffected by the compresence of others, but as they overcome initial discomfort, they glance about to see what the others in the room are doing. The initial isolative trend is broken, at the beginning, at the refreshment table, where the children find themselves in proximity as a group. If no one initiates a conversation, the therapist attempts a neutral type of conversation, such as transportation routes to the treatment center, the weather, or news of athletic teams.

As the boys and girls leave the room as a group, they are again thrown together, and some of them may walk with one or two others. As a result of these stray contacts, children may feel more at ease and approach one another at subsequent group sessions on the basis of their manual occupations or other events. An extended period of interindividual contacts follows, with the group as an entity seemingly remaining in the background of their awareness. Although it usually requires a long time, individual relations grow into an awareness of group, aided by the introduction of trips, refreshments in restaurants, and outdoor picnics.

The details of planning and the management of these enterprises cannot fail to generate an awareness of the supra-individual existence; that is, the group as an entity becomes involved in their lives. Then a coalescence of the native social impulses into a larger gestalt appears, and the group enters into the children's psyches to serve as a socially therapeutic force. Thus, the therapeutic agent now becomes the group in what is termed *therapy through the group.*

The modality of the process in analytically oriented groups is more individual, that is, each seeks relief from his difficulties and from time to time becomes the center of attention of the group. This is termed *therapy* (of the individual) *in the group.*

IV

The Physical Setting for Activity Group Therapy

ID, EGO, CHARACTER, AND THE ADAPTATION MECHANISMS

While the raw materials for structuring of the ego are genetical endowments, they are conditioned by neonatal imprints, life experiences, imitation of and identifications with parents and other adults of importance in the child's life, and relationships with siblings in the family. What is commonly known as "character" in an individual is the product of a very complex network of hereditary, biological, and psychological assets and their adaptations to external demands during formative years. Ethos and mores play a salient role in shaping both the personalities and the characters of individuals.

We have defined character as the disposition and capacity to direct and inhibit native atavistic (instinctual) and egoic urges. The ego is the part of the individual's character that mobilizes these powers; it is also employed in overcoming obstacles and difficulties that arise on the way. In a real sense character and ego are synonymous. However, while the ego, as a psychodynamic construct, is the organizing and executive force in the human psyche, character includes the broader scope of values and that which Glueck (1928) spoke of as "the capacity to make the right decision even though it has no relation to possibilities of immediate reward or punishment . . . the ability to postpone satisfaction of desire to an ever-ready future" (p. 736).

Character is "the building up of our lives into substantial purposes which will weather the vagrant urges and lures of the present moment" (A. Myerson). It is "an enduring psychological disposition to inhibit instinctive impulses in accordance with a *regulative principle*" (A.A. Roback). Character thus incorporates in its structure the superego as well as the ego.

It is important for parents, educators, and therapists to recognize that the shaping of the personality complexion, of which character is a part, cannot effectively be achieved merely by training. It is rather an outcome of actualizing inherent power resources of the individual through favorable physical and psychological growth. To attain maturity is at once "the most difficult task of education and the greater burden imposed on civilized man" (Myerson). It can be successfully achieved only through orderly psycho-organic development in which the micro- and macrocultural conditions are favorable and where adequate identifications and values automatically become part of the individual's psyche; that is, they become *internalized*. The "regulative principle" is an unconscious mechanism derived from the totality of experiences in the home, in school, with playmates, from contacts and interactions with individuals and groups in neighborhood and region, and from the ideology of the larger world. Character emerges from all the purposeful and incidental influences to which an individual is exposed.

The process of adapting to the impact of environmental influences molds what may be termed the complexion of personality; but in terms of its structure, three definite components are required: will, power, and endurance—an impelling desire, the power to carry it out, and the endurance to withstand resultant stresses. With growing maturity and emerging ego strengths, adaptation gives way to a more dynamic, interactive process which is termed *adjustment*, as contrasted to the malleable *adaptation* to external demands, which is suitable in early childhood. Adjustment involves dynamic interactivity with environment in which the individual affects it as it, in turn, affects him. In this process the ego of the individual is strengthened, giving him varying degrees of mastery over his own destiny; but to achieve this salutary state considerable discipline is essential, particularly self-discipline.

Maturity can best be defined as *controlled spontaneity* and character as the totality of the adaptive mechanisms with which the individual deals with his instincts, drives, and anxieties, and the constructive demands on him of the outer world. Character is thus the resultant of the struggle between inner pleasure-seeking urges and outer "reality" demands in dynamic interactions during the individual's formative stages. It is therefore the permanently achieved resolution of the struggle between ego forces and the id or instinctual strivings through the mechanisms of repression, sublimation, reaction formations, and expression.

AGT IN THE LIGHT OF BIO-PSYCHO-SOCIAL FORCES

AGT derives its theoretic rationale from the above hypotheses. Since character is fundamentally a result of the interaction of intrapsychic forces with outer actualities, its correction can be achieved through conditions that counteract the original crippling influences that shaped it. This is particularly true of the as yet malleable psyche of the child, still in a state of plasticity and flux, unrigidized by habits and defenses and by final identifications. The child *becomes what he does*, i.e., what he experiences. This is only partially true of adolescents and much less so of adults. This psychological law underlies the principle of "corrective reexperiences."

BASIC FEATURES OF AGT SETTING

AGT is designed to affect improvement in behavior through a nonverbal therapeutic modality. It is essential not only that the process be emphasized but also that the physical setting is such as to evoke the process. To achieve this, the physical setting needs to be compatible with children's natural interests at their ages and developmental levels. The arrangement of a therapy room and the materials and implements provided are based on these factors.

The therapist should consider the crucial fact that, for the most part, the technological world is physically and functionally designed in all respects for the needs and comforts of adults. It is assumed that children easily accommodate themselves to these settings, but the demands placed on their capacities are extraordinary. In the home where children spend so much time, the kitchen, living room, bedrooms, bathroom facilities, and furnishings are of adult size. This is also true of all things in the outer environment, except, perhaps, in playgrounds, which are available to negligibly small numbers and utilized only for brief periods.

From his earliest years, the child experiences a physical environment that is restrictive and forbidding. He is taught very early to respect the sanctity of things. Even rumpus rooms must be orderly! While such strictures may be suitable for adults, to a young child they are unwieldy, restrictive, and uncomfortable. Not only are insufficient provisions made for children's comfort, but their expressive needs are neglected. What has been said of the home applies even more to schools. A few feeble attempts have been made, but only in recent years, to design equipment more suitable to the growth needs of children.

As much as the world to which the child is constrained to adapt is unsuitable for him, just as much must an AGT treatment room be *child-oriented*. Its overall design, its furnishings, supplies, and equipment should be devoid of anything resembling home or school. The furnishings are made of plain, unpainted wood, the floor is bare, and everything in the room is free of an "upholstered" appearance. All work and other benches, tables, and closets are arranged around the walls, leaving a large free area for play and movement in the middle of the room. This setting suggests freedom of locomotion without concern about marring, soiling, spoiling, or breaking anything. The room is, from the child's point of view, entirely utilitarian. Everything in it is designed to free him and accommodate his physical size and his motoric, play, and work interests and needs.

RATIONALE FOR EMPHASIS ON SETTING

The child's early adaptive mechanisms being the foundations of character, the corrective climate must be in every regard different from that of home and school and of the adult community. It must be designed to evoke more suitable responses, which as indicated, become internalized to form part of ego functioning and character. For example, the discovery of a benevolent rather than critical, dominating, antagonistic adult in the person of the

therapist has an indelible effect upon the child's psyche. His benevolence (permissiveness) must be reflected in the nonprohibitive
physical setting as well as in the unrestricted communicative and
interactional opportunities. Such experiences are crystallized into
feelings and attitudes. The AGT setting is therefore designed to
represent freedom and evoke responsiveness. The activity therapy
room is planned to suggest manual individual and cooperative
activities and interpersonal interactions of a corrective nature. To
a casual observer, such a room may appear to be merely a
simple, relatively uncomplicated arts and crafts setting, but it
actually is the result of a carefully planned design in which
nothing is left to chance. Furnishings, equipment, and supplies
are all painfully placed in terms of their relationship in use
(*function relatedness*). This arrangement of the room brings into
visual focus all the objects that are used together in performing
any task (*visual stimulation*) and, in addition, obviates unnecessary movement by the young workers, which would create a nontherapeutic, chaotic, hyperactive atmosphere.

Practice has shown that departures from these standards in the
setting and the resulting functional discordancies not only vitiate
outcomes, but actually create deleterious effects. Discordancies
might stem from inappropriate furnishings, materials, and tools,
inappropriate room size and layout, as well as from faulty selection and groupings of patients (to be discussed later). Prevention
is particularly crucial to AGT because it is a nonverbal modality;
hence the subtlety of the setting and the climate must be preemi-
nently suitable for the ends of reconstruction of character and
personality.

In play therapy with an individual child, which relies partially
on interpretive and quasi-analytical procedures (stemming from
the play content of patients), the therapist may function effectively even in a setting not entirely suitable with respect to room
size and other appurtenances. As long as the necessary play
objects are available, the therapist can make accommodations as to
space without seriously hindering the therapy. This is feasible
because inquiry and interpretation by the therapist are significant
elements of the patient-therapist communications: feelings of
discomfort or frustration on the child's part can be dealt with

on a verbal level. In AGT this flexibility is not available, since the children act out their annoyances instead of "working them through" verbally. The effects of an excessively small or an over-large room in AGT, for example, make it impossible to maintain treatment levels. Here, the discomfort is immediately acted out by the group, and since the therapist must maintain a neutral and passive role, countertherapeutic chaos results.

EFFECTS OF UNSUITABLE SETTINGS — ILLUSTRATIONS

Perhaps several illustrations of inappropriate settings may serve to emphasize the importance of avoiding deleterious outcomes from inappropriate room conditions.

On reading the weekly protocol reports of a group of boys about eleven years of age, the therapist's supervisor raised the question of one boy's repeated drilling of holes in the floor of the therapy room, which was in this case a store on the street level. In reviewing the case history of the boy, no evidence could be adduced as to the psychological meaning of the persistence of this obviously nonproductive and damaging occupation.

Fulfilling his permissive role, the therapist, employing the standard strategy for preventing damage to the building, placed a small board under the brace and bit so that the boy could satisfy his need for this activity, but without damaging the premises. However, at the start of each session, as the other boys found various occupations or play interests, the boy in question resumed drilling the floor.

It occurred to the supervisor to ask the therapist if there was anything particularly special about the floor. The therapist thought for awhile and said that he did not think so. The building was an old one, but could withstand heavy wear; otherwise there was nothing especially outstanding about it. "Are there any cracks in the floor boards?" the supervisor asked. "Oh yes," was the ready reply. "There are large numbers of cracks in that old floor." "Well, this seems to be your key to the problem. There is a possibility that this boy is acting out some sexual fantasy by his persistent act. Let's have the floor put in good condition or, if necessary, cover it with heavy linoleum." After this was done the boy discontinued his drilling.

In reading the protocol record of a session of a group of twelve-year-old girls, the same supervisor was struck by the subtle change in the climate of the group at that session. Although the girls continued with their accustomed activities, a pervasive restlessness and unusual shifts of interests occurred. When questioned by the supervisor at the weekly supervisory conference, the therapist seemed unaware of any radical change in the conduct of the group. The supervisor mused almost to himself, "Something happened in that room." He then put the question to the therapist, "Was anything done to that room?" "Oh yes," the therapist responded, "the room was painted." "What color" "Light brown," the therapist replied. "What color is the floor?" "Bright red," was the response. "Well, that's your problem. Ask your district supervisor to have the floor repainted, preferably black." This done, the group returned to its normal state. Obviously, the color of the floor reminded the girls of their menstrual flow and sex, about which they felt uncomfortable, setting off anxiety that caused their restlessness and distractability.

In one of the rooms of a child guidance clinic used for AGT was a deep, unused cubbyhole on the floor level, a structural peculiarity of the building. Two members of the ten-year-old group of boys made a practice of crawling into the cramped space, closing the doors after them, and spending most of the group sessions huddled in these closed quarters. The therapist, wishing to maintain his permissive stance, was concerned about these developments, suspecting overt or covert sexual implications, but he could not prohibit this activity and make his suspicions and concern manifest, nor could he make the space inaccessible by placing a lock or nailing down the small door. (Past experience has proved in similar situations that the boys would remove these impediments.) The supervisor then suggested that an artificial wall-like structure be built six or ten inches inside the space, thus rendering it unsuitable for entry. This solved the problem.

The manner in which the problems were met demonstrates the principle of *situational restraint*, as differentiated from *direct restraint*, which must be used in nonverbal therapy. The latter never fails to arouse resentment and rebelliousness and uncontrolled acting out.

In another treatment center a group of boys in latency were assigned to a room with three doors. The therapist was at his wit's end coping with the turmoil and hyperactivity of the group. Aside from the inclusion of a severely hyperactive youngster — probably a borderline psychotic — who would have created insuperable problems to the group and the therapist in any case, the unprecedented violence and excitement during the aimless running about, screaming, shouting, chasing each other in and out of the room were made possible by the many exits and entrances. Because of the lack of understanding by the therapist and his supervisor of the basic requirements for situational therapy, they were at a loss to recognize the causes of the disturbances in the group and permitted it to continue for several months. The problem was solved when the chief instigator turned up at one of the sessions with a knife to kill the therapist.

This event led us to assume that the instigator was psychotic. But if the room had been more suitable for the purpose, the intensity of the acting out would not have risen to such heights and the latent psychosis of the instigator would not have been activated to the degree of attempted homicide. His attempt can be understood as the result of a loss of ego control, a condition the therapist permitted to be escalated beyond the boy's ego limits by remaining passive, and for which the boy unconsciously blamed him.

The negative outcomes of unsuitable equipment and the setting of a room were tangibly demonstrated in one child guidance clinic where the one group it maintained could not get under way. The group members did not seem to settle down to the usual constructive work and relations for many months. The clinic building, being situated in a suburban community, had a back yard and an extensive front lawn. No matter what strategies were devised to entice the boys to stay in the room, they insisted on playing outdoors.

Even though the therapist's personality was unsuitable for this type of work, the continuous balking by the boys at engaging in occupations usually appealing to boys of their age puzzled us. Upon visiting the center, we discovered that the otherwise suitable room contained a motley of discarded chairs, some overstuffed, others plain armchairs of various sizes. A massive antique polished table was the only other piece of furniture. The equipment was equally unplanned and, in addition to being skimpy, was unsuitable. It was inevitable that, under the circumstances, the boys sought refuge in outdoor play.

LIMITATIONS ON DOORS

The matter of doors is extremely important in the physical setting of an activity therapy room. No doors, whether in the walls or closets, can be locked against the young patients. To all children, especially to those requiring therapeutic ministration, doors have special meanings, since in homes, doors are used as instruments of exclusion and rejection. The doors of bathrooms and bedrooms, both areas of intense curiosity to a child, are always locked against or forbidden to them, and doors are also used to lock them out as punishment. Doors, therefore, assume symbolic meanings.

There should be only two doors in an AGT room: one for entry and exit and another leading to the lavatory. Even doors to built-in (walk-in) closets should be avoided. Such closets are often used for self-isolation or isolation with a companion. Often doors of a closet serve the children as a means of struggle when one inside the closet is kept from reentering the room. Removable storage closets against the wall are preferred. Extra doors should be covered by plywood and painted so that they become part of the walls. The range of conditions in which most forms of therapy can operate effectively is much greater than it is in AGT. Here, the conditions of the setting are closely and inextricably involved with the therapy.

LOCATION OF THE TREATMENT ROOM

Whenever possible the treatment room should be located where no other activities are going on. It is also preferable that it be located in a building other than the clinic. The location should be such that the children are not distracted or their interest diverted from the therapy group; nor should the sounds from the group interfere with or annoy others, who may complain and force restrictions on the freedom of acting out by the children as well as on the unavoidable sounds incidental to hammering, sawing, screaming, and running about. A therapy room located in close proximity to a business office, interviewing rooms, or in a residential apartment, for example, is an open invitation to difficulties. A badly located room is bound to create annoyances affecting all concerned.

Experience indicates that the best location for an activity group is one that is not contiguous to other settings or occupations or residences. A loft in a quiet manufacturing building. an airy, light basement, or a private small garage building are examples of suitable locations. If, however, the therapy room must be maintained within the confines of a child guidance agency, a neighborhood settlement house, or an out-patient clinic, it is essential that it be located peripherally so that it will not intrude on other services. Groups that meet on weekends can be more easily located than those that meet on weekdays. It should be kept in mind that AGT groups meet after school hours, which facilitates obtaining locations for them.

If locations cannot be provided with optimal requirements, compromises may have to be made. The compromises, however, may not seriously counter the essential requirements of freedom of action for the children, nor should they present temptations for distractions and disorder.

SIZE AND DESIGN OF THE TREATMENT ROOM

A floor area of approximately 450 to 500 square feet is adequate for a therapy group of eight children. This is its maximum size. A convenient formula for area determination is approximately 50 square feet for each member and the therapist. If

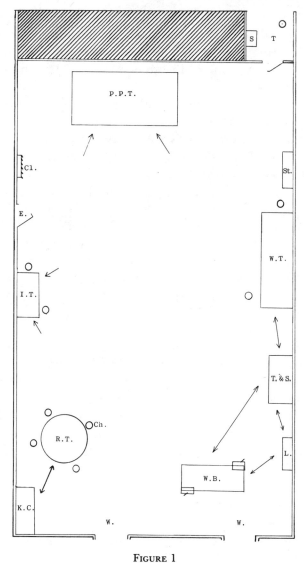

FIGURE 1

Treatment Room for Activity Group Therapy

Ch. = Chair. Cl. = Closet. I.T. = Isolate Table. K.C. = Kitchen Cabinet. L. = Lumber Storage. P.P.T. = Ping-Pong Table. R.T. = Refreshment Table. S. = Sink. St. = Storage Cabinet. T. = Toilet. T.&S. = Tool and Supply Cabinet. W. = Window. W.B. = Woodwork Bench. W.T. = Worktable. E. = Entrance. Connecting arrows illustrate the principle of function relatedness.

65

possible, the shape of the room should be such as to provide open space, unencumbered by pillars or alcoves. It can be square, rectangular, even circular. The dimensions should be more square than rectangular.

As mentioned above, access to the room should be by one door only. Adequate ventilation and heating, of course, are necessary, as are other facilities such as electricity for lighting and at least two outlets for electrical appliances (an electric cooking plate, for example) and a lavatory, with a sink, opening into the room. The room should be well lighted by daylight and have electric lighting fixtures for dark late afternoons in the winter. Walls and ceiling can be painted off-white or any other plain color. It is wise to use a water-based latex-type paint and to have a reasonable supply of this paint and brushes available for future use when scribblings and graffiti have to be covered over. (Occasionally, children deface the walls with crayon and water paints, and it will be necessary, after they have left the room, for the therapist to paint over the parts that have been so defaced to prevent suggestion to other groups or to the same group at subsequent sessions to deface the walls further. In one instance, girls, upon learning that the boys' groups met in the same room, water-painted their names and telephone numbers on the walls.)

Of all factors involved in meeting space design, the question of adequate room is probably the most important. The size of a room and the utilization of its space influence the degree and type of mobility that takes place. Therefore, the following considerations should be borne in mind:

There should be free and easy access to all parts of the room and sufficient space between worktables and other furniture to enable children to apply themselves unencumbered to various activities. For example, a woodwork bench should be so placed that children can use a saw, hammer, or plane without interference or crowding one another when working at the same bench. Furniture should be placed along the periphery of the room, leaving the central area free for passage, moving about, running and play.

A corner of the room should lend itself to use as a kitchenlike unit, for preparing and serving food. A small sink in this area is helpful, though not essential, as water can be carried in a basin from the lavatory faucet.

EFFECTS OF ROOM SIZE ON CHILDREN'S BEHAVIOR

Therapy rooms that depart in many respects from the recommended size and layout — that are either excessively large or too small or contain encumbrances that interfere with free mobility — vitiate the therapeutic climate on two levels: they may frustrate or disturb the children and complicate the role of the therapist. An excessively large room tends to suggest that children run helter-skelter or chase each other, thus generating random, unproductive motility and hilarity that at times may not end without the therapist's intervention. This abrogates his role in the *primary group code*. The unverbalized primary group code consists of two basic elements. One is that the children are completely free to act out their impulses; the other is that the adult unconditionally accepts the children's conduct. Any diversion from these principles confuses the young patients as to where they stand — what they are permitted or not permitted to do — thus the *knowable* quality of the group is abrogated, replicating the children's schools and families that caused their difficulties in the first place. In addition, an overlarge room also diminishes opportunities for interpersonal contacts and prevents emergence of relationships.

An illustration of the effects of an oversized and underequipped therapy space was presented by a setting in a child guidance center in a section of New York City during the early years of group therapy. The huge, high-ceilinged room that could easily seat 150 adults was used exclusively for a few groups of boys in latency. The room was completely bare of any furnishings, except for a punching bag and playground seesaw. Because of a misunderstanding of the intricacies of AGT and the subtle conditions under which acting out becomes therapeutic, the boys were let loose in that bare room to do what they wished and "interact" in whatever way they fancied.

As could be expected, the area of the room, its bareness, and its height stimulated the children to run about, tumble over each

67

other, wrestle, and wildly chase one another. One of the unique occupations the overwrought youngsters stumbled upon was systematically demolishing one of the huge walls. The boys were supplied with hammers, and a visitor was informed that the clinic had the wall replastered regularly every year during the summer months when the group was not in session.

The rationale for such a bizarre setting was the director's and staff's misunderstanding that activity group therapy was *completely* unrestrained acting out to reduce tensions and ventilate hostility. Having no channels for sublimating these feelings through suitable materials and constructive play and occupations, the children used the room like an open-air playground. One can also assume that another error made in planning the project was the inclusion of unsuitable children for this type of therapy.

On the other hand, when a room is too small, the effects of crowding are keenly felt. It was empirically demonstrated that the hindrance effects of small rooms impinge on the therapeutic process.[1] The children feel physical constraint giving rise to annoyance and aggression to ward it off. Hyperactive children are deprived of adequate space for discharging motoricity trends and grow tense, "jumpy." As a consequence, they act provocatively and disturb the group. Others defensively withdraw, and the schizoid are frightened by the closeness. They, too, grow tense, flight-oriented, wary, increasingly defensive; the period of acclimatization cannot occur, with the resulting relaxation essential for the adaptive process. A confining room thrusts child against child with an impact that cannot be comfortably sustained for long periods.

The therapist's neutral role is also affected in the confinement of a small space. He cannot as easily set himself physically apart from the children and avoid becoming involved in their activities. This is particularly deleterious in the early sessions of a group, because the children are unable to assess him and his intended role. Under these circumstances the physical closeness puts him in the position of an unintended restraining factor.

---

[1] It is probable that man automatically reacts against excessive violations of "personal" space. Animals react defensively to "foreign" intrusions on their living space (territory).

THE FURNISHINGS

All furnishings should be arranged as far as feasible in functional relatedness so that space can be used efficiently and with a minimum of movement. Viewing the room for the first time a child should get an impression of its utilitarian character and its suggestiveness for creative activity. As already indicated, all furnishings should therefore be simple. Global perception of the room should be of a setting that not only invites use but can also stand abuse, in contrast to early conditioning in the home, school, and everywhere in the community. Heights and sizes of tables and chairs must be suitable for the age group under consideration, e.g., eight to twelve years of age. The woodwork bench must be firmly fixed to the floor to prevent shifting when in use. A set of low sawhorses is recommended for use in sawing wood.

The following are specifications for basic furnishings for an activity room for both boys and girls. Consideration is given to the probability that the room will be used by more than one treatment group, the usual practice in child guidance and hospital clinics and social service agencies. The dimensions given for the table surfaces are optimal, but minor modifications may be made to fit circumstances dictated by varying space availabilities in rooms.

Worktable

Dimensions: 6 feet by 2 feet, 28 inches high. Surface may be made from finished joined planks of 6 by 1-and-1/4 inch, or, more easily, from a 3/4-inch plywood sheet. Supporting legs may be made from 4- by 4-inch posts, strengthened by 2- by 4-inch braces.

This table is placed with a long side against a wall and is accessible from three sides only. Initially, the table is used by the therapist for displaying the crafts materials and some of the tools so as to suggest their use by *visual stimulation*. After the first sessions, as the children become familiar with the setting, the materials are no longer displayed. They remain in the storage cabinets, which are opened or unlocked before the children arrive. The boys or girls help themselves from the cabinets. The table is usually occupied by several children, each at his own self-selected job. The children may be working independently or cooperatively. It usually becomes a place of assembly. Functionally, it can also be used as a supplementary woodworking table, should the actual one be fully occupied.

Refreshment Table

The refreshment table should be round and large enough to seat ten persons comfortably. The shape of the table enables all to be in view of each other, which promotes feelings of belonging. This table serves as another assembly point as the group develops and is then usually used as a congregation point for quiet talk and table games.

The children's tendency to use the refreshment table as a gathering place undoubtedly flows from its initial use as a place for eating. In this context it is closely associated in symbolic meaning with the therapist, the giving person, and the family. Therefore, this table, because of its placement near the "kitchen area," assumes, in the psychic economy of some of the children, more significance than other parts of the room.

A round table surface may be made from two semicircular sections cut from 3/4-inch plywood, with a supporting frame made from 4- by 4-inch posts, with 2- by 4-inch braces. When used for refreshments, it should be appropriately covered with a tablecloth. At all other times its top is uncovered. Because of its shape and its special significance, girl patients usually gather around it to do their handicrafts, forming a friendly, intimate circle. There are, of course, always some individual girls who take up activities considered more suitable for boys, and they work away from the group. A round table as specified above may be purchased ready-made. The refreshment table should be located so that all parts of its surfaces are accessible, yet it should be close enough to a wall and not extend too far into the room and thus encumber the central space. Its most suitable position is near the kitchen area where the food is prepared and served.

Isolate Table

This is a small table, suitable for use by one or two children.

Dimensions, 4 feet by 2 feet, 28 inches high. This table can be fabricated from the same type of lumber suggested for the other tables or readily purchased in a home supply store.

The isolate table is usually situated in or near a corner of the room, with two of its sides accessible. It should be in a part of the room minimally utilized by children, but not too far from the center of activities. While the other tables are intended to be occupied by more than one child simultaneously, the isolate table is aimed to accommodate one or at most two children who are either diffident or otherwise as yet unready to feel comfortable in the proximity of fellow group members and have to slowly grow out of their defensive isolation. From the relatively safe position of the isolated table such children move slowly as they acquire security in the group, first physically and later also emotionally.

An insecure, very timid child may remain in this isolative location for many weeks, relinquishing it only momentarily from time to time to get something from the supply closet and warily join the group for refreshments. The transition from isolation to group participation is most often made as other children join the isolate fleetingly to see what he is about. Usually no word passes between them. On occasion, the curiosity seeker may ask the self-sequestered child what he is doing. Such episodic contacts serve as beginning steps in socialization of isolates. Sometimes an aggressive child preempts the isolative table. This occurs rarely and is unlikely to continue beyond a segment of a session.

Woodwork Bench

There is a tendency to employ makeshift devices for woodworking benches, partially because of their cost but mostly because of the inexperience of professionally trained personnel in such matters. But if children are to enjoy working with lumber, and to gain in ego strength through their efforts to master such a highly resistive material, frustration due to inadequate equipment must be avoided at all costs. Commercially manufactured woodwork benches, such as those used in woodwork classrooms of elementary schools, are most suitable for activity therapy groups and can be purchased second-hand. The benches have two vises, and if second-hand benches are to be used, they should be checked as to the working condition of the vises and their sturdiness.

In lieu of a commercial workbench, a satisfactory one can be made from rough, heavy lumber. Dimension: 4 feet by 2 feet, 28 inches high. Two vises can be attached at diagonally opposite ends. Small hand clamp vises are not adequate, as they easily work loose, irritating children, who, as a result, give up work on their projects. The work surface and the legs of the woodwork bench can be made from 4- by 4-inch hardwood. All woodwork bench legs must be firmly bolted or screwed to the floor using heavy-duty angle irons. The following should be kept in mind in locating the woodwork bench:

The bench should be placed at a sufficient distance from a wall so that all sides are accessible for use, and close to the tool closet.

Its location should be at a distance from parts of the room that are frequently used for passing from place to place.

Other tables should be placed at a sufficient distance from the woodwork bench so that children using woodworking tools may feel free to manipulate them without accidentally hurting others.

The four tables described are sufficient. Additional work surfaces tend to scatter the group members and prevent contiguity, thereby reducing the potential for bringing about personal contacts — one of the important aims of the manual occupations.

Supply Cabinet

A supply cabinet is needed to store the tools and the crafts materials. In the event that more than one group will use the room at different times, separate cabinets (not tools) are preferable to one used in common, though this is not essential. There are several reasons for this exclusiveness in arrangement. From a practical point of view, some of the crafts media and the tools used by different groups vary in age and gender. Further, each therapy group tends to look upon its cabinet in a proprietary manner, and the children of one group are annoyed by alterations in replacement of the closet's contents by other groups. Later in a group's development this is not as important a factor, because by then the children are capable of sharing with other groups.

Either metal or wood cabinets are suitable. The important requirement is that the shelves are deep enough to hold the supplies and tools, and further, that all shelves are within view and easily accessible. Tall closets, in which shelves are above eye level of the children, are unsuitable. An additional closet is required to store "works in progress" by various children. Just a few open shelves may also answer the purpose. Each object so stored must have the name of its owner clearly marked.

By following the principle of function relatedness, the supply closet should be placed in reasonable proximity to the locations of the worktables and yet not so close as to interfere with passage to and from the tables, or with children who may be actively at work.

Kitchen Cabinet

This cabinet is used to hold the dishes, cutlery, cooking utensils, towels, soap, and other appurtenances used in serving light refreshments. There are no particular requirements for such a cabinet beyond the need for it to hold the necessary kitchen supplies and to have a surface to work on these preparations. Cleaning-up supplies should be near or next to the closet. The closet can have cloth curtains or doors.

Kitchen facilities should not be kept under lock and key. It is important that the children feel free to use them when they become ready for it and wish to assume the responsibility for preparing and serving food.

Seating Arrangements

Chairs and benches must be appropriate as to height for the ages of the children. If folding chairs are used, they should be of good quality. Only enough chairs are needed to seat the members of the group and the therapist, with one or two additional for visitors that group members may bring with them. Two high stools are also necessary for some work at which children may wish to be seated at a higher level than ordinary chairs provide.

Clothes Hangers

Clothes hooks can be attached to a wall of the room out of the way to provide for outer garments, thus preventing their being strewn about and creating an aspect of disorder or causing possible damage to the garments.

Water Supply, Lavatory, and Cooking Arrangements

An activity therapy group should have water available for some of the activities and, especially, for preparing refreshments. Most desirable are a sink and water faucet incorporated into the kitchen area. If that is not possible, they must be part of the lavatory that opens directly into the workroom. When this is the case, it may be advisable to have a medium-sized plastic basin for carrying the water to the kitchen area.

If a sink is available within the room itself, a table or wide shelf should be built or supplied contiguous to it to facilitate heating the refreshments. The table should be partially covered by a thick asbestos pad on a tin frame upon which a two-burner electric plate rests. The electric outlet should be nearby so the children will not stumble over electric extension wires.

It is essential that the lavatory open directly into the main body of the room, preferably at one end. For obvious reasons, it should not be located where the children have to leave the room to get to it. Such a location serves as an escape from the group, with varying consequences. In one instance where this arrangement could not be prevented, we had considerable difficulty as children were constantly disappearing from sight. Some inaugurated games outside the room, including splashing water on each other. Others went down to the street unsupervised.

Function Relatedness

The furnishings of a room, including tables, chairs, cabinets, closets, kitchen corner or alcove, and all other articles of furniture, should be placed in such positions as to have function relatedness to each other. This reduces movement, makes for more work efficiency, prevents annoyance or frustration, and fosters a calmer atmosphere. Thus, the woodwork bench is located close enough to where the tools and wood materials are stored so that a child may have easy access to them. This also applies to the central table, on which the therapist displays much of the material when a group is first started, and which becomes the focal point of the group's activities. If there is a sink within the room (in addition to one in the toilet), the cupboard holding the kitchen settings and the refreshment table should be located close by. The location of the ping-pong table, which is set up at a distance from the other furnishings, allows for the children's play and vigorous movement without the risk of interfering with the quieter work of others.

Conditions Affecting Safety

As already noted, an activity therapy room is designed to stimulate interest and freedom in its use. Any conditions that make it necessary for the therapist to limit children in their free movement and action vitiates his neutrality and permissive role. Rooms must therefore be devoid of any physical hazards. Under no circumstances must the therapist be placed in a position of having to caution, limit, or protect children. Their self-direction and personal autonomy must be assured, which requires meticulous anticipatory preventive measures.

A room optimally designed as to its structural elements and furnishings prevents children from injury and from generating anxiety in the therapist, which spares him from unnecessary involvement and interference. To achieve such a climate of safety, attention should be given to the following considerations, among others:

Glass Surfaces

Glass, or any other shatterable material, should be avoided. Thus, glass panels in doors, closets, or partitions are taboo. Where they unavoidably exist, they can be replaced by plywood or covered by metal screenings of mesh wire, heavy gauge. Such precautions reduce the possibility of their being shattered if accidentally struck by an object, or if a child falls or leans against them. Whenever suitable, there is an advantage in using translucent glass with wire reinforcement.

Inevitably a child may wish to open or close a window, either for the purpose of ventilation, or to look out. To prevent accidents (and therapist interference), window stops at proper heights in the frame slides can be nailed, thus limiting the extent to which the lower half of the window is openable. This and similar strategies are in conformity with situational restraint that avoids the therapist's direct control.

An extreme example of this was the equipment of a therapy room in a former commercial establishment one story above the street level with a display window the width and height of the entire room. Full partitions were built dividing the floor in half, which then provided the appropriate size for a therapy room. To safeguard the children against injury, we built a picket fence about 4½ feet in height across the room in front of the window and stretched wire meshing from this fence to the ceiling. The fence prevented bodily impact against the huge window, and the wire mesh kept it from being struck by flying objects. The columns holding up the ceiling beams were padded with felt, and the glass panel on the entrance door at the street level was protected by a removable frame of heavy mesh placed on the inner side of the door so that boys playfully pursuing each other down the stairs would not impetuously push their hands through the glass panel.

Protruding Structural and Breakable Objects

Any structural parts that extend into the room or stand entirely within the room present possible hazards and should be enclosed or padded. This includes such objects as radiators, steam-pipe risers, columns, and various sharp corners.

First-Aid Kit

Despite all anticipatory precautions, it is inevitable that children as active as those in AGT will have slight injuries, such as scrapes and cuts of the skin. A standard small first-aid kit or odd items like a painless antiseptic, surgical cotton, tape, Band-Aid, and small scissors must always be on hand.

CRITERIA FOR SELECTING SUPPLIES

We have seen that the therapeutic climate of the treatment group has to foster a feeling of freedom — a sense of emancipation from the all too familiar restrictions imposed by parents, teachers, and others in the community — and at the same time supply motivation to explore new avenues of experience in work, play, and human relations. While it is the attitude and conduct of the therapist that initially convey freedom, it is the work and play materials that become the experiential modality through which the children's varied growth and corrective needs find active fulfillment. Therefore, it is essential that careful consideration be given to the choice of materials, through which children's growth needs can be fulfilled.

The basic criteria for choosing supplies are that they be intrinsically interesting and meaningful. More definitely, materials should be familiar to the young children, evoke curiosity, tap creative potentials, meet play needs, and provide for discharge of aggression. Such materials help the process of sublimation, foster socialization, and promote a feeling of competence and accomplishment which have been denied them in the past.

Choice of materials has to be geared to the developmental capacities, age levels, and the degrees of competency. Materials and tools should be of the simplest type and appropriate to the gender of the children, as well as to their age. While many crafts and games are equally suitable to both boys and girls, it would be counterproductive to provide boys with sewing supplies and girls with woodwork or machine tools. In a general sense, there may be some merit in a boy's knowing how to sew a button on a garment, and for a girl to be able to do simple carpentry. However, one must be mindful of the fact that the problems that beset disturbed children are often related to matters of sexual identity. It is, therefore, necessary that therapy fortify appropriate sexual identifications by any means available, and the working equipment in a therapy group should reinforce such identifications through judicious selection of materials for activities. We have found, for example, a record player with popular, semi-classical, and dance music salutary for preteenage girls, but inappropriate for boy's groups. This is also true of sewing, knitting, and some artwork materials.

THE ELEMENTS OF "RESISTIVITY" OF
MATERIALS AND ACTIVITY CHOICE

In keeping with the findings of projective psychological tests, the child's choice of and use of materials to work with serves as an indication of his psychic state and, at times, also of his basic nature. The timid and diffident—the "weak" boys—initially choose materials of low resistivity, i.e., materials that readily yield to shaping and require little effort and aggression: crayons for drawing, plasticine for molding, leather lacing for lanyards, and in some instances, pewter, not copper, for hammering out ashtrays.

The more aggressive group members may start with copper or wood, which requires greater effort and aggression and, perhaps, also concentration. Some may even initiate projects such as building a small stool or a shoeshine box but, finding them too difficult, may abandon them after one or two sessions. In many instances they return to these enterprises months later, after they have acquired the know-how (and perhaps also self-confidence) to succeed at the earlier, overdifficult undertakings.

Most girls turn to projects more consistent with their culturally derived self-image; small rug weaving, drawing, painting, knitting, making dolls, or sewing aprons, blouses, and occasionally even a simple dress. There may be one or two who undertake more boylike activities, such as hammering out an ashtray, or sawing wood, often without special aim in mind. These choices are made on the basis of their identities arising from home conditions.

The movements of children to more gender-appropriate projects and toward more resistive materials as the group sessions proceed are valid indicators of strengthening egos and corrective identifications. These evolve slowly, require periods of different lengths for different children, and can occur only in a setting in which free choice is offered.

ORDERLINESS AND CONSISTENCY OF THE SETTING

As one of the goals of psychotherapy is to help patients grow emotionally calm and stable, external orderliness has to be consistently maintained in the treatment room. The physical setting is planned and *maintained* to prevent inconveniences, irritations, and frustration. Physical disorder tends to increase disordered emotions; orderliness promotes feelings of inner order and security. Sameness and constancy of the setting in the early stages of a group aid in this process, which is an essential ingredient of a therapeutic climate in nonverbal therapy (the "knowable nature" of the group). Changes of furnishings and their placements and new crafts media (unless requested by children) tend to disturb the emotionally unstable, rendering psychic energies less readily available for personality improvement and creative achievement. Unexpected demands for new accommodations and distracting alterations in the environment in the early stages of a group's life add to anxieties and tensions. Little change should therefore be made during the lifetime of a therapeutic activity group. As we shall see later, added tests of frustration are planfully introduced in the fourth quarter of the two-year period, and the reactions of each member are carefully recorded.

Orderliness, convenience, and consistent storing of tools should follow these principles. The woodwork tools, which are used more than any others by boys, should be hung on special brackets or nails on the inner faces of the doors of the supply closets. (This positioning not only is practical and efficient but also provides visual stimulation for initiating occupations.) Nails, screws, and angle irons of different sizes are best stored in a box with small square compartments or in separate metal or plastic containers. It is exceedingly frustrating to anyone, and especially to a child with unstable emotions, when working with lumber, for example, to have to search lengthily for the proper size in a mixed jumble of different sizes of nails and screws. Since the children use quantities of poster color paints, these should be supplied in pint jars. This makes it unnecessary for a child to move back and forth for separate items, prevents spillage, and aids orderliness.

During group sessions, the consistent initial orderliness of the room and setting found *at the start of every session* is quickly disturbed by the activities (which may be creative and purposeful, playful or boisterous). It may be advisable at times, when the room acquires too chaotic an appearance, for the therapist unobtrusively to restore some of the discarded objects, tools, and materials strewn about, thereby preventing possible injury to someone by stumbling over them; also to restore an orderly aspect in the room. Tools discarded by the busy workers may have to be returned to their regular places so that children in need of them during the progress of their work will not be forced to search for them. Paintbrushes, particularly, require attention to prevent the mess they create.

There are important reasons for the therapist to perform the tasks indicated. By acting in this manner, he is also demonstrating orderliness and responsibility, without pressing the children or communicating in any fashion that they are remiss in creating the disorder. His conduct also has educational, and in many instances reeducational implications. The chores the therapist performs, especially in the early stages of the group's life, are eventually mirrored in the behavior of the group as its members take over these responsibilities voluntarily, later also purchasing food, setting the table for refreshments, washing the utensils, and straightening up the room. Thus, the group grows more involved as times passes.

THE THERAPIST'S PART IN FOSTERING RESPONSIBILITY

The manner in which the therapist applies himself in the early stages of treatment to maintaining order and cleanliness by replacing tools and equipment to their assigned places in the storage cabinets is therapeutically effective only when he does it in a quiet, unhurried, and unobtrusive manner. It is more important that he does not follow up on situations where children fail to rectify their carelessness or indifference, as when they let tools dropped to the floor lie there, for example. To do so implies criticism and disapproval. Often patients in their impetuosity drop outer clothing to the floor or place it on a chair or table, instead of hanging it on the hangers or hooks provided for that purpose. It would be a serious error for the therapist to correct a child's carelessness immediately. This he does unobtrusively some minutes later, which prevents the child's placing him in the category of his critical parent or teacher. The rigid rule is that a therapist by his behavior must in no way remind the patients of these adults.

CONDITIONED VERSUS CONTROLLED ENVIRONMENT

The design of the setting for AGT and its climate have often been incorrectly referred to as a "controlled environment." The concept of control is alien to AGT in any connection. Nothing is as diligently eschewed by this therapeutic modality as are control and authority. In fact, members of groups introduce variables from time to time by bringing in toys, tools, and other objects which are integrated by them into the standard work appurtenances supplied by the therapist. They also bring friends as visitors to "show off" the "club" to which they "belong." The environment of an activity therapy group is more correctly identified as a "conditioned environment" in which active and adaptive functioning may produce results in the character structure of children.

LIST OF SUPPLIES

Woodwork
Tools:
1 try square rule
1 ruler, metal
1 yardstick
2 bit braces, 10-inch sweep
Auger bits, 2 each, 1/4-, 1/2-, 3/4-, 1-inch for above brace
2 screw drivers, 3/8 inch
2 wood chisels, 1/2, 3/4 inch
1 C clamp, 5-inch
1 hand drill with sets of drill bits
Wood files, 10 inches, 1 each, flat, half-round, full-round
4 file handles for above

3 claw hammers, one 12-ounce head, two 10-ounce heads
1 ball peen hammer, 8-ounce head
1 metal snips, 10-inch
1 block plane, 9 inches long
1 block plane, 6 inches long
1 combination pliers
4 coping saws 6-1/2-inch and extra blades
1 crosscut saw, fine, 22-inch
1 rip saw, 26-inch
1 keyhole saw, 10-inch
2 nail sets, 1/8-inch
1 miter box, hardwood
Brads, 1-, 1½-, 2-inch
Nails, 1-1/4-, 2-, 2-1/2-inch
Wood screws, 1-, 1-1/2-inch
Screw eyes, various sizes
Sandpaper, sheets, coarse, medium, fine
Lumber (no hardwoods):
 Pine, planks, 1/2 by 6 inches by 4 feet
 Pine, planks, 1/2 by 8 inches by 4 feet
 Plywood, 1/4-inch in 2-foot squares
 Dowels, 1/4-, 1/2-, 3/4-, 1-inch

Metal Work

Foil, copper, or aluminum, in sheets or roll, 36 gauge.
Embossing tools for pressing foil
Disks, copper, pewter, or aluminum, heavy gauge, for molding
    into ashtrays or plates
2 shaping mallets, hardwood, for above
2 molds, hardwood, for shaping disks
Wire (bare, rolls), copper and aluminum

Leather Work

Squares, irregular pieces or rolls of leather or less expensive
    synthetic substitutes, for working into wallets, comb cases,
    pencil holders, purses, etc.
1 hole puncher, rotating head

Snap fasteners and assembly tools
Lanyard clips and lanyard leather string, various colors

Plastic Work

Plastic ring tubes, for cutting and shaping finger rings
Plastic squares, 3/16-inch, for cutting and assembly
Plastic cement, tubes

Linoleum Block Printing

Battleship linoleum squares, 6-by-6 inches
1 set linoleum carving tools
Block printing ink, assorted colors in tubes
1 3-inch rubber roller for above

Woodburning

1 pyropencil, removable tips, for woodburning

Models

Airplanes
Boats

Art and Drawing Supplies

Show card poster paints, water-base, assorted colors, in plastic jars
Artists' brushes, 3 each, 1/4-, 1/2-, 3/4-inch
Newsprint, heavy white, large sheets
Construction paper, assorted colors, large sheets
Tracing paper and carbon paper
2 boxes of crayons, assorted colors
3 pencils
2 6-inch scissors
1 stapler, extra staples
Paste, jar
Shellac, bottle or can

Clay

Plasticine, 1-pound blocks
1 modeling tool set

Games

1 ping-pong set and table, 4 rackets, extra balls
1 Nok-Hockey set, extra sticks and pucks
1 checker set and board
1 Chinese checker set and board
2 jacks sets, for girls

Additional Items for Girls' Groups

Pipe cleaners, bundles, assorted colors
Crepe paper, rolls, assorted colors
String, balls, assorted colors
Needles: sewing, simple crocheting
Thread, wool, cotton
Felt cloth, other suitable materials for needlework
2 looms for pot holders
Cotton loops, bags, colored, for pot holders
Note: Girls' activity groups can use most of the standard items
    supplied for all groups.

Kitchen Items

1 dozen cups
1 dozen saucers
1 dozen salad plates
3 dinner plates
2 saucepans, 1-, 2-quart
1 dozen each, spoons, forks, knives (stainless)
1 hotplate, electric, double, preferably with open coils
1 asbestos board, 2-by-3 feet
1 dish drainer
Napkins, dishtowels (disposable), paper hand towels in dispenser
Soap and soap powder

General Supplies

1 waste basket, large
2 brooms, push type
1 dust pan
1 mop
1 pail
Cleaning rags
Newspapers for protecting surfaces from soiling by paint
Plastic table cloth
Balls of twine

Items in Reserve, Not Visible or Accessible to Children

Paint in cans and paintbrushes, to restore walls to original condition when they are marred by children. This is done only after a therapy group has left the room.

Note: It is not necessary to install the full complement of tools and materials listed above at the outset of a group. Rather it is advisable to supply essential items in each of the categories and gradually add others in the early sessions. Often children request these as they need them to proceed with their projects.

V

The Nature of
the Therapeutic Activities

THE INITIAL SHOCK EFFECT

The basic intent of AGT is that child patients may discover for the first time a life setting and an adult devoid of the psychonoxious influences to which they had been exposed in the past. Initially children react to these with some shock and considerable discomfort. The unrestricted freedom of choice and action generate anxiety equally in the aggressive and the diffident, manifested in facial expressions of wonderment and uncertainty. Most children remain briefly standing motionless, surveying the room and its accouterments, somewhat puzzled, as though expecting to receive instructions from the therapist, who greeted them in a cordial and friendly manner, but returned to his work project as though he were ignoring them. After a brief period of being at a loss, the child, without uttering a word, turns impassively to examine the tools and supplies.

The therapist continues in his absorption with his job, seemingly unconcerned until the child *discovers* with some discomfort that here he is on his own. After perfunctorily touching or handling some of the objects, which helps decrease his discomfort, he takes up some materials with which he may be acquainted from past experiences, and following the example set by the therapist silently proceeds to work. The simplicity of the material and equipment is important. Were it to consist of unaccustomed objects, children would not find their way around on their own. The principle of

87

visual stimulation operates by acquaintance with the commonly employed tools and materials in schools, homes, and the community generally. Some, after a period of perusal, turn to the therapist and ask what they can do. The therapist responds in a friendly manner by enumerating some of the many possibilities for making things, emphasizing the word "making." Note that he does not use the term "do," but rather suggests that one can make things. Nor does he use a blanket or generic phrase of "making anything" the child wishes. He responds rather with a list of specific possibilities that the equipment offers, leaving it to the child to make a choice. To respond with a blanket permission to make *anything* might prove rather bewildering to a youngster who has had little or no experience in arts and crafts and has quite likely been exposed to continual suggestions and controls.

THE ELEMENT OF SIMPLICITY AND FIRST STEPS

It must be noted again that the implements and materials in the room consist almost entirely of ordinary object that a child in a modern home, school, and neighborhood has seen and perhaps used. There may be a small number of objects with which some children may be unacquainted and the use of which they learn later in the course of their attending the group through observing the therapist or some other sophisticated fellow group member. The more curious and enterprising children may experiment with them and discover their nature by trial and error, or by asking the therapist.

The element of acquaintanceship with the objects in the room that we emphasize proves here of prime importance; nothing should arouse intense or prolonged curiosity. The therapist must keep in mind the foundational objectives, libido fixation (so as to prevent random, uncontrolled, and violent acting out), socialization (through cooperative activity, mutual helpfulness, and sharing), and evolving a feeling of competence and achievement (thereby improving each child's self-image and self-confidence). Playing up the physical environment and things in it that would arrest overintense interest, such as scientific toys or equipment, would prolong intellectual pursuits, which is counterindicated. Such materials are productive in a "learning" situation, but delimit expanse of personal and social development, which is the major aim of our therapy.

The activity group therapy equipment, especially work materials, are so elemental that a child, even at the outset, can complete a project in a single session. As the group progresses and the patients' skills, self-confidence, and concentration span expand, they can undertake projects that take up several weekly sessions. Thus, when the therapist enumerates possible projects in response to a child's initial query as to what he "can do," the list should consist of things that can be accomplished in an hour and a half of working time. He may suggest an ashtray, a small box, a lanyard, a model boat, clay (plasticine) modeling, or a (water color) painting.

The shyness of the first child at his entry into the room is usually lessened in children who follow. Finding a child of his own age present or already at work relieves the newcomer of the discomfort of remaining alone with a strange adult. Where more than one child is already at work, the initial diffidence is greatly reduced. Nonetheless, the first session is for a time a strain on all which is manifested by immobility, silently observing others at work from a distance, and seemingly being at a loss.

Period of Acclimatization

A period of acclimatization is characteristic of all animals, not sparing man. Dogs, for example, when visiting a strange home with their owners, explore by sniffing at every corner of the room. Once that period is past and all or most of the members of the group settle down to work, each following his self-chosen interest, they soon discover and are impressed that no controls are placed on their use of equipment and materials. Occasionally a child may ask permission to use some tool or material. The therapist matter-of-factly replies that here he "can use anything he needs." Further direction or suggestions are usually not necessary. In this manner the therapist conveys the important message that everyone is free to decide for himself what he wishes to make. However, the newness of the total setting keeps children in a state of unease for some time, which is revealed by their turning their gaze from time to time toward the therapist to see whether he is observing them. *It is most important that the children do not surprise him looking at them.*

There are times when a dependent child complains to the therapist, usually in a plaintive voice, that he does not know "what to make." Even in such instances the therapist avoids specific suggestions so as not to fortify the child's dependency. The therapist needs to recognize that the child, replicating his past, is less concerned with "making something" than with becoming involved in a dependent relation with him. The response of the therapist, therefore, should be to enumerate quietly the various possibilities available, leaving the decision to the child. This technique, which may appear as a rejection of him, greatly depends on the manner in which it is carried out. Experience confirms the validity of this clinically determined procedure to help children move toward autonomy. However, with the over-dependent child, the therapist must become alerted and give him special attention: he may walk over with the child to examine the materials and tools displayed on the table and closet, enumerating possible projects. The visual stimulation and verbal support invariably result in the child's making a choice. The special attention helps the child in making a decision.

CHOICE OF ACTIVITIES AND THEIR MEANINGS

We have laid considerable emphasis on the selection of materials suitable to the age and skills of children, the manner in which they make use of them, and the extent and nature of the therapist's involvement. These materials, supplies, and tools, in addition to being simple, are suitable for discharging physical and psychic energies and serve the ends of catharsis and displacement. Boys who select work with materials of high resistivity involving "assault" in banging, cutting, sawing, and hammering may do so to discharge aggressive trends and perhaps anxiety. Observing the manual work of such children at the beginnings of treatment, one is impressed with the extraordinary quality of their anger and the aggression that flows from it through their manner. In addition to its cathartic effect of displacement of hostile resentment against persons, the major value of the work lies in the child's discovery

90

that he can act aggressively, without fear or guilt, and achieve ego gratifications by creating a useful or ornamental object that brings recognition and praise from other children and not infrequently from members of his family.[1]

At times an aggressive child may "attack" materials with no intention of fabricating anything, just to destroy them. He may hack or hammer away at a piece of wood that happens to be clamped in a vise, or saw it impetuously into bits or pound away with a mallet on a copper disk or at a wad of clay, with no intention of making an ashtray or a statuette. His manifest purpose is destruction, i.e., release of anger.

In either case, the therapist's response to such diffuse aggression is pivotal not only in the relation to the aggressive child, but also in relation to all the other children, for if he becomes disturbed, prohibitive, or punitive, his image as a strong, permissive person will be affected and he will forfeit his value as an object of identification. If the therapist reacts negatively or punitively toward any one child, even if this is justifiable by ordinary standards, he will become in their eyes a potential threat to all of them, which will inhibit them from freely acting out.

It is most unlikely that a child in AGT will persist for any length of time in destroying materials in the manner just described. If such behavior does continue for more than several sessions, the child's anamnesis and psychologic and psychiatric evaluations must be reviewed, for it may be associated with psychotic or psychopathic disturbances, brain injury, or deepseated neurosis. In that case, removal from the group and referral for a more appropriate therapy is indicated.

However, in the course of prolonged therapy, any child may display disturbing reactions at a session. This is often caused by a distressing experience immediately preceding his coming to the group, which we identify as an *antecedent experience.* In such instances, the therapist must unconditionally accept the behavior until it is dissipated, or he may subtly support the disturbed group member. This may take the form of physically moving

[1] To assure the latter, work with parents and/or other members of the child's family is sometimes indicated.

91

closer to him. Such supportive proximity, without comment, may afford sufficient relief to a youngster. Or, should it be necessary to supply more direct solace, the therapist may ask the child to help him with his, the therapist's, project or invite him to play a game of checkers or ping-pong. These techniques are examples of action interpretation: their meaning to the child is as though the therapist said, "I understand that you feel unhappy, and I would like to help you relax." In this role the therapist acts also as a *supportive ego* to his patient.

In contrast to the aggressive children, insecure, frightened, and diffident ones tend under the same circumstances to remove themselves from contact with, or even being in the vicinity of, others. They work in isolation or in the proximity of the therapist or a fellow group member with whom they instinctively feel safe. Such children may prove to be "good workers," but their concentration is a form of self-encapsulation and militates against socialization. The lack of manifest aggression leads them to select types of crafts work which do not require energetic physical output and usually to choose materials of low resistivity. They work with plasticine or spend their time unobtrusively painting, sketching, braiding leather lanyards and similar occupations, usually at the isolation table. They eschew activities that involve noise, such as hammering, which seems to frighten them. If such a child accidentally drops a tool, he instantly grows tense and peers about to see whether others have noticed it.

However, in time, after he has assessed the total group situation from his safely removed stance, and when he has confirmed through extended observations of the therapist and the other children that he will not be in danger if he attempts to participate with the others, the passive child slowly begins to explore new pursuits. The therapist would make a serious error should he attempt to draw such a child into activities or relations before he does so spontaneously. The child must be allowed to grow at his own pace. The testing or acclimatization period is much more extensive for the withdrawn child than it is for the others. Even as . his self-assurance begins to emerge, his intial attempts to widen his operational horizon in the group are for a time tentative. He is fearful of the reactions of others to his venture outward.

The behavior of a diffident child in these circumstances can be likened to that of crustaceans who project their appendages before initiating movement to explore the safety of the environment. If no danger is sensed, the animal moves ahead. Should anything be present which may threaten it, it quickly withdraws the appendages and remains inert. Sensitive humans, and especially children, react in a similar manner. Should an initial step of a diffident child in an activity group be in the slightest way rebuffed, or his pace accelerated, he, too, will at once withdraw again into his isolative shell.

What is even more important to recognize is that even a friendly gesture and an offer of help may be felt as an invasion of such a child's threat area, causing him to withdraw. Under special circumstances, the therapist may at times take the initiative in blocking some aggressive group member who may attempt to interfere with the diffident one by diverting the former's attention, such as asking him for help in doing his (the therapist's) work. However, our observation of the reactions of numerous AGT members is that they evade making contact with strongly withdrawn fellow members. It is as though they perceive the problems of the shy child and let him be. This is poignantly demonstrated in the film "Activity Group Therapy."[2]

While the therapist needs to be cautious before attempting to make contact with such children, it may sometimes be necessary for him to volunteer assistance in overcoming a real work difficulty so as to prevent failure and discouragement. This is best accomplished without verbalization, and the therapist should remove himself from contact as soon as his assistance is no longer needed. This procedure accomplishes several things: the child is helped over a point of frustration; his defensive social insulation is not overwhelmed; he is reassured by the circumspect behavior of the therapist; and he is thus prepared to sustain a relation with the therapist and later with children.

[2]A film made over a period of two years and available to professionals from the Film Library, New York University, Washington Square, New York, N.Y.

CONSTANCY OF MATERIALS

The supply closet should be replenished before materials are completely used up. For a considerable time there should be little modification in, or additions to, the basic equipment and tools. From time to time, always in response to a special request from a child, some new item may be added. The fulfillment of such requests fortifies the perception of the therapist as a giving person. There may be therapeutic advantage, however, in introducing moderate new stimuli for new experiences when the children's interest in the standard equipment appears to lag.

When it is realistically and/or clinically indicated that an individual's or even a group's requests for special supplies (which occurs rarely) are too costly or indicative of an exploitative attitude, the therapist cannot refuse them out of hand. Rather, he introduces an outer authority in the person of the "office," by displaying a letter addressed to him stating in simple terms that the particular item exceeds the budgetary limits and cannot be supplied. The therapist opens the letter in view of the group and, after reading it, places it on the main table so that the children can read it for themselves. Not only may the therapist not deny anything to his group members, but he cannot be the harbinger of frustrating news. Should any resentment be generated by the denial (which is unlikely), it can then be directed at the anonymous "office" and not toward the therapist, who must maintain with no variation his neutral and benign image. This strategy has the added value that it makes the children aware of reality elements beyond the perimeter of the group.

REMOVING MATERIALS FROM THE GROUP

All finished projects belong to their creators and may be taken home. However, occasionally, a child may ask permission to take home an unfinished piece of his own work, some materials which he has not yet begun to use, such as drawing paper, a piece of plastic, or lumber, or to borrow a tool. These requests do not always flow from the simplistic fact of need or desire to continue an occupation begun at the group session. They may also stem from other sources, and the therapist's dealing with them appropriately is important. The motivations may be testing the therapist's genuineness as a giving adult, a desire to carry over the felicitous feelings of the group symbolically into the home, a test of unconditional acceptance, or to enrich the home experience. The latter is likely to be the case with children from homes bereft of opportunities for suitable activities, toys, or other engaging possibilities.

The therapists should respond positively to such requests, as unreasonable as they may appear. When basic tools, the absence of which may create a problem for the group as well as for other groups that follow on other days, are involved, he must still accede to the child's request but says, "Yes. But please bring it back next week, because others will need it."[3] Such extreme permissiveness is especially pivotal during early sessions so as to fix the image of the therapist as a positive person, unlike any other in the children's experiences. If removal of objects from the group becomes endemic, a letter addressed to the therapist is presented to the group reading, "It has come to our attention that your club has been using up more materials (and tools) than our budget allows. Will you please see to it that your boys (or girls) use only as much of these things as they actually need in the club and waste none." (Any name of an officer of the sponsoring organization will do for a signature.) In fact the therapist may dictate the letter himself. All such letters should be typewritten and presented to the group as already described.

The result of premature refusal to allow taking materials and tools home is illustrated by an episode during the early years of an AGT project. The director of the project, a nationally noted psychologist, in conversation with one of the present authors, stated with emphasis that the children must accept the fact that "the group's materials are for the group's use, and individuals cannot take advantage of it." "Shall I tell you what has happened?" we asked. "What?" somewhat taken aback, the other queried. "The boys began to steal." "That's right!" was the surprised admission.

Stealing is an inevitable reaction to the inconsistent role of the therapists from boys who mistrusted adults. The inconsistency of group "leaders," in being prohibitive and denying, replicates the

---

[3] For a detailed discussion of this, see Chapter VIII.

treatment youngsters have received at the hands of all other adults in the past, and they react accordingly. The therapists placed themselves in the same category—enemies to defeat. Children and adults are natural enemies, and the latter, being more mature, and hopefully having better judgment, must find ways to allay this enmity. AGT is designed to do this. To force patients in any type of therapy to suppress their psychomalignancies is to maintain the psyches in status quo, if not magnifying their problems. The corrective process requires that malignancies be revealed so that they can then receive therapeutic attention. They are the chief grist in the therapeutic mill, which arbitrarily imposed external controls and ethical standards prevent from coming to the fore to receive treatment.

A more appropriate method of dealing with a similar situation was used in one of our groups. After a prolonged period of unflagging permissiveness in a group of boys about eleven years of age, the therapist observed one of the group stealing on a number of occasions by concealing objects in his clothing as he was leaving for home. One evening after the group session the therapist planfully detached himself from the group on the way to the subway and joined the boy in question. The therapist then said to him, "George, I noticed that you are taking things from the club when nobody is looking. You know that I always let you take things when you ask me. Shall we leave it at that?" Having said this, the therapist abruptly walked away and joined the other boys. No incident of stealing occurred after that.

The effectiveness of this strategy depends on the absence of moralism, a genuine noncritical, nonpunitive accepting attitude on the part of the therapist, and the manner and tone of voice employed. "It is the tone that makes the music," runs an ancient proverb. Patients respond to the mien and tone of such an encounter, not only to its content, and to be effective the therapist must be sure of their quality when he faces a patient with so highly sensitive a matter. Another element in the above encounter that proved it so effective was the abruptness with which the therapist walked away after he made his statement, thus preventing the "culprit's" denying, making excuses, or offering retribution. It also served to strengthen the boy's identification with the therapist and his superego. In the several hundred groups the authors have observed, exploitation of therapy groups by patients has never been prolonged. As the boys and girls become convinced of the therapists' benevolence, all untoward acts disappear. An adult who, by disposition or his own personal characteristics and difficulties, is unable to sustain faith in children should not undertake the trying task of conducting activity therapy groups.

Of course, a child placed erroneously in a group may persist in noxious and group-infectious behavior. This should be considered an indication that he is unsuitable for this form of treatment and may require individual psychotherapy and, in extreme cases, commitment to a rehabilitative institution. As indicated in Chapter VI, it takes just one seriously acting out child to block the emergence of a therapeutic climate of a group and destroy it with no benefit to himself. In most instances, children inaccessible by AGT grow worse in a permissive environment.

THE TIE BETWEEN HOME AND GROUP

A child who openly removes objects, sometimes nothing more than a scrap of wood, from the group may do so from a desire to carry over the pleasant continuity from the group to his home. In such instances he should be allowed to do so until what might be described as sentimental attachment automatically abates. Such feelings in a child, representing emotional ties never before experienced, are most significant to the corrective process of his personality. He may also signify by this act his wish that his home might be as satisfying as is the group. In some instances children describe the group as "just like a home." They are particularly impressed when the therapist busies himself setting up the table preparing refreshments. One boy, speaking in a low, meditative tone to himself, said, "Just like a home."

The tie between home and the group also has group and individual transference significance. We have observed that as children internalize the effects of the group and recognize the therapist as an ideal parent, the conduct of many of them toward their parents and teachers greatly improves. Without benefit of guidance or therapy for the parents, the children grow more amenable, less troublesome, and generally more adaptable and obedient. We have labeled this phenomenon *transference in reverse.* Improvement extends to schools and neighborhood peers. In one instance an assistant principal of a school took the trouble to call one of the authors to convey her gratification with the improvement of a particularly troublesome youngster of long standing. She terminated her enthusiastic recital by saying, "I don't know what you did to him, but it's a miracle!"

PLAYING WITH FIRE

At some point it is almost inevitable that some boys will experiment with fire, which the use of the electric plate in the preparation of refreshments and the electric wood-burning stylus suggest. Most often the experimentation is carried out by igniting small pieces of paper. Such partially atavistic interest should not be squelched out of hand in the setting of AGT. (As already noted, precautionary measures are taken by providing a large asbestos-lined pad.)

In addition to its psychoanalytical meanings, fire setting carries other significances for boys (Girls have never become involved in playing with fire in our groups.) A timid child has to overcome many fears and achieve considerable ego strength before he can attempt, or participate in, such an activity, and when he does, it constitutes a major break toward improved mental health. Aggressive boys discover that they are able to control the dangers and fears with which the prohibitions against fire and matches had been set up for them in the past. The fact that the therapist accepts it and displays no anxiety as other adults had always done enchances security and feelings of potency in children.[4]

MAINTENANCE CHORES

A number of chores must be performed in maintaining the treatment room, such as sweeping the floor, removing rubbish and waste, purchasing, preparing, and serving food, washing

[4] A scene of fire setting and the boys' own safety steps appears in the film mentioned in this chapter, footnote 2.

dishes, keeping the storage closets orderly, replenishing materials before they are completely used up, and generally tidying up after sessions. The many and varied activities during the sessions give the room a disordered appearance: chunks of lumber and other waste products, tools, and games are strewn about. This disordered condition may be the result of normal activity, but may sometimes be a result of, or augmented by, boisterous play.

While the room is unavoidably littered during sessions, it must be neat and in perfect order when the children arrive. A disordered room at the start of a session induces disordered emotional reactions and acts. At the termination of the ninety minutes intended for manual occupations, the therapist wordlessly begins to set the room in order without announcing the fact or in any way interfering with the children's ongoing occupations. He returns the unused tools to their assigned locations in the closet, replaces materials, brushes tables, sweeps the floor, and places the sweepings in the basket. The therapist works "around" the children at their various occupations. These acts on the therapist's part signal the termination of the session and serve as a demonstration of orderliness and responsibility. Before handling food, he washes his hands and dries them on a paper towel within the sight of the children. He thus tacitly demonstrates cleanliness without verbalizing or commenting when they do not wash up. Invariably, after a few weeks the children follow his example and wash their hands as well.[5] For many sessions the therapist proceeds with these routines without attempting to involve the children, until such time as they voluntarily join him in doing the chores, which they later completely take over.

When some child first volunteers to help the therapist with the cleaning up, the therapist accepts this cooperative gesture without comment. The gesture may be an attempt to establish a preferential relationship with the therapist, which usually leads to tension among the others and jeopardizes his neutrality. Or it may stem from feminine identification in a boy, in the correction of which AGT is eminently successful. It may also be a repetition of a role imposed in the home, but the group members soon learn that

[5] This is part of the reeducational and desirable habit-forming process.

their relationship with the therapist is in no way conditioned or enhanced by such "helpfulness." Participation and responsibility must rather grow out of the feeling of belonging and emerging maturity.

Ordinarily, the therapist secures the refreshments on his way to the sessions, but when in his judgment the group members have reached a level of responsibility, it is not unusual for him to leave the room to purchase them. This strategy serves also as a means of testing the children's self-control to continue in an orderly fashion with their activities in his absence. Soon some child asks permission to do the purchasing, and almost always he invites another one or two to come along. The therapist then places money on a table (instead of handing it to anyone), thus preventing the appearance of preference.

TRIPS AND EXCURSIONS

After a therapy group has met for three or four months and the children have been acclimated to the permissive setting and have begun to establish relationships with the therapist and with each other, another dimension is added to the treatment experience through all-day excursions outside the treatment room. Such excursions, or "trips," as the young patients are accustomed to calling them, are held on weekends and school holidays and are substituted for regular weekday sessions. When the group sessions are ordinarily held on weekends, trips are arranged for the same day.

Trips are made to such places as restaurants, museums, parks, aquariums, amusement centers, movies, theaters, circuses, and rodeos. Trips are also planned around recreational activities such as rowing, bicycle riding (which is especially valuable for boys), walks and cook-outs, in which basketball, baseball, and softball are included. An outing may consist of several activities, depending on location and availability in the town or city where it is planned and on the age, readiness, and interests of the children.

Values of Excursions

The excursions, which are an integral part of the overall therapeutic design of AGT, have values beyond entertainment and diversion. An obvious value lies in the fact that the therapist's image as a giving and kindly person is further cemented through them. However, their service is even more important as a means for widening the children's experiential horizons. In most instances their lives have been limited to their homes and immediate neighborhoods. Many young ghetto children are frightened at the prospect of travel beyond their familiar precincts and are strengthened by ventures under the protective shield of the therapist and the group until they acquire a sense of security in new settings and untried experiences.

Experiences in traveling considerable distances from home and the familiar treatment room by various types of conveyances — bus, subway, elevated railroads, ferries, excursion boats, indoor escalators, and elevators — enhance the security and confidence of many children so that even at the age of ten they grow able to undertake travel for considerable distances on their own to and from the treatment sessions, often requiring changing busses or other conveyances en route. Of no little significance, for example, was the experience of one boy who finally undertook a ride on a "cyclone," a very rapid and highly stimulating ride in an amusement park, after having fearfully avoided it on several previous excursions. Another youngster insisted on climbing the circular stairway by himself from the base of the Statue of Liberty to the crown a second time, after having made his initial climb with great trepidation and in close proximity to the therapist.

The opportunities for achieving a sense of mastery and accomplishment at outings, such as learning to ride a bicycle, row a boat, throw and catch a football, or make an outdoor fire, are ego-expanding experiences of considerable magnitude for children who had been subjected in the past to directions, limitations, and controls. Other experiences and learnings that excursions provide expand the sense of reality and serve to increase capacities for reality testing and social learnings. Among these are the incidentals involved in such enterprises as purchasing tokens, transferring from one form of transportation to another, purchasing food for picnics, dining out in cafeterias and restaurants, learning to manage money allotted for expenses, and similar details.

101

Initiating and Conducting Excursions

The idea of trips is usually first introduced by the therapist at a time when he feels the children are ready. The therapist may inform the group at the refreshment table that "the office" has provided the group with finances to go on a trip should they so desire. The children may then suggest the places to visit and decide on matters involved. Group members who are absent when the announcement is made may be informed by mail or at the next session. From the very outset the children assume responsibility for handling money, which the therapist distributes to each member, with which to pay fare, order food of his own selection in a restaurant or cafeteria, and pay admission to places of entertainment.

INCIDENT, TREND, AND PATTERN

An isolated act that a child and even a group may commit, as damaging as it may seem, must be overlooked by a group therapist as an *incident*. This may be an impulsive act, a trial balloon, or even an act of hostility or aggression. This rule applies also to incidents of "stealing." To make an issue of a first transgression, a mistake parents and teachers always make, is to invite its repetition and the consequent conflicts, deceit, and evasion. The therapist must under all circumstances avoid making an issue of such an isolated act, but he should take note of it and observe whether the act is repeated. However, should the deviant act be repeated several times, it becomes a *trend* and should be dealt with to prevent its becoming an individual or group *pattern*. This was tangibly demonstrated by the manner in which the stealing incident reported earlier was managed.

Before such direct action is taken, however, where the practice of purloining, for example, assumes the character of a trend or a pattern, measures of situational restraint instead of direct confrontation can, and in most instances should, be tried first. At the stage of a trend, objects involved may be removed for several weeks and later restored. One of the most frequent undesirable acts is a boy's asking for a "loan" of money. In the first instance the therapist ought to comply. But if the same child does not repay the loan the following week and requests another "loan," the indication is that the original incident is moving toward a trend and that steps should be taken to prevent it. The therapist, in giving the boy the small amount of money the second time, says, impassively, "Now you owe me (mentioning the sum of the two loans).[6]

These procedures are employed only when a child repeats his malignant acts and ignores the therapist's subtleties. When the therapist becomes convinced that they will not automatically cease, he takes the direct steps suggested in Chapter VIII.

THE CRITICAL EVENT

In all psychotherapies the therapist must be on the alert for the occurrence of the *critical event* in the therapeutic unfolding of each of his patients. By critical event we mean a manifestation — which may be a verbal communication, an extraordinary emotional upheaval, or an overt act — of the beginning of a resolution of a patient's *nuclear problem*. The simplest example of this is when a very frightened, isolative, and withdrawn boy stands up for the first time against a bully in the group. Whether or not he is successful is at the moment not important; the very fact of offering resistance is a critical event, since it signifies a step toward overcoming a nuclear problem, which may be a fear of being hurt or defeated or, perhaps, a fear of his own hostility. In this instance the event is the first sign of change of the patient's characteristic adaptive pattern and the beginning of his ego reorganization more in consonance with mental health. It may also be an indication of improved self-image and a sign of growing confidence not only in relation to peers, but also in other areas. A rather startling occurrence during a refreshment period in the advanced stage of an activity therapy group illustrates an unexpected verbal emergence of such an "event." As he, his fellow group members, and the therapist were conversing, a boy, with no apparent reason, burst forth with the statement, "I really want to be a girl." Little heed was given by the others to this unusual declaration, except for the mental note the therapist made of it.

The significance of this statement is enhanced by the fact that

---

[6]For a more detailed discussion of this topic, see Chapter VIII.

on the basis of the boy's conduct in the group, the therapist's supervisor had indicated a number of times that the boy's sexual identification was defective and that he really wanted to be a girl. This boy's impulsive statement signaled a change in his self-image and constituted a critical event in his therapy.

The critical event of a boy who is customarily aggressive may occur when one or several of his group mates overwhelm him and he discovers the unreality of his blustering, bullying manner. Sometimes the act of a therapist constitutes a critical event when he "generously" gives money to a child who has been repeatedly denied and punished by his parents, or when he helps one at a point of difficulty with his work. When a dependent, infantilized, and overprotected child tells his mother she no longer needs to accompany him to the group sessions or call for him, as he can now travel by himself, which happens often in AGT, he has demonstrated a critical event of considerable magnitude.

The critical event is psychodynamically an initial experimental, but *spontaneous,* attempt of the newly strengthened ego to test its improvement. If the reaction to a patient's testing or experimental move is a negative one—when he is forced to withdraw or when he is defeated—it can be considered only as a symptom of awakening of inner forces and may be a precursor of a critical event that will manifest itself later.

THE SOCIALIZATION EFFECTS OF CHILDREN'S ACTIVITIES

Children are inevitably brought into contact with one another through the manual activities, games, and the planned setting. The contacts take the forms of cooperative and mutually agreeable outcomes such as a shared craft project, or helping one another with work, or playing a game involving two or more group members. Contacts may initially be of a conflictual nature leading to arguments and even physical encounters, though the latter occur rarely in a well-constituted group and are fleeting and perfunctory. The therapist must restrain himself from entering into such rifts, allowing the protagonists to resolve their difficulties on their own. In fact, the therapist must refrain even *from looking* directly at the contestants. To prevent possible injury, however, he should place himself where he can observe the proceedings peripherally.

The strategy of withholding direct gaze has special meaning. For the adult to observe unacceptable behaviour and not react signifies to children approval, or at least acceptance, of that behavior. By averting his gaze, the therapist indicates his non-acceptance passively, which serves as a mode of action interpretation. While in AGT *we accept the child unconditionally as a person, we do not accept all of his behaviour.*

Open conflict among children in an accepting, nonpunitive, and non-guilt or fear-arousing climate such as an activity therapy group is in itself socializing. As the protagonists resolve their contentions on their own, without (adult) interference, they discover the modus of benevolent relationships. It serves to arouse in them benign rather than hostile feelings as they discover the benefits of cooperation and mutual compromise. The adult's noninterference, which is in contrast to the children's past experiences, brings home to them the advantages of solving interpersonal problems amicably. Allowing children to resolve conflicts, especially physical encounters, may place the therapist in a trying position, but if he has confidence in himself and his charges, experience will prove to him the safety and soundness of this procedure.

Conflict situations arise from quarrels over materials or the use of tools, arguments as to game rules, and discussions having to do with group decisions about refreshments, trips, and other matters in which the group as a whole is involved. Such developments, and their outcomes, represent the working level of the group therapeutic process. The psychological elements involved in such interactions are tension induction (created by the conflict situation), confrontation, discharge of emotionality, recognition of reasonable alternatives, and eventual conflict resolution, all of which lead to alloplastic personality.

It is for these reasons that equipment which might serve genital, anal, urethral, and oral regression, such as that used in analytically oriented group therapies, is barred in AGT. The materials chosen here place a premium on corrective and integrating maturational opportunities. Unsuitable media invite regressive acting out and, since no interpretation is employed, prevent psychologic growth.

In activity-interview and play group therapies with young children — practices that depend on interpretations of behavior — materials are provided to foster responses related to early fixations associated with oedipal and preoedipal etiology and activate the unconscious and preconscious. Such materials are impermissible in AGT. Instead, games where two or more children can participate are especially suitable for interaction and socialization. The most common of such games are ping-pong, Nok-Hockey, checkers, Chinese checkers, tenpins, and others of a similar nature. The children are placed in situations where they can gain satisfactions by cooperation and sharing. Thus an overabundance of tools and supplies should be avoided. An advisable dearth of materials and occasional shortages of tools at later stages of treatment often favor social interaction, conflict and ultimate sharing. In an activity therapy group materials and equipment are chosen, in addition to their other values, for their potentials for positive and negative interpersonal encounters.

VI

Selection and Grouping

BASIC CRITERIA

Selection of patients for a nonverbal, situational therapy such as AGT is, at best, problematical. No criteria can be completely relied upon, for whatever clinical standards are employed, they can be rendered inoperable by the vast variety of characterological traits of prospective candidates. These traits must be considered not only as such, but also in their degree of intensity and manner of manifestation. Clinical entities, as well, need to be evaluated, or estimated, in the light of the same and similar considerations. This is tangibly illustrated in neuroses and neurotic traits, in preoedipal and oedipal behavior disorders, and in sociopathic-like behavior.

Guides for inclusion of patients in groups and for grouping them are set forth in considerable detail in *An Introduction to Group Therapy* (Slavson, 1945). The emphasis placed there on character traits and behavior has proved valid after many decades of trial. It is of utmost importance for the practitioner of AGT to hold fast to these pragmatically established and validated criteria as the bases for selecting patients for AGT.

The two basic criteria for inclusion of children in AGT are (1) a basic potential capacity—as weak and as distorted as it may be—to relate to others, which we term *social hunger,* and (2) the capacity or flexibility to alter attitudes and conduct through corrective experiences. In the first instance, the anamnesis must reveal that the child has had at least a moderately positive relation with one or more persons in his nuclear or extended family (such as grandparents, aunts, uncles, cousins), or that he has

107

related to one or more peers or a teacher. That is, the child's psyche has experienced *relatedness,* which can serve as a basis for amplifying and extending it in the favorable climate provided in AGT. In the second instance, the child's history must reveal that he has made at least moderate adaptations to variables in conditions of his life, as slight as they may be, such as school, friends, and camp. A child who has been consistently in difficulties in all these and similar contacts could not be assimilated in free-floating groups like AGT groups.

CLINICAL COUNTERINDICATIONS

These two criteria exclude constitutionally atypical and organically defective children, borderline or full-blown schizophrenics, psychoneurotics (who require an individual transference relation), psychopathic characters (who are exploitative of and unable to relate to others constructively), and neurotic characters (whose hypermotivity has been structurally integrated into character, though such problems are found only infrequently among children of this age).

One also occasionally encounters children who had been so harshly treated and seriously neglected by parents from infancy that they have internalized severe, pervasive anxiety. Such children have an adverse effect upon groups, since their tensions and diffuse aggression disturb some and infect others, resulting in a horrendous group climate. Latent homosexuals (or perhaps homoerotic) children, too, generate anxiety even in the latency children who constitute activity therapy groups. The riotous behavior of the group filmed (see page 116) was caused by the presence of one such boy. Once this youngster was replaced, the tensions that led to disorder disappeared.

However, it must be noted that transient homoeroticism is present in girls' groups. This seems to be a pervasive magnetic feeling among them which persists later also in women as a result of the role of the mother as a nuclear love object. We have not observed any negative outcomes from this situation in our groups, except in a few instances when two girls became overattached to each other and spent much of the group's sessions dancing together. In such instances we separated the girls by transferring one of them to another group immediately or when it was reassembled for the second year.

SOME CLINICAL INDICATIONS

As to clinical criteria favoring inclusion of patients in activity therapy groups, they are, as already indicated, preoedipal and oedipal primary behavior disorders, habit disorders, certain character disorders, children with defective sexual identifications, youngsters with neurotic traits or mild neuroses, some who suffer from situational anxiety, mild latent schizophrenics, and some schizoid personalities.[1]

CHARACTEROLOGICAL COUNTERINDICATIONS

Negativistic children with inadequate ego development, absence of minimal superego, inability to establish relationships, regressive infantilism, intense castration anxiety in boys, excessive generalized aggressiveness, mental deficiency, and similar problems and conditions that would prevent the emergence of inner controls of impulsivity through normal group pressures and without jeopardizing the therapist's neutral role, should be barred from or placed conditionally in activity groups. We shall indicate presently the importance of such potential inner controls in view of the absence in AGT of external controls, of rules and regulations, rewards, and punishments that are inherent and essential to the life and survival of all other groups, including the primary group, the family.

POSITIVE INDICATIONS

Children whose character traits and behavior patterns are modifiable by new experiences and relations are eminently suitable for activity therapy groups. Among these are confusion as to sexual identification (effeminacy in boys and masculinity in girls) immaturity without neurotic or compulsive elements, overprotected

[1] See Slavson, 1945.

children, timidity and withdrawal (without pathological involvements), disobedience at home and at school (without deep-rooted emotional complications), sibling rivalry, self-centeredness stemming from either success or failure in sibling rivalry or as a result of being only children, desire for peer relationships (social hunger), and social awkwardness or inexperience.

TABLE 1

INDICATIONS AND COUNTERINDICATIONS FOR
ACTIVITY THERAPY GROUPS FOR CHILDREN IN LATENCY

Indications
Clinical
☐ Oedipal primary behavior disorders
☐ Some preoedipal primary behavior disorders
☐ Character disorders
☐ Mild neuroses
☐ Situational anxiety (anxiety hysteria)
☐ Some latent schizophrenics
☐ Some schizoid personalities

Characterological
☐ Confused sexual identification
☐ Effeminacy (in boys)
☐ Masculinity (in girls)
☐ Infantilization
☐ Overprotection
☐ Nonpathological withdrawal
☐ Inadequate ego development
☐ Social hunger
☐ Only children

*Counterindications**
Clinical
☐ Severe psychoneuroses
☐ Psychoses
☐ Psychopathy
☐ Neurotic characters
☐ Severe anxiety states
☐ Latent homosexuality
☐ Disturbances in libido development

Characterological
☐ Absence of minimal ego development
☐ Absence of minimal superego development
☐ Inadequate capacity for object relationships
☐ Regressive infantilism
☐ Castration anxiety
☐ Excessive generalized aggression
☐ Excessive aggression toward adults
☐ Physical handicaps and deformities
☐ Stigmatizations
☐ Mental deficiency

*Children included in this category of counterindications cannot be placed in groups even when they receive individual treatment. They can be referred to groups only after the basic personality problems have been corrected through individual treatment, and they may require a period of "socialization."

GROUPING

Our experience leads us to conclude that a child who is suitable for an activity therapy group, according to indications outlined, will find his way in it on the bases of his personality traits and accustomed behavior responses and that individual and group influences will find their mark in improving him and his conduct. It is only when an error is made by including unsuitable and especially insensitively aggressive and habitually destructive children, that the therapist is placed in a dilemma and the group fails in its aims for everyone involved — the children and the therapist.

Since an activity therapy group has no "curriculum" and personality changes result from meaningful experiences only in a therapeutic climate of a psychologically well-balanced group, the free flow of interactive experiences makes possible resolution of personal problems and social conflicts. Any grouping problem that creates doubt in the mind of the therapist as to the correctness of placement of a child should be resolved on the side of caution. For example, a child who has been subjected to brutalization, either from members of his family or from children in school, should be spared from conditions of grouping which might perpetuate such painful experiences. It is wise to avoid placement where there is any possibility of a child's basic problems being further exacerbated. *The effectiveness of AGT is in direct relation to the care taken in selecting and grouping children correctly.*

DYNAMIC EQUILIBRIUM

To be effective, an activity group has to be so constituted that over a period of time, the personalities and behavior of the children will have established reciprocal relations that foster emotional health. In grouping children, consideration has to be given as far as possible to psychological needs common to all as well as to the requirements of individual group members. A well-structured therapy group ultimately fosters relaxation, security, trust, empathy, and feelings of achievement. To attain these outcomes, a group must be *psychologically balanced.*

Even the best constituted activity therapy group goes through initial periods of upheaval, which also recur later in the life of a group. These episodes are an essential part of corrective experiences, provided they are transient and the group reestablishes its own equilibrium without external interference or control. The temporary upheavals and their self-evanescence are analogous *in action* to *working through* problems in analytic groups of older persons. The interpersonal interactions among members of an activity group are in the instrumentalities for personality changes in patients. Where a condition of *static equilibrium* prevails, it may have educational consequences, but little therapeutic efficacy. To have such efficacy a group in a climate of nearly absolute freedom has to be in a state of *dynamic equilibrium*, i.e., continuously passing through nodal and antinodal phases. On the other hand, an activity group so constituted that aggression and conflict are of unreasonable intensity or predominate beyond a reasonable time, without spontaneously reestablishing antinodal phases, is countertherapeutic and potentially injurious to the mental health of its members.

GROUP BALANCE

Beyond the clinical and characterological principles for suitability, the dominant criterion for grouping is the behavioral patterns of prospective patients that will determine the climate of the group. Among these are the degree of combativeness, capacities for self-control, primary relatedness, physical size, and other similar considerations and potentials. It is obvious that forming a group of all or mostly timid and frightened children will result in static equilibrium with little or no therapeutic interaction and corrective experiences. On the other hand, an activity group composed of predominantly acting-out, aggressive children will result in chaos and inevitably involve the therapist. In either case the therapeutic process will be aborted. To create the necessary therapeutic milieu for AGT, a judicious blending of aggressive and passive children with a number who fall between these categories will set in motion interactions of mutual benefit, bringing the group under self-control through that blending. The timid child has to find that assertiveness is not only tolerable but beneficial to himself and the group, while the customarily aggressive youngster discovers limits to his overassertiveness. He also discovers that gratifications can be obtained by means other than being overbearing and pugnacious. To achieve such a therapeutic climate, the group personnel needs to be psychologically in balance by the inclusion of *instigators, neutralizers, and neuters.*

INSTIGATORS, NEUTRALIZERS, AND NEUTERS

It is operationally convenient to characterize group members' behavioral contributions in a group as instigators, neutralizers, and neuters. We have adopted these characterizations of children to identify the role each plays or may be expected to play. Some children by temperament or because of the roles they have played in the past act as catalysts, stimulating in others positive or negative activity and/or interactions. These children we have labeled *instigators.*

A child is a *positive instigator* if his effect upon the group is psychologically and/or socially beneficial. Such children mobilize and reinforce inherent strengths of others, but what is more important therapeutically is that they set off in their fellow group members intra- and interpersonal beneficial interactions. *Negative instigators,* on the other hand, promote disharmony, hyperactivity, rancor, and hostility. They are *true centers of infection,* and unless checked may destroy the group (see below).

It is therefore important that an activity therapy group (this is true for all groups) comprise also members who can counteract the effects of negative instigation by blocking destructive processes without adding to a group's tension and conflicts. We characterize such individuals—persons who are more reasonable and whose impulses are under better control—as *neutralizers.* Their calming conduct benefits all members of a group by serving as a healthy identification model as well as by aborting destructive aggression and uncontrolled hilarity. Their calm and resourcefulness lead their group mates to substitutive and sublimative alternatives.

Inevitably a number among any group of individuals can be characterized as *neuters.* This term is intended to identify persons with floating or weak identities, who easily succumb to influences of stronger personalities. As treatment progresses, however, and the neuters are strengthened, their roles change and they become more active, assuming at various times roles of instigators and

113

neutralizers. As one of the aims of AGT, indeed of all psychotherapy, is to lay in the patients bases for wholesome self-identities in the future, characterological neuters are prepared by the activity group therapy climate for more assertive and self-sustaining roles in the future.

Children who initially withdraw from social contacts as defenses against their own aggressions and those of others, and children with schizoid tendencies find in the group an arena for overcoming their timidity and fears. Such children remain for considerable periods peripherally in the group. We have observed that even the assertive children sense the isolative schizoids until they tentatively test-move into limited contacts. We have also found that as an assertive child establishes a relation with a withdrawn, his own behavior is to a degree modulated. Isolates thus subtly contribute positively to their group mates and the group climate as they themselves grow more related and communicative.

FOCI OF INFECTION

For reasons of special personality characteristics, initiative, and imagination, some members in a group tend to infect others to disturbing behavior. The followers are not necessarily attracted to these instigators; they are rather victims of the dynamic of *emotional contagion,* which not infrequently causes disturbance and chaos. One can assume a degree of a charismatic quality operating here. However, the ready spread of contagion among all children (as well as adults) indicates a covert tendency for regression to infantile levels by the mechanism of "the return of the repressed." As can be readily seen, the influence of such individuals is far from being sanguine in a group of children with personality problems. When this effect reinforces destruction or hyperactivity without automatic amelioration, it has a detrimental impact on a group and its members. It is the chief reason why active delinquents and patients with psychopathic personalities cannot be included in AGT, where adult restraint is taboo.

Members of groups who consistently set off disturbances or instigate destructive acts we characterize as *foci of infection;* they should receive special attention from the therapist. The type and format of such therapeutic attention are conditioned by the nature of the personality problems of the individuals involved. Is the drive toward such destructiveness merely a replication of conduct in the family? Is it a bid for attention or transferential displacement of feeling toward a parent or parents? Does the psychic source of the conduct proceed from stress in sibling rivalry, or does it emanate from overreaction to fear and insecurity? Or, is it a deeply ingrained character structured by intra- and extra-familial culture?

The perceptive therapist, adequately trained, will deal with such a child in the light of the special syndrome that the anamnesis reveals supported by his own intuitive judgments. In some instances special attention tactfully and unobtrusively directed to the offending child may resolve or diminish the difficulty. In other instances direct impediment of intolerable conduct by confrontation can be employed,[2] *but not in the presence of the other members of the group.* When the causes of behavior are not deeply rooted in the personality, as in the case of testing the therapist, or are a nonneurotic displacement, it is best overlooked to allow self-corrective group process to take over. However, most often children who turn out to be completely unmanageable foci of infection are found in groups as a result of bad judgment and inexperience of the intake person, who was responsible for including such a child in the group. Not infrequently, errors emanate from inadequate or erroneous case histories or from concealment or oversight of facts by the person who presents the case for intake, usually a parent.

True and Pseudo Foci of Infection

A greater source of challenge is presented by a child who infects the group or some of its members not by acts or behavior but by the essential nature of his personality. This being the case, i.e., where to all appearances the conduct is normal and acceptable, the therapist or supervisor needs to have the perspicacity to recognize the intangible effect the "culprit" has on the group. To identify the contrast between the two types of foci of infection, we suggest the terms *true focus of infection* and *pseudo focus of infection.*

---

[2] The method is detailed in Chapter VIII.

In the first category fall children who can be covertly recognized as setting off the group on the path of nontherapeutic activities and interactions. However, the observable or apparent focus sometimes only reflects another, who by his covert personality generates anxiety that sets off the seeming true focus of infection, which in turn activates the group. This subtle phenomenon is tangibly illustrated in the film described on page 93.

After a particularly raucous group session, it became clear that the group was not in psychologic balance, and a conference was called to discuss the matter. The participants were the group therapist, the director-supervisor of the project, and the casework assistant. The question for consideration was the source of the general "restlessness" of the group which culminated in the chaotic session. One of the boys was seemingly the obvious cause of it. This boy was inordinately hyperactive, highly distractable, and hyper-motoric, and he was understandably selected by two members of the reviewing trio.

However, the supervisor suggested that another boy with whom the first developed a close working and social relation was the true center of infection. According to him, the source of the group's tensions was the second boy, whose visible conduct was otherwise faultless. The discussion grew somewhat heated, and the supervisor suggested the compromise of "trying" his idea, which could easily be corrected later should he be proved wrong. The boy was accordingly removed from the group and referred for intensive individual treatment by a female caseworker, with salutary results. The first boy, who appeared to be the cause of the group's tensions, proved to be the pseudo focus of infection, set off by his quiet companion. The cause was the strong homosexual tendencies of his newly found friend (the boy who was removed). This generated anxiety in him, which he acted out, infecting the group.

"Supportive Ego" Relations

One of the major therapeutic dynamics in AGT is the phenomenon of *supportive ego*. This term is applied to a relation of two members of a group in which one, usually of a stronger psychic constitution, helps the other grow toward improved mental health. The nature of the relation is usually either *symbiotic* or *anaclitic,* the latter being more frequent. The operational pattern in this relation as it appears in an activity therapy group is that each member of the dyad finds some element in the personality of the other that attracts him. In such instances each supports the healthier elements in the ego functioning of the other as they work, play, and commune, thus helping each other keep their respective regressive ego trends in abeyance and promoting more adequate ego integration.

There are, however, ego-supportive relations of an anaclitic nature where one of the dyad is the recipient of help from its second member. Such a relation probably stems from libidinal and identification sources in the more mature child of the two, who lends his strengths to the other. It is our impression on the basis of observing these phenomena in a large number of instances that children who enter into either supportive relation gain more from the group experience and improve more rapidly than others who do not develop such affiliations. Even an anaclitic ego-supportive relation seems fruitful to the stronger of the two by virtue of his or her exercising guidance of, and sharing with, the less mature group mate.

There is little likelihood that one could plan for or predict in advance the probabilities as to who of the prospective group members would strike up supportive relationships. This matter has to be left to fortuitous developments as the group becomes operational. However, after a period of a group's operation, a perceptive therapist can planfully add a child who will serve as a supportive ego to one who is in need of it.

SCAPEGOATING

The phenomenon of scapegoating is almost inevitable in groups of children in any type of aggregate and is a frequent occurrence among adults as well. Scapegoating is almost a socially acceptable pattern of discharging aggression and latent hostility even among the most so-called "civilized," and is more prevalent among males than among females at all ages. Indeed, so characteristic is it of the male species that it can be attributed to a sexual component of maleness stemming from rivalry for male excellence and perhaps also for covert homoeroticism.

117

Among children, it seems to be derived from, and an extension of, sibling rivalry, usually instigated by one of the group with others joining in (by emotional infection) as it obviously meets the latent susceptibility for it in them. Scapegoating seems to have universal appeal where individuals are in close and active contact, as in competitive games, and may hold different significance for individuals which would require closer scrutiny. However, whatever these are — specific and common — every leader of a group of children and, even more so, of adolescents, is faced with this problem and its effects upon the group and its consequences.

Of special interest, and even concern, to the activity group therapist is the target of his group's scapegoating propensities. By and large, the victims of scapegoating, which is not always just humorous attack, are individuals who invite it because of some characteristics, by their unconscious masochistic needs that arouse sadistic feelings in others (as extensions of family relations), or because they histrionically seek to attract to themselves the attention of their group mates. Such children activate the free-floating hostility and aggression in a group against themselves either by the disguise of "fun making" and risibility or by disturbing acts.

Unlike some other negative transitory developments in an activity therapy group, scapegoating may prove to be a source of considerable difficulty for the therapist. Particularly is this so when it takes the form of physical aggression involving all or most of the group members. The nature of the acting out and the underlying feelings generate a countertherapeutic climate, which if it persists for too long may lead to the dissolution of the group. The heightened anxiety level, even in the participants who appear to enjoy the process, eventually becomes intolerable, and they quit the sessions. The therapist, therefore, needs in such cases to observe closely and thoughtfully the covert reactions of its members and take steps to reverse the group's activities.

Fortunately, scapegoating in permissive groups such as in AGT, where the adult does not become involved and thus does not add to the gratification of the perpetrators (which is usual also in other congregate situations) gradually subsides as the normative dynamics of AGT begin to operate. Chief among these are displacement by manual creative interests, the assertiveness of the neutralizers, and above all, the tolerant, accepting, and sanguine attitude of the therapist. However, occasionally a target of the scapegoating proves to have an insatiable need for being the center of attention and continues in his efforts beyond the well-being of the group. In such instances he has to be removed (as a true focus of infection) and his nuclear problem leading to his malignant conduct worked through in individual treatment. Where sloughing off does not occur, working through has to be applied.[3]

ROLE MODIFICATION IN THE GROUP

While it is possible in composing a group to hypothesize with a fair degree of accuracy the typical roles that each child may be expected to play, it should be kept in mind that these roles are subject to modification as the group progresses in consonance with the goals of therapy, namely, to effect changes in character and personality. As these occur, the roles children assume change. A child who was initially prone to stimulate others toward motoric behavior becomes less catalytic as he himself becomes less hyperactive. On the other hand, isolative children may develop into more moderate instigators as they come to feel secure in the group after a considerable time in treatment, during which they discover that being assertive is permissible and that they are able to enact, in varying degrees, the roles which they observe other group members playing.

It is not sufficient that frightened, isolative children merely move toward participative social contacts. The distorted and exaggerated feelings of danger at being aggressive that dominated these children prior to therapy must be modified through direct experience. One whose role in the group was that of a neuter at the start becomes more alert as his ego strengths are built up. Such children expand creatively and instead of remaining suggestible and noncontributory begin to offer opinions and display vitality. In fact, the social maturation of the entire group improves as each member's capacity to act in an active neutralizing role grows.

[3] One of the reasons for barring children with physical handicaps and other stigmatizations (see Table 1, this chapter) is to prevent supplying the group with a ready target for scapegoating.

119

VII

The Therapist:
His Qualifications and Training

The practice of psychotherapy, in any of its forms, requires the therapist to be adequately endowed by temperament and personality for the task. He must possess a comprehensive knowledge of dynamic psychology and psychopathology, and have specialized training in the field. Other types of professional work which are not concerned with behavioral matters, such as engineering or accounting, can be competently executed despite any personal idiosyncrasies of the practitioners. In psychotherapy, however, personal attributes are an overriding consideration, for the course of treatment is conditioned by the intrinsic qualities of the therapist.

Patients' feelings and responses are governed not only by the specifics of technique employed but also by their perception of the therapist as a person. Thus, even a most comprehensive intellectual grasp and possession of technical skills on the part of the therapist do not by themselves assure therapeutic proficiency where essential personality qualities are lacking.

Probably the most important qualification for the practice of therapy is a desire to help human beings. This must be a real motivation, for it is unfailingly sensed by patients. Its essence is inevitably detected in many subtle ways. It is unlikely that pretense and technique can succeed in communicating to the patient a feeling of empathic understanding, if it is not intrinsically in the therapist. This is particularly true with children, who possess a hyperperceptive ability to assess the personality, feelings, and motivation of adults.

Special Personality Attributes of Therapists

The special personality of the practitioner is a *sine qua non* for the successful practice of psychotherapy. In addition, personality variants qualify some therapists better for particular age groups of patients and for specific methods of psychotherapy. Children and adolescents demand an unusual degree of sensitivity in the therapist and a temperamental fitness which will resonate to their special needs. Under emotional stress they cannot tolerate the feelings of separatedness, or distance, which characterize the more or less detached attitude of a therapist who employs traditional forms of individual therapy with adults, for example. This external detachment with adults is predicated on sound psychological premises in that it allows for the associative flow of a patient's thoughts and emotions without interference or influence from the therapist. In the treatment of children, however, such clinical detachment "turns them off" emotionally. They respond to it as if it were, in fact, an evidence of rejection and lack of interest.

An activity group therapist who took the bidding of uninvolvement too seriously was approached by a member of his group as both happened to meet on the way to the group session. The boy greeted the adult, who did not respond. As they walked along together, the boy explained his absence from the group at the preceding session, without any comment from the adult. Probably quite embarrassed by what must have seemed a rebuff, the boy asked what had transpired at the preceding session, again receiving no response. When asked by his supervisor as to the reason for his complete uncommunicativeness, the therapist stated that he understood the rule of "neutrality" and his function, therefore, did not permit any contact with his patients. Obviously, an adult so devoid of humaneness is not fit to work with children in any capacity, regardless of the extent of training, and he was promptly fired.

The essential personality of a child therapist should mirror some of the qualities of childhood: imagination, curiosity, and warmth. These elements must be integral to his character. The therapist has to be able to maintain psychological contact with a child, respond appropriately, and quickly perceive his spontaneous needs, but without abandoning at the same time his objective, clinical stance by becoming emotionally involved. This requires a special empathy for children which may be traceable to the tribulations of his own childhood.

HIGH LEVEL OF FRUSTRATION TOLERANCE

An activity group therapist requires a high degree of frustration tolerance. As could be expected from the type of children selected for AGT, their behavior for a considerable period is impulsive and at times violent. The accumulation of resentments, their hostilities and aggressions, and their egocentricities have full sway in an activity group, and the resulting conduct and treatment of each other often rise to great heights of inconsiderateness and even cruelty. Their attitudes and values do serious violence to the sense of decency and fairness ingrained in the adult personality chosen to lead therapy groups. The therapist, therefore, needs to have superior tolerance and resilience not to be affected by these transgressions. This capacity cannot entirely be learned. Although it can be strengthened by supervisory guidance and acquired understanding of children's mental processes and their vagaries, the basis for such attitudes must reside in the personality of the therapist. Fatigue after group sessions is a common complaint of beginning therapists of boys' groups. The fatigue results from the controls they must exercise in the presence of the unfairness with which their clients treat each other, and scapegoating.

As compared with adult patients, children rapidly and relatively easily accept therapists as significant relationship objects. This facile, psychological accommodation is in response to their need for closeness to parents, of which they have been to varying degrees deprived. Their dependency needs are readily transferable to other adults, particularly to one who is permissive and giving as is the therapist in AGT. To be fully effective, the therapist must not feed these feelings or become enmeshed in deep emotional relations. His neutrality and passivity are tools with which he can achieve this much better.

COUNTERTRANSFERENCE REACTIONS

The acting-out behavior of emotionally disturbed children has potentials for inducing intense negative countertransference feelings toward seriously offending members. This is due to the fact that much of children's conduct, in its primitiveness, is implicitly directed against adults. The therapist's unconscious awareness of this makes it all the more important that he have insight into his own psychic processes, so that he remains in command of his feelings. It would be fatal were the patients to detect any signs of disturbance or fear induced in him by their acts. The therapist must not in the slightest degree display such feelings by word or act, and especially not by facial expression.

Being free (or successful in concealment) of these feelings is essential not only with respect to negative reactions. The therapist needs also to manage the positive countertransferential feelings that may be aroused in him by children whose personalities or behavior touch his own earlier conditionings. Sensing the favorable impact such children have on him, they may persist in good behavior, thereby blocking their own therapeutic gains. Of even greater hazard is the resentment which signs of favoritism evoke in other group members, which inevitably leads to spitefulness against the therapist and aggression against his favorite or favorites.

CULTURAL BACKGROUNDS OF PATIENTS

A child therapist should also have familiarity with the social and cultural backgrounds of his patients and accept their manners and personalitites. This is especially important if they are products of material and cultural circumstances at variance from his own. Personal habits manifested by children may seem coarse and uncouth to a therapist raised in more favorable circumstances, but he must, nevertheless, in no way react to them by overt or covert disapproval, displeasure, or annoyance. What may appear to him as personal or habit deficiencies may actually be normal in the patients' culture, having no etiological relationship to their clinical problems. It is hoped that identification with the therapist during a two-year or longer contact will modify their behavior patterns favorably.

USE OF LANGUAGE

In therapy with children, the therapist needs to be concerned with each child's language capacity and his own ability to verbalize on their level. These factors are not without significance in all forms of psychotherapy, and with all age groups. However, they have more pertinence for disturbed children, who find it easier to discharge feelings by aggressive acting out or withdrawal. Language is not always adequate for expressing the intensity and complexity of their emotions.

In analytical types of therapy use of language for interpretation is essential, but while a therapist may at times communicate verbally in AGT, his major means of communication is through behavior, i.e., by action interpretation. Any tendency of the therapist toward conceptualization with child patients in AGT, except, of course, on occasion during the repast, not only falls on sterile grounds but jeopardizes his neutral role and image of permissiveness.

ROLE CONSISTENCY

We have made reference to the importance of the knowable character of an activity therapy group; this includes consistency of the therapist's role. Children generally, and especially those who require psychotherapy, readily detect alterations in a therapist's mien, demeanor, and language overtones that represent a departure from the norm. Because they are emotionally disturbed and insecure, even minor alterations in his attitudes, moods, and customary functions increase children's insecurity and call forth overdetermined reactions: they relive the mordant effects upon them of parents' inconsistent and threatening treatment to which they had been exposed.

The therapist must make every effort to maintain a positive transference in the children toward him consistent with clinically valid effectiveness, for only then can he serve in a supportive role, as a model for identification, and ride the crest of transient negative feelings toward him. It is comparatively easy to achieve this in AGT, since no exploration or interpretation is employed and no verbal clarifications are sought. The neutrality and passivity of the therapist demand consistency.

THE SCOPE OF KNOWLEDGE

Children anticipate that a therapist will be knowledgeable in areas that affect or are important in their lives. They expect a therapist to comprehend matters relating to school, teachers' attitudes and behavior, hobbies, street and community situations, television programs, sports and current movies, which they discuss during the refreshment periods. He needs to be moderately proficient in children's games, such as checkers, chess, ping-pong, and indoor hockey and participate in them when invited by patients. He also needs to possess a variety of manual skills to a degree that he can help his patients when they seek his help.[1] While these requirements apply to all types of therapy with children, they are particularly important in AGT, where crafts are an integral part of the treatment modality.

TRAINING FOR PSYCHOTHERAPY

Though trained to deal with emotional disturbances and pathology, therapists must have thorough knowledge of the sources and nature of the behavior of "normal" people; a therapist's knowledge of human personality and behavior cannot be limited to pathology. Since pathology is a deviant from the ordinary human condition and conduct, the "healthy" state needs to be understood as a frame of reference. The basic biological needs of children and their requirements for vasomotor activity in gross and rhythmic expression must be taken into consideration in dealing with them. There are many phases in a child's development, each having its own place and exerting its own influence in the orderly formation of the final product, the adult. During normal growth, the child passes through stages which are *manipulative-exploratory, practical-inventive, intellectual-epistemonic*, and *social-participatory* (see Slavson, 1934, pp. 290-296).

Each is an essential phase of development, and each leaves its imprint upon him. The lack of fulfillment of any one phase does injury to the harmony of the body-mind and the integrative processes of the personality. Mental health can be achieved only

[1] See also Chapter VIII.

when full growth in each phase is achieved in fullness, so that the subsequent levels can then be fully attained. It must be noted that all forms of child therapy involve vasomotor activity consistent with the ages of children. In AGT the room and its equipment are designed to engage the patients bio-psychologically in suitable occupations that involve the vasomotor systems.

To understand normal development dynamically, one must recognize the stages of nurture, training, discipline, and education in the orderly growth of the child. Personality problems and emotional disorders have their roots in inappropriate treatment of the infant and young child during these four early phases.

The earliest needs of the infant are met by nurture: he requires absolute protection; his wants and needs require immediate satisfaction; his survival securities must be assured. The stage of training sets in with regulation of oral, alimentary functions: eating and voiding. This training is replaced successively by discipline, schooling, and education as the child grows older and ideally should bring to realization the potentialities of the individual.

The involvement of the neuromuscular, the vasomotor, and the endocrine-affective systems as a total and unitary organism in developmental growth and education is too evident to require elaboration, and one who is not aware of these dynamic processes and their place in total health will inevitably overlook many therapeutic considerations. Conduct and reactions can easily be misunderstood unless one understands the total human personality.

This perspective of child development provides the scientific base for the study and practice of psychotherapy. It also yields a fuller appreciation of the complex phenomenon known as man and the critical importance of individual differences. While men are alike in gross structure, they are vastly different in many and important details. Temperamental dispositions and congenital and hereditary variants are too great among individuals to warrant our anticipating from them identical, or even similar reactions, or expecting them to possess the same capacity to bear stress and tolerate frustration.

Good psychotherapy is based on these broader insights and

appreciation of the numerous and complex elements involved in the nature of individuals. Dealing with people is predominantly an art and much less a science, but the art element in psychotherapy is rooted in science. It is in the science of man and his society that the art of dealing with human beings is refined. Science also serves as a check upon the effectiveness and direction in which art is practiced.

PSYCHOTHERAPY AND THE TOTAL PERSONALITY

Sound psychotherapy addresses itself to the total personality as a unitary bio-psycho-social entity; it does not merely treat symptoms as isolated entities. The various elements that go into the making of a personality and their dynamic interrelationship must be understood and considered. A therapist has to be familiar with the structure of the human organism, its dynamics, and the integrative processes in the body-mind organization of man. Despite his major preoccupation with man's psyche, Freud did not fail to note this unitary nature. He affirmed that stimuli travel from the soma to the psyche, and from the psyche to the soma. This fact is the foundation of psychosomatic medicine and is the origin of somato-psychological phenomena.

The interrelationship of somatic and psychogenic factors as a predisposing condition for the development of emotional difficulties can be seen in children. They develop emotional and social problems when they suffer prolonged frustrations in the areas of neuromuscular activity, in creative self-expression and human relationships. Motor activity serves as a sublimation, yielding ego gratifications, and meets the requirements of a child's basic dynamism. We see clearly how authoritarian, repressive, rejecting, and hostile attitudes of parents and teachers affect children emotionally. Not so clear is the fact that interference with the learning process itself, and the frustration of motility and active dynamism are equally damaging to both the physical and mental well-being of the child.

In training persons to practice psychotherapy, the following content areas and supervised practice are recommended: [2]

---

[2] Part of this section appeared in *A Textbook in Analytic Group Psychotherapy* (Slavson, 1964, pp. 412-429).

1. Basic studies in embryology, anatomy, physiology, neurology, endocrinology, social psychology, group dynamics, and sociology.

2. Professional courses in child development, abnormal psychology, depth psychology, basic psychiatry, psychopathology, diagnosis, individual psychotherapy, and group psychotherapy.

3. Most important of all is prolonged internship and practice in a clinical setting under competent training supervisors.

The aim of the orientative courses is to give trainees a basic understanding of the total personality as a biological and social organism. The professional courses and internship, on the other hand, should be considerably more intensive and related to definitive areas of clinical knowledge and practices. The first group of courses leads to knowledge of the relationships between affective disorders and somatic dysfunctions. A child therapist must be knowledgeable of the developmental aspects of physiology, because manifestations of children's somatic disorders differ in important respects from those of adults. Emotional stress in the young child may produce mild gastric signals, the "tummy ache," for example. In the adult the anxiety outcome may prove more drastic, such as an ulcer.

Endocrinology and neurology contribute to a better understanding of how the body's hormones and neural processes are related to physiological functions, to behavior, and to the development of personality. A nonmedical therapist though not equipped to treat medically related problems, must still be able to recognize symptoms that require medical attention. A knowledge of genetics, gestation, embryology, and fetology sharpens the appreciation of the influence of heredity and the dramatic biologic complexity that determine the beginnings of a human being and of organicity.

It is of paramount importance that a therapist have a comprehensive knowledge of the dynamics of personality development necessary in establishing the nuclear and peripheral elements in a presenting problem, and for tracing etiologically the points at which pathogenic events have taken place. Such information helps him to determine points of fixation, the onset of extraordinary habits and conduct, and the emergence of neurotic traits or symptoms and to identify the nuclear problems. This knowledge also contributes to the therapist's grasp of diagnosis in a dynamic sense.

129

The nonmedical therapist needs also to be informed in basic psychiatry and psychopathology, which helps screen out cases of psychoses, severe psychoneuroses, and organic defects and disabilities. Medical training is not necessary for the practice of the art of psychotherapy. It is the professional responsibility of the nonmedical practitioner, however, to be able to discriminate between patients and not to attempt treatment of disorders that exceed his training and competence. In working with children, the therapist frequently encounters somatic symptoms, e.g., gastrointestinal complaints, vomiting, and stomach aches, constipation, allergic reactions, asthma, marginal neurological symptoms such as tics, twitches, insomnia, and other physical symptoms. It is important that a psychiatrist and other medical specialists, if necessary, be consulted with respect to all signs of organic illness. It may be necessary in some instances to supplement psychotherapy with medication. This decision can safely be made only by psychiatrists.

Internship and residency supply the pragmatic experiences where theory and practice are integrated and refined. These pivotal processes occur as the prospective and beginning therapist in training operates under supervisors who have had advanced training and wide experience, and possess teaching skills. Without special training, psychiatrists per se are not qualified to practice or supervise group therapy (or psychotherapy generally), but they may serve as consultants and control on individual patients, leaving the supervision of the actual practice to senior group therapists.

Since there is no one method of psychotherapy that can be universally applicable to *all* emotional disorders of children (and others as well), it stands to reason that a therapist, supervisor, and psychiatrist will need knowledge of various specific types of psychotherapy of proved merit, and should confine themselves to the practices of which they have knowledge. It is desirable that a therapist be well versed in the theory and applicability of as many types of therapy as possible. His first clinical task is to ascertain the nature and clinical problem of each patient and to select the treatment modality most suitable for him. Unless the therapist can exercise such clinical discrimination, he is unable to avoid biased decisions with no or indifferent results. Frequently, a misapplication of a treatment method for any length of time renders patients difficult to motivate to another more suitable form of treatment. Thus, a therapist who has had widespread training in various types of both individual and group methods will be less liable to make errors in selection and grouping. In most instances, senior knowledge and experience should be enlisted in making these decisions.

THE NONMEDICAL THERAPIST

It is becoming increasingly evident that community needs for psychotherapy cannot be met by the relatively limited availability of medically trained psychiatrists, and that this lack is not likely to be met in the foreseeable future. Despite the increase in the number of persons suffering from emotional dysfunctions because of increased tensions and complexities of our society in transition, facilities for treatment are critically inadequate. Moreover, the prohibitive cost of private treatment makes it available to comparatively few, and social work agencies and out-patient hospital clinics are in most instances not equipped to meet fully the demand for comprehensive psychotherapeutic services.

It is also becoming increasingly evident that medical training, as such, is actually not essential for the practice of psychotherapy, provided that nonmedical practitioners do not attempt to deal independently with full-blown psychotic and organic patients who may require medication. The nonmedical therapist cannot be too cautious in this respect, and he must be able to discern patients who do not fall within his purview and be bound, both legally and ethically, not to undertake to give treatment beyond his competence without psychiatric guidance and consultation.

ADVANCED TRAINING IN METHODS OF GROUP THERAPY

In increasing the number of persons qualified to do group therapy, it has become necessary to involve practitioners from the fields of clinical social work and clinical psychology who have had training and extensive supervisory experience in individual psychotherapy. Because of their advanced standing their training is focused mostly around group therapy. It then consists of: (1) a seminar in dynamic psychiatry; (2) seminars in group therapy; (3) group supervision; (4) intensive supervision on an individual basis; (5) internships in hospital and agency clinics; (6) psychiatric consultations; (7) a review of the history and current practices in group psychotherapy; (8) analysis of the literature in the field; (9) administration, recording, and steps in integration of group therapy into the comprehensive treatment programs of institutions and agencies.

INDIVIDUAL AND GROUP THERAPY: DIFFERENCES

Therapy with groups is in many respects more complicated than dealing with individuals. In treating an individual, the therapist is to a considerable extent in control of the therapeutic situation. He may act in various ways according to his understanding of the client's needs at a given time: he may be passive and uncommunicative; give an interpretation; encourage or stimulate the patient's productions; direct the interview by means of leading questions or remarks. In groups, this autonomy, and in some respects also the power, do not remain the exclusive prerogatives of the therapist. They are either greatly diminished or are often altogether denied him. The catalytic effect of group members upon one another, whether in conversation or through acts, is such that the situation is largely taken out of his hands.

In individual treatment the therapist has to adapt himself to the emotional state of only one patient and to follow the trend he pursues. In a group, the therapist must also adapt himself to numerous situations and a network of interpersonal tensions that are not present in individual therapy. It is for this reason, among many others, that only highly skilled and self-confident therapists can function well in a group treatment situation.

GROUP THERAPY IS PART OF GENERAL PSYCHOTHERAPY

Psychiatrists and other psychotherapists who have had extensive training and experience in analytical methods of psychotherapy of both individual and group types have commented on the fact that group psychotherapy places more demands on them than do even difficult cases in individual treatment. Yet, group therapy is not a specialty separate from the total practice of psychotherapy;

it belongs with general psychotherapy. A group therapist must have the knowledge that an individual therapist has; he must know and understand the background of each of his patients, their individual intrapsychic problems and treatment needs. One cannot master the group techniques apart from the general understandings that are essential to all psychotherapy. Only persons who are qualified through a thorough knowledge of psychopathology and experience in individual psychotherapy should undertake the practice of group psychotherapy. This is as true of activity groups as it is of the various analytical types of activity-interview and play therapies. No one who has not had thorough training and prolonged experience in general psychotherapy should attempt to do group therapy in any of its forms.

Group Psychotherapy with Children

A considerable body of clinical material has accumulated over a period of almost four decades to establish that group therapy is the major treatment modality for children. This includes analytical forms, such as play group therapy for preschool years; noninterpretive methods based on psychoanalytical understanding such as AGT with latency children; and a combined activity and interpretive method, activity-interview group therapy with disturbed prepubertal patients.

Knowledge of how the unconscious influences manifest behavior and the latent meanings that underly it is called for regardless of the method of therapy employed. In groups interpretation may be less mandatory, but a therapist must still be aware of psychodynamic processes and have psychoanalytical understanding. Because of its nonverbal nature, AGT places even greater premium on such insights and perceptions required in *reading patients' conduct,* its nuances and meanings.

Latent Meanings of Behavior in Activity Group Therapy

The therapist in activity groups is called upon to recognize the latent meaning of behavior as well as the statements children make, if his own responses are to be correctly formulated. This was apparent in the instance of a boy who asked the therapist for the key to the entrance door of the treatment room, unlocked it, and then unlocked the materials closet. At first blush it may seem that he wished to be helpful. Actually this is not always the case. Through such an act a child may be manifesting vicariously a desire to displace the father (or the mother) in the family. Where the reality circumstances are such that the father (or the mother) is a weak person or is absent from the home, the boy strives to become worthy of the mother (and the girl of the father). He (or she) therefore attempts to play the role of an adult, which he (or she) also does in the group.

Another common example is the child who runs breathlessly into the therapy room. This is usually derived from sibling rivalry. He rushes to the group in order to be the first one. Unless there is an element of neurotic anxiety permeating *all* his behavior, this is, in most instances, an expression of primogeniture rivalry. The therapist has to perceive the hidden meanings of sometimes rather simple statements that overtly appear to have no special significance. The following example is typical.

While the therapist was cutting a cake, the boys sitting around the refreshment table were discussing food. They were making plans for refreshments for the next session. Each expressed his preference. Some voted for chocolate, some for pineapple, others for apple cake. As if he were participating in the discussion, but really addressing his remarks more pointedly toward the therapist, one boy said, "*I* like any kind of cake—chocolate, pineapple, most any kind." In saying this, the boy tells the therapist that he is pleased with whatever the therapist chooses for him. It is an act of submission which is in consonance with the submissive role he has played in his family circle.

First Understanding, Then Correct Procedure

Understanding the conscious and unconscious motives of children's behavior and statements are, however, in themselves not sufficient. In all therapy, and especially in AGT because it is a nonverbal form, the skill lies in *dealing* with them. Where the child seeks to displace the therapist, the latter must be very careful not to play into this pattern. In the first example cited—of the boy who asked for the key—the therapist did not perceive the concealed intention of the boy, and later in the session asked him to go out to buy the food for the group. This technical error gave consent to the boy's strivings to displace the therapist and to live out the fantasy of being better than the adult (father). When the therapist reinforces such strivings, he is acting in opposition to the child's maturing process.

In the case of the submissive child, it is quite evident that the treatment goal is to help him build up his ego strengths and autonomy. This can be accomplished through support by the therapist, through assurance of status in the group, and by successful achievements. The therapist in this situation lends himself as a focus of attention, but through subtle strategies gradually removes himself from the center of that attention. The other children (group) then become increasingly efficacious as a therapeutic force in promoting maturation. In dealing with defective ego development, the therapist serves as a temporary prop only.

In the case of the boy with intense rivalry, the therapist does not attempt to deal directly with the problem other than through his fundamental, positive role of acceptance and permissiveness. The rivalry problem the child has to work out by himself through the other children as sibling substitutes.

TRAINING FOR SKILLS IN CRAFTS

Part of the training of the therapist for AGT includes learning how to use crafts materials and tools. A therapist has to be acquainted, not necessarily proficient, in all media provided for an activity group so that he will be able to assist children who may encounter difficulty in their work endeavors. Many urban children can acquire skills by work experimentation or by observing other children and the therapist. Prospective group therapists can acquire skills by work with groups under supervision, where the trainer enacts the same role toward the trainees which the latter are expected to play in a treatment group. Although it is seldom fully possible, the trainer-therapist should not teach didactically the use of materials and tools. It is better to leave the trainees to their own devices to explore the setting, make experimental attempts with the materials and tools, experience frustration and failure so as to identify better with the strain his patients will experience. Whereas the therapist prevents frustration and work failure in his patients, the trainer-therapist allows failure during the training of prospective AGT therapists so that they will appreciate corresponding feelings in children. However, the above is an idealized situation. In practice, direct instruction may suffice.

The trainer-therapist also volunteers assistance, wordlessly, at appropriate moments and in the same manner as this is practiced in AGT. He also demonstrates reasonable and judicious use of praise, precautions against injuries, preparation and serving of refreshments, methods of terminating a session, and other functions within the therapist's role in AGT. The effect of this "immersion" of the student-therapists in a learning and working experience in a reenacted group treatment setting goes beyond acquiring proficiency with tools and crafts, however. When trainees actively experience the role of patients, they become more realistically and more sensitively aware of the meaning of corrective reexperience than it is possible to convey didactically. This laboratory experience adds a dimension in training which crystallizes the theory and principles underlying AGT. We have found that adults considered for leadership in AGT are sufficiently skillful with the simple arts and crafts provided for groups. However, at times they require help in specific situations. The supervisor can supply it or suggest sources where it can be obtained.

THE BASIC CHARACTERISTIC OF THE THERAPIST

Although gentle and accepting, the therapist *must* possess a strong personality. His gentleness and tolerance cannot stem from weakness or a vacillating character. His gentleness should rather be a matter of an adaptive pattern superimposed upon his strengths, which the young patients readily perceive. Weakness or hesitancy evokes and mobilizes children's hostility toward an adult which they mercilessly heap upon him. Random mobility and disturbing hyperactivity and destructiveness are vastly enhanced when children operating in a permissive environment sense weakness in the "leader."

Children selected for AGT have more than their share of

intuition for acts that would disturb or outrage an adult and are unsparing in committing them. Any trace of fear, distress, or uncertainty on the part of the therapist is taken full advantage of by a group. As a result, a chaotic and antitherapeutic climate sets in. It is the members' recognition of the therapist's inner strength, not alone his reactions or actions, that holds children in check.

The therapist's personal strength is essential for preventing continuation of extreme acting out; it also serves as a model of identification. If the therapist's *laissez-faire* attitude proceeds not from weakness or indifference but from choice, his strength communicates itself to his patients and serves to strengthen their egos by identification. But if the therapist is basically a "weakling," the ego identification necessary for character reconstruction will be lacking. In addition, the fumbling and weakness of the therapist generate anxiety in children, with resulting overreactive behavior.

One must be especially vigilant against assignment of effeminate men and latent schizophrenics as therapists. The first will have varied effects upon different members of a group. Some are abashed and moderate their acting out, but most react spitefully and intensify their destructive conduct, infecting others and thus presenting the therapist with an unenviable situation. However, since attendance in the group is entirely voluntary, the outcome is that many of the boys drop away because of their heightened anxiety.

Similar reactions have been found in groups where the therapists were unrecognized latent or nuclear schizophrenics. Added to the mildness of manner in these men, is that a basic indecisiveness and tentativeness creates insecurity in children, to which they react by never-ending violent and destructive behavior. In the several instances when the error had been made in assigning latent schizophrenics to activity groups, they failed so miserably that they had to be removed. Most meticulous and detailed supervisory suggestions, though faithfully carried out, did not alter the group's conduct, since the children reacted to the *essential personality* of the adult rather than to his actions. It is also not impossible that children react with such violence to the inhibited or controlled hostility in the adult which is an integral part of the schizophrenic syndrome.

The choice of female group therapists should be based on the consideration of their basic maternal feelings, which they must be able to hold in check, and act upon their latent character strengths. For obvious reasons, the personality of the therapist is not as critical in groups of girls as it is with boys. As to pathology, the remarks concerning male therapists hold also for females.

VIII

The Therapist: His Functions

ROLE OF THE THERAPIST

As we have seen, the position of the therapist in an activity therapy group is different in every respect from that of a leader of a social club or any other type of group. Here the adult is a source of security, but only minimally so. He does not actively guide the group through the maze of emotions that arise, a function that is proper for other groups, including other therapy groups. Through planful strategies the activity therapist has to withhold entering into interpersonal interactions with his patients and into the relations that arise among the members.

FIGURE 1

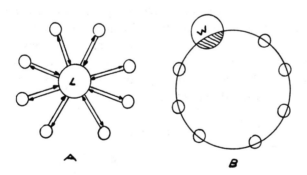

In Figure 1, *A* illustrates schematically the interindividual (bilateral) relations between the leader and each member of an ordinary club. The leader (*L*) is the central person here. The interpersonal (multilateral) relations in an activity therapy group are shown in Figure 1B, illustrating that the therapist, in his "neutral" role, is only partially included in the group circle.

Since the aim of AGT is to strengthen the autonomous potentials in children, this role of the therapist is essential because, among other things, some of the children selected for the groups have, as a result of overprotection, been rendered overdependent, while others are too "self-reliant" as a result of rejections and deprivations. Children deprived of primary relations cannot be included in AGT. They first require an experience in relationship with an individual adult before they can deal adequately with multiple relationships in a group, and should be first referred for individual treatment. This plan is recommended also for overdependent children who, because of their intense affect hunger, seek to monopolize the therapist and thus create tensions in the group. In both instances parallel individual and group treatment or guidance are recommended.

Dealing with Children's Attitudes

We have so far described relationships between patient and therapist from the point of view of the latter, but each child comes to the group with definite attitudes toward adults which he inevitably projects or displaces upon the therapist. The dependent child may have to go through a period of dependency; the deprived or inadequate may need support; the rejected usually redirect their rage upon the therapist and the group. By definite strategies (to be described later) the therapist meets these variegated psychologic needs and reactions of each of his patients in a manner that does not encourage continued reliance on him and discourages emotional ties with him.

Figure 2

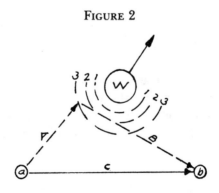

Figure 2 is a schematic representation of the "deflective process" the therapist employs to help a child establish relationships
with his contemporaries, rather than with himself. At first, line *A*
was extended to *W* (the therapist). The therapist however, withdrew gradually, as shown by arcs 1-1, 2-2, 3-3, until *a* found it
necessary and was able to relate to *b*. Line *B* is the deflective
relational line. Later *a* is able to relate to *b* directly (line *C*),
omitting the therapist (*W*). This role of the therapist is vastly
different in activity-interview group psychotherapy and in play
group therapy. In these groups the therapist is active both
emotionally and physically. Each member develops a transference
relation with the therapist, which is encouraged and utilized as
part of the treatment process. The therapist is the central figure
and is an integral part of the group treatment. In purely activity
groups, on the other hand, the therapist's role must remain
throughout a recessive one.

THE THERAPIST AS AN "IDEAL" PARENT

In a real sense, the role of the therapist in AGT can be likened
to that of an "ideal" parent.[1] Since interpretation and insight
formation are not part of this modality, his effectiveness depends
primarily on his attitudes and demeanor. In trying to emphasize
how important it is for a therapist in AGT to subordinate his
psychological and psychiatric knowledge and his training and
experience in clinical methodologies to the more indispensable
factors of role performance, the authors have avoided employing
technical terminology in describing the therapist's functions. The
earlier cognomen we used was "worker" rather than "leader" or
"therapist." This was designed in the early years to foster a humanistic perception of the therapist and to offset a tendency toward
technical and clinical orientation in the *practice* of AGT.

It would be helpful at this juncture to visualize the therapist's
role from the child's position. The child perceives the therapist
within the context of his own past and present relationships with
other significant adults—parents, teachers, and others. His later

[1] In fact, some boys spontaneously turn to the therapist and announce, "You are my
father." And when adults in a subway inquired about the group the boys would say, pointing to the therapist, "He is our father."

141

assessment of the therapist as a person evolves from the positive elements of his relationship with the latter—of trust, security, gratifications, and fondness. Such feelings, always present in a positive transference, become integrated into the child's psyche and stand out in contradistinction to earlier negative and traumatic relationships with adults. As a good and understanding "psychological parent," and because of his neutrality, the therapist makes it possible for each of the children to use him variously according to their emotional needs: to unburden themselves of hostile feelings; to maintain a sense of security and support; and as an object of anaclitic dependence and a source of oral gratification.

Image of the Therapist

As already emphasized, the therapist remains as passive and uninvolved as circumstances permit. This neutral image can be likened to a blank movie screen on which fantasies of each child are projected. Each uses the therapist as a variable template. An astonishing demonstration of a therapist's failure in this respect occurred during a concealed observation by one of the present authors of a group of ten-year-old boys in Stockholm, Sweden, in 1957. While his other group mates had been variously occupied, a boy sat by himself at a table apparently composing a tune which he quietly hummed to himself. As he did so, he accompanied himself by beating the song's rhythm with a small, thin stick and seemed deeply absorbed in what he was doing. Close by was a piano, which the children ignored (it obviously was being used for other purposes in the clinic's work with patients). Being attracted to, and perhaps impressed by, the melody, the male therapist (a male and a female were conducting the group) sat down at the piano, and began to follow the tune. In an instant, without even a glance at the therapist, the boy jumped up, dropped the stick onto the table, and briskly walked out of the room to the back yard. This reflex reaction was extremely impressive and demonstrated the sensitivity of children to invasion of their self-assertiveness and creativity. We found later that the therapist had a keen interest in music, and had attempted before to interest his young patients in that art.[2]

NONINVOLVEMENT OF THE THERAPIST

The therapist demonstrates his noninvolvement most obviously when he avoids entering disputes and physical struggles of his young patients. Individual and group decisions remain the prerogative of individuals or the group. The children know full well that they can depend on the therapist in real need, but they also discover that he does not usurp their opportunities for self-expression and decision making. As already indicated, in the beginning children are surprised and even shocked by the permissiveness of the therapist and may comment to each other about the seeming absence of controls. Some test his forebearance by acting out in a manner that was always immediately prohibited by adults in other settings. The therapist, however, accepts the untoward conduct without seemingly even noticing it. By remaining impassive, he *neither approves nor sanctions it but accepts the child as a person.*

UNCONDITIONAL ACCEPTANCE

Children with primary behavior disorders, who have experienced prolonged nurture deprivation, rejection, and extraordinary degrees of frustration, and who have responded to these psychotraumatizations with anger, aggression, and highly energized forms of behavior, require much emotional reconditioning. *Unconditional acceptance* of their behavior by the therapist must extend for long periods of time before abatement and sublimations of aggression can evolve. Only unconditional acceptance is proof of *total love.*

Children who, as a result of parental overprotection and overindulgence, suffer from infantile fixations require internalizations of controls and, in order that they may do so, need to experience reasonable restraints from without. In AGT these controls come

[2] The clinic director told the visitor later that after some months of the group's life, not being convinced of its value, he contemplated disbanding it. However, on "second thought," he said, he telephoned the parents of the children for their reactions, and all of them reported that their children had improved. He then decided to continue the group.

from other children in the group in the form of direct limits on silly, disturbing, and sometimes manic behavior. It is difficult even for an immature child to continue to ignore for long admonitions, criticisms, and limits imposed by his annoyed peers. Only in extraordinary circumstances may the therapist restrain an overdisturbing child in a specific manner, to be described elsewhere, that would not shake him up or frighten all the others. Infantile children, as do also the withdrawn and diffident, gain most, and more readily, from AGT.

SEEING WITHOUT LOOKING

The climate in an AGT treatment room is often explosive, especially in the early periods of a group's life, with possibilities for personal injuries. The therapist, therefore, has to be vigilant as to the activities of his group members. He needs to be aware at all times of everything that transpires. In addition to being helpful to his young patients, he must be alert to the onset of frustration in some of them and note significant behavioral manifestations of individual children and their interactions with each other. This global percipience, in addition to other values, enables the therapist to detect deviant behavior and characteristics that may have been overlooked at the time of initial referral.

Activity groups have proved effective instruments for differential diagnoses. Constitutional defects such as mild brain damage or glandular imbalance may be overlooked, and are frequently first recognized by their conduct in free acting-out groups. However, it is most important that the children are not made conscious that they are under observation. The groups have been described to them as "clubs," and they should therefore feel free in their behavior. Making the young patients self-conscious through focused observation would defeat the intent of the group. Even extreme forms of acting out, such as high levels of boisterousness, teasing, fighting or wrestling, provoking, scapegoating, destruction of some of the equipment in the room, and fire setting, must remain "unobserved" as far as the group members are concerned, but must be within the global awareness of the therapist so that he may step in when real danger is impending. However, this has hardly ever been necessary in the hundreds of groups under our supervision for almost four decades.

It is our unorthodox belief, sustained by our experience in liberated schools, neighborhood clubs, and therapy groups, that children do not intend to hurt themselves or others. They rather do so as displacement of anger and resentment against some adults, usually a parent, a teacher, or others in authority. Were we to claim to allow freedom in groups and at the same time limit and control, chastise or punish, violence and injuries would be replete.[3] The reasons that AGT groups are free of catastrophes are the group climate and especially the consistent benign, accepting attitudes of the therapists.

Pointed observation of children makes them both uncomfortable and resentful; freedom "to be themselves" is curtailed by it. Equally important is the fact, to which we already called attention, that a child observed in an antisocial act without comment or counteraction from the adult feels that he has approval. The therapist must therefore learn to see *without looking*. Some examples follow.

The therapist noticed from a distance that Steven was vigorously sawing a length of wood in an inappropriate manner. The board was secured by him in the vise by one end, and instead of holding the other end with his free hand Steven was awkwardly grasping the wood so that part of his hand was directly below the saw. If he kept his hand there, it was not unlikely that he would injure himself. The therapist walked over to the bench and wordlessly steadied the plank with one hand. Then, with deliberateness, he took Steven's left hand and placed it on top of the plank to steady it. Having done this, he walked away. Despite his intense preoccupation with his work, Steven flashed a quick smile of gratitude at the therapist. The fact that the therapist did not verbally correct or *instruct* him on the "proper" way of woodcutting, but rather helped without asserting his superior knowledge, was the pivotal element in this deceptively simple encounter.

During an altercation between two boys, one of them held a hammer over the head of the other, angrily threatening to strike

---

[3] Note the appearance of stealing when their taking things from the group was prohibited by the therapists, see p. 95.

him with it. Being aware of the first boy's impulsivity, the therapist calmly walked over and extending his hand said, "Let me have it, please. I want to use it now." The boy relinquished it and spontaneously blurted out, "That's good!" He was obviously relieved by the therapist's resolution of his conflict. This further cemented his positive attitude toward the therapist.

In still another group, two boys, after wrestling rather vigorously on the floor arose, squared off against each other in a fighting stance. The therapist walked to the supply closet and in so doing planfully passed between the two combatants. This momentary interference broke the tension. The boys withdrew from each other, and each returned to his occupation. The therapist employed this stratagem because in his judgement a physical combat between those particular boys was contraindicated and could have led to more serious developments. Walking deliberately between two combatants is a technique to terminate an impending fight and has always proved sufficient to dissolve such conflict situations. This indirect strategy obviates overt interference by the therapist, who retains his neutral role while accomplishing his end, and is an effective face-saving device for both children involved.[4]

MOBILITY AND WORK ACTIVITIES OF THE THERAPIST

Throughout every session the therapist must not be idling or moving about the room observing the children's activities in a supervisory manner as do teachers in school. From the very first session and thereafter, he sets the example of constructive activity. While seated in an area of the room that sets him somewhat apart from the center of the children's activities, he may work with some craft material, repair a tool, or engage in other work related to the setting such as puttering around the "kitchen" area, straightening out the storage cabinets, or working on a crafts project.

Another advantage of the therapist's keeping busy is that he

---

[4] Tl e strategies cited are not standard. They are employed only when from the therapist's knowledge of the participants the possible outcomes are counterindicated. Ordinarily, developments are allowed to take their course.

thus becomes less accessible than if he were sitting idle. His pre-occupation tends to throw the patients more on their own resources rather than needlessly seeking help from him. This favors self-reliance and resourcefulness. It also prevents the therapist's becoming overinvolved in the group. When a child has to interrupt an adult's work in order to get his attention, he is less prone to approach him, and is more likely to seek him out only when he really needs help. On the other hand, his mien should not be prohibitive so that children hesitate to consult him or seek his assistance. When help is requested, the therapist immediately leaves whatever he may be doing and responds to the request. The immediacy of the response reconvinces the child that to the therapist, he, the child, is preeminent.

Before they grow in confidence, infantile children in the early stages of treatment tend to demand attention excessively from the therapist for a period of time, and he must respond without hesitation. Later he may delay the response interval by saying, "As soon as I finish with this, I'll come over to you," and if the child resumes work on his own, the therapist may omit his visit, or approach the child and say, "That's fine. You are doing well. You don't really need me." Such strategies are in keeping with the principle of "action interpretation"; they also help children to become aware of their powers and skills.

It usually takes some time for a very timid child to make contact with a therapist, certainly to the point of interrupting him when he is engaged in crafts work or performing a chore. A diffident child learns vicariously at first through observing the more assertive, less fearful children, who "demonstrate" that while the therapist may be occupied, he is never inaccessible. Thus, timid children eventually move into direct contact with the therapist, assured that they will not be denied. The therapist should avoid unnecessary movement about the room that will distract the children at work or at games. Moving about also has the effect of overemphasizing his presence and focusing attention on himself.

Dealing with Obduracy

In situations where boisterousness, bullying, or pugnacity by a boy or an uncontrolled hostility or querulousness of a girl disturbs

147

the climate of a group without a letup for an extended time, the therapist may take steps to terminate the disturbance, but only when he concludes that other members of the group will not or cannot bring the offending child to book. However, steps should not be taken before the therapist assesses the cause or causes of the offending behavior. Is it abreaction to some anxiety or resentment against an offense before the session, or was it failure in some recent conflict that disturbed the boy or girl? Or has something occurred in the group that set off the culprit? Whatever the reason, if the disturbance continues beyond a reasonable time during a session or sessions, the therapist asks the child quietly to come with him, and both repair to the hallway or to an adjoining room where they cannot be heard by the other children. The therapist then says, "You know, Jimmy, we come to the club because we all have fun here. The way you've been behaving nobody is having much fun, neither you nor the others nor I."

Having said this the therapist abruptly turns about and returns to the activity room, not giving the child an opportunity to defend or explain himself, thereby diluting the impact of the therapist's declaration. The child follows on the heels of the therapist, somewhat chastened and a bit meekly and either returns to his work or initiates some occupation. This episodic interruption usually brings a child under control. There may be instances, however, when the inner pressures are more compelling than are the ego strengths and the child sometimes later resumes his disturbing conduct. The therapist then fixes his gaze on him — not with anger or as chastisement — but rather as a gesture to remind him what transpired between them not so long ago. Almost always the child terminates his disturbing conduct. Should he ignore the therapist and continue to act out or return to it again soon after, the therapist walks over to him and *quietly* tells him to go home.

This extreme step needs to be resorted to very, very seldom, if the selection of the group members and their combination have been well planned. But when it becomes necessary, for whatever reason, the banishment of the child must be carried out. The therapist must not renege. No matter what the child may say in his defense, the therapist should pay no attention. He simply repeats, "Go home, Jimmy, go home." It is most unusual that a child will not pick up his outer garments and leave. But should he fail to do so, the therapist wordlessly places the palm of his hand on the child's back and, gently pressing it, walks toward the door (picking up his garments on the way) and helps him out, closing the door after him.

This dramatic enactment has profound effect on everyone, whether or not overtly involved. It would be unique if this profound departure from his passive role and customary benign attitude were not to arouse feelings in the therapist, as well, while the group members who witness the encounter and the therapist's unaccustomed role cannot but be shocked, but the greatest impact will be on the culprit. The significance of what transpired makes the children and the culprit realize that the blame must be his, for unlike all other adults, the therapist has consistently demonstrated his unfailing kindness and acceptance of everyone. Hence, the fault must be with the child. It is this discovery, perhaps for the first time in the children's lives, that alters hostile attitudes and acts against grown-ups.[5] The most critical sequence of the occurrence, however, is the reception the culprit receives upon his arrival at the next session, when the therapist acts toward the child as though nothing untoward had transpired. This is pivotal to the restoration of the positive relation between the two.

Obviously, the stratagem of dismissing a patient cannot be employed during the early life of a group. It is effective only when the image of the therapist as a benevolent person has been adequately imprinted on the minds of the children. It is in the *unusualness* of the act that its value lies. Should this episode occur before that image has been securely established, the therapist falls in the category of all adults, and his therapeutic effectiveness is destroyed. In fact, most of the children who might witness the transaction too early in the life of a group may not return, nursing the thought that if the therapist can be "cruel" toward one of them he can be so to all.

If through an oversight a compulsively incorrigible boy is included in a group and the therapist is convinced that his behavior will not abate by itself, the process of removal will have to be

[5] This dynamic we term *transference in reverse.*

149

initiated outside the group. The boy and a parent will have to be seen by the therapist or better still by a colleague before the next group session, and an interim of individual therapy should be recommended before he rejoins a "club."

CONTACT WITH PARENTS

To maintain his own neutrality and the nonclinical image of the group, the therapist cannot have any contact with parents of his patients. To do so will make the children suspect him of being in alliance with the parents against them. Contact between therapist and parent may also reveal the clinical nature of the "club," which will alter the children's attitude toward it and its "leader." The group must retain its character of a living, rather than a treatment, situation. Knowledge of such contacts with parents will cling to the child's fantasies that adults are in league *against* him and that he can no longer trust any adults. This will block the free flow of the child's action catharsis and action communication, the mainstays of AGT.

In agency practice all problems of communication with parents can be avoided by referring them to a social worker or psychologist on the agency's staff on a continuing or occasional basis, as the requirements may indicate. In private practice the situation is more complicated, and parents may be seen by the therapist. The child must be informed of the fact, however, and the general content of the interview should be imparted to him in the therapist's office, not at the group session.

Not infrequently a particularly anxious or uninformed mother, when accompanying her child to the group, insists on inquiring about her offspring and his adjustment in the "club," or she may wish to impart to the therapist some information about the child's conduct and proceeds to do so despite the fact that the latter informs her that someone at the (agency's) office can give her the information and that all he does is "lead the club." When a parent becomes so intransigent, the therapist walks toward the door of the room, thus forcing the parent to accompany him. As they reach the door, the therapist opens it, saying, "I'm sure the office will give you all the information," and bidding "good-bye" closes the door. Should there be a pressing matter that realistically falls within the therapist's purview, such as a traveling problem that may require his help or attention, he should talk to the parent only within the child's hearing so that the latter will have no fantasy projections.

Experience with AGT groups has yielded a small list of frequently occuring situations and standard methods of dealing with them. This section will be devoted to outlining them. Some have already been mentioned rather perfunctorily but are here reemphasized because of their significance to the therapist's role.

Helping Children with Their Projects

While the intent of AGT is to render its young patients self-reliant and confident, the therapist should not overload a child's ego and thus increase his anxiety by denying him help when he requests it. When asked for assistance with work or for a specific material, the therapist is required to stop *promptly* what he may be engaged in, walk over with the boy or girl to where he or she is working, and give the assistance requested. However, if the request is made when the therapist is engaged in assisting another child, he may say, "As soon as I finish with George, I'll come right over to you." The child's request for help when the therapist is engaged with another is not always genuine; it may stem from jealousy, sibling rivalry, or antagonism to the fellow group member receiving the therapist's attention at the moment. Sometimes still another child may require help. Then the therapist explains to him that after he finishes what he is doing, he has to help the other, mentioning his name, who preceded him, and then his turn will come.

If the request is for help with work—sawing, for example—the therapist takes several strokes with the saw and then, leaving the tool in the plank, wordlessly returns to his own occupation. The therapist must make sure that the child does not inveigle him, indirectly, into doing all his work. However, when a child for one of a variety of possible reasons displays anxiety about finishing a project—as the end of a session nears, for example—the therapist cooperates extensively, even to the point of taking over the last steps in finishing the job which the child is anxious to take home and display to members of his family.

When a patient is at a loss for an interest and asks the therapist what he can do, the therapist should respond by saying, "You can make . . ." suggesting several possibilities, not just one. Note that he substitutes the word "make" for "do." He must convey the idea not that a child can *do* whatever he likes at the group sessions, but that he can *make* whatever he desires. This differentiation was derived from an incident when a provocative boy at the very first session asked the therapist, "What can I do here?" The therapist mistakenly replied, "You can do anything you like." "Can I?" exclaimed the boy sarcastically and laughingly raised his arms as though he were making a dive into a pool of water.

Supporting the Weak Child

In the course of working on a project, a child may manifest confusion, discouragement, frustration, or anxiety by grimace, posture, or facial expression. The vigilant therapist will register the state of the child; but unlike a school or community center situation where the teacher or leader verbally offers help, the therapist finds some excuse to move his own project within the proximity of the child. This physical nearness often raises the level of confidence in the child, and he readily finds a solution to his problem. Usually, as the child becomes aware of the therapist's presence, he turns and smiles at the therapist in recognition of the helpful gesture and proceeds with his work with new vigor. By taking up this position the therapist makes himself available to the fumbling child, and at times the latter will turn to the adult and ask how to proceed with his project or request direct help. This gesture by the therapist is another demonstration of action interpretation.

Withdrawal from a Child

A child who is seeking to monopolize or ingratiate himself with the therapist or is drawn to him through positive (transferential) feelings may locate himself close to the therapist. When such strategies should not be encouraged for reasons already enumerated, to counteract them, the therapist, after remaining in the child's vicinity for a brief period, becomes occupied elsewhere by puttering in the refreshment area with the food or dishes, arranging the materials and tools in the closet, repairing to the washroom, or finding some other plausible reason for escape. However, if a child is impelled by fear or insecurity to seek the therapist's support or protection, the therapist remains in his original position and may even flash a smile of encouragement to the child. But when the same child later finds his place in the group, and feels more comfortable and more secure, the therapist initiates the withdrawal tactic.

Picking Up Discarded Clothing

At the early sessions of a group—and in some instances also later—some children drop their outer clothing to the floor or place it on a chair in their haste to begin their manual work, especially when upon arriving they find others already at work and become either curious as to what they are doing or feel outdone by them in point of priority. The therapist allows the clothing to remain where it is discarded for about five minutes; then as he passes by he nonchalantly picks it up and hangs it on a hook provided for the purpose. This he may repeat a dozen or more times, until the children become aware of the need for orderliness in the room and on their own begin to hang up their clothing.

Cheating on Transportation

When going on a trip, the therapist supplies each with fare and whatever is allowed for refreshments before departing from the room. We have noted that some of the children, instead of depositing the fare into the turnstiles of the subway, crawled under them, thus indulging in the cheating game customary in their neighborhood culture. In such an eventuality we suggested that the therapist wordlessly deposit the appropriate coin (now token) and turn the turnstile by hand. At first this maneuver caused consternation among the boys and brought outcries of disapproval. The therapists were instructed, however, not to respond to these protestations and let the children draw their own conclusions. Soon there was no "stealing of rides."

Scrambling Residence Numbers by Therapist

On rare occasions some child expresses a desire to visit the therapist at his home and asks for his address. Such inquiry and intention can be viewed as proceeding from warm feelings for the adult and the child's desire for a closer relation with him. Because of the general plan and intent of AGT, such transferential feelings and emotional dependency cannot be encouraged. (Unless transference in a psychotherapeutic relation can be interpreted, its emergence has to be discouraged.) However, the therapist cannot reject the inquiring patient. He, therefore, should give the child his address but, while retaining the street name, scramble the house number of his residence, e.g., turn 1367 to 1637. The same strategy is employed with telephone numbers, should a child ask for one. Actually, we have had only one instance of a patient in AGT carrying out the intention of either calling on or telephoning a therapist.

Answering Personal Questions

All other questions put by the children such as age, marital status, and parenthood should be answered, forthrightly and honestly. Stemming as these queries do from a wish for emotional closeness and feeling of belonging, the information concerning the *person* of the therapist is valuable to the process of reconditioning alienation from adults. Sometimes children inquire why he bothers to "lead the club," to which the response should be, "Because I like to work with boys [or girls]."

Dealing with Denial

As can be expected, some demands for materials, food, money, and trips by children from ghettos may be prohibitive or out of line with the basic intents of AGT. Also, overgratification may be as bad as deprivation, but the therapist, nonetheless, must maintain his image of a "giving" person. To circumvent the dilemma, the therapist responds acceptably, but suggests that he will have to ask "the office" whether funds are available to meet their requests. However, the therapist needs to exercise judgment when a rule has to be subverted to the psychodynamics of a specific patient's personality.

Ruth had a "habit" of asking the therapist for various things to take home. Since these were often major items necessary to other groups, such as tools and implements, the therapist pointed out as tactfully as she could that the items could not be removed because they were needed by others. Ruth then modified her approach, asking to "borrow" supplies. This too, the therapist thought she had to deny. Finally, at one session, when the girls had left, Ruth returned so that she was alone with the therapist and asked whether she could have a role of crepe paper. The therapist suggested that she wait until the following week, when she could "make something" from crepe paper in the "club" and then take it home.

As could be expected, Ruth did not appear the following week or for three weeks thereafter. It took a month during which the therapist routinely wrote a letter each week telling Ruth that the "club missed her" before Ruth returned. (Such letters are written to all members who absent themselves.) It took even more time to restore in the girl the earlier friendly feelings toward the therapist. Obviously, Ruth needed the material things as an assurance of being loved. It was incorrect for the therapist to deny the tools and equipment out of hand. In the crepe paper incident, however, signals were being communicated by Ruth which the therapist failed to register. Ruth was giving the therapist second and third chances to meet her need. This was a glaring case where the "rule" should have been broken; Ruth should have been permitted to "borrow" the things she asked for, because the items were not as important as their symbolic value to the girl. *Rules serve as guidelines only,* and are necessary to help beginning therapists, but there is no rule that can adequately meet all circumstances. The experienced know when and how to dispense with or modify rules.

On Praising Children

The therapist's neutrality precludes volunteering praise as well as blame. To offer unsolicited praise implies power of judging and evaluating the child's work and a tacit expectation of its being acceptable to the adult. But children at times approach the therapist asking for an appraisal of their workmanship. The therapist's response must be positive—neither negative nor conditional—but at the same time not fulsome or exaggerated. Neutral statements like, "That's pretty good," or "It looks nice," are quite sufficient. When a product is glaringly poor, the therapist says, "Pretty good for a first try." In any event the therapist must avoid giving suggestions as to ways of improving or altering the performance, thereby negating the child's autonomy and worse, replicating the critical practices of parents and teachers to downgrade the child's self-image.

The therapist should keep in mind that being praised is a novel experience to his young patients, and as such may prove embarrassing. Praise must therefore be moderate, for fulsome praise makes children uncomfortable. In one such instance a boy's response was, "That's what I hate—*dishonest* praise," which put the therapist in his place. One has to be circumspect to the potential reaction of some children even to something as positive as praise: some are distrustful of adults, others are shy and frightened by gratuitous or exaggerated praise; in others it may arouse anger, as in the case just quoted; others may become anxious and some will be embarrassed.

However, in the case of a particularly shy or slightly schizoid child, or one with low self-image, who because of these conditions refrains from group participation for a long period and avoids contact with the therapist, the latter may in passing quietly remark about his handiwork, "That looks pretty nice," and pass on. One of the remarkable developments toward ego integration and good mental health is manifested by children who in later stages of group treatment spontaneously praise the work of fellow group members. This is quite common in AGT groups.

On the Use of "Thank You"

Any act on the part of a child which has communal (group) intent, such as replacing tools or materials, sweeping the floor, or setting the table for refreshments, should not be rewarded by grateful acknowledgment from the therapist. Contributions to the life of the group have to be taken for granted as from members of a family. However, any *personal* service ought be so acknowledged. For example, if a child hands the therapist a knife, brings him his coat, or lets him pass ahead of him—such acts call for a "thank you" as a demonstration of appreciation as well as of good manners. This is part of the educational process of AGT.

Meeting Challenge from a Patient

Very rarely a boy may attempt to defeat the therapist or challenge him. These attempts must be handled with great acuity, for the therapist is placed in an anomalous situation. He can neither allow lowering the group's esteem of him nor react punitively toward the child. Therapy requires that a patient may discharge without fear his feelings toward the therapist, but when challenged, the therapist must maintain his status. Any real threat to his image is dynamically a threat also *against the group*. Usually when a child attempts to defeat the therapist, other members of the group reprimand him or actually attack him, but the therapist needs also to anticipate and deal with such entrapments that weaken his position. The therapist did so in the following incidents.

One day, at the request of the boys at the previous session, the group went to a neighborhood playground that had a basketball court. The boys chose sides and asked the therapist to referee. After a while, Mark suggested that the teams change and the therapist should also play. Mark contrived to have the therapist on the team opposing his. The therapist had the unmistakable feeling that Mark was setting things up as a challenge situation. Mark had, in the past, demonstrated in various subtle ways a tendency to defeat the therapist. However, at no time had he tried so openly to maneuver the therapist into an obvious competitive position.

As was expected, when the game started, Mark immediately took it upon himself to make the therapist "his man." This meant that if Mark had the ball, the therapist was supposed to get it, or at least to prevent Mark from scoring. The therapist permitted Mark to score a basket. Mark chortled, "I did it; you couldn't block me." A bit later, when Mark again was in possession of the ball, the therapist retrieved it from him, in an impressively easy manner, and without overdoing it, demonstrated his superiority.

When this "message" had been communicated to Mark *and the group*, the therapist excused himself from the game.

In this incident, the therapist revealed himself as capable and strong. This was conveyed without attempting to overwhelm the child, or "showing him up." Mark and the group needed a potent therapist.

Another example of a threat against the position of the therapist occurred in the following episode.

Two of the boys were painting graffiti on a wall of the activity room. From a distance the therapist could make out what appeared to be numbers. The action drew the attention of others in the group. A kind of "game" seemed to be involved. Finally it became clear. Mike said to several boys, "Read it." One replied, "It's only number 611." Mike laughed, added a few quick strokes and "611" became a well-executed, unmistakable set of male genitals. Mike roared with laughter: *"Now* read it!" Others snickered but only murmured to each other. Mike shouted across the room to the therapist: "Hey, Mr. F., I want to show you something." The therapist walked over, some leather he had been working on still in his hands. Mike again drew "611." Again he quizzed: "Read it." The therapist did. Once again Mike quickly converted the numbers. Now two male genitals were starkly portrayed. Mike loudly and challengingly demanded, "Now, what is it?" The therapist matter-of-factly answered, "It's a prick," and turning his back returned to his work. The boys guffawed, all except Mike, who stood dumbfounded. Mike had his "answer": the therapist was not weak. No one was defeated. Rather, by preserving his image, all the boys were again reassured of the therapist's essential emotional strength.

A boy may sometime use profanity and lewd four-letter words, uttered not directly to the therapist, but to the setting, the environment. However, this can be interpreted as a challenge to the therapist, as an adult. In such a case the therapist gives no indication that he has heard the words and continues with whatever he may be doing.

Tests of Frustration Tolerance

Toward the end of the treatment—which is usually two school years—the therapist tests the maturity of the children by submitting them to a series of frustrating situations. One is denial by the "office" of requests that involve money expenditures for some trip or a movie. Another is the therapist's "forgetting" to bring along the keys to the materials and tools closets, or the office's cutting off funds for food by written note on the pretext that the group has exceeded their monthly allotment.

The reaction of the group and of individual children to these changes in routine, the degree of manifest frustration and their resourcefulness in dealing with them are reliable tests of the maturational headway they have made during the course of treatment. Were these denials and frustrations to occur in early periods of the group's life, some would react with depression, and still others would complain, become cantankerous, or act out aggressively. But when we exposed them to these denials later in treatment, we found impressive objectivity and calm in all our groups. When the therapist of a girl's group, for example, informed them that she had forgotten to bring the keys to the supply closets, the girls calmly made appropriate suggestions to fill the time with walks in the neighborhood, play in nearby parks or playgrounds, or in games of checkers in the room. Boys usually suggested sport games in nearby playgrounds.

Playing Games with the Children

One of the situations in which the therapist is pitted against a child, requiring keen perspicacity on his part, is when he becomes involved in a one-to-one competitive table game with a patient at the latter's invitation. The games are most often checkers, ping-pong or table tennis, and occasionally, chess. On general principles, it is damaging to a child's self-image to prove himself more skillful or superior to an adult in any regard. Such triumph may be permissible as a corrective strategy, however, but it must be managed by the therapist discriminately and with full awareness of the psychodynamics involved.

If a particular child is "weak" because of a succession of

159

failures in other areas in his life as a result of which his self-image is at a low ebb, the global value of the group and therapist's supportive efforts lie chiefly in supplying him with a series of successes. As already indicated, praise by the therapist, though honest and realistic, should be of an encouraging nature. The consistent building of a wholesome self-image in such a child is particularly tested in a one-to-one game, however. Should the child be constantly defeated by the therapist, his failures will confirm his feelings of weakness and inadequacy. The therapist, therefore, will underplay his skill to permit the child to win games. However, he must not be allowed to win *all* the games, only enough to realize that it is possible for him to succeed, a feeling which he may never or seldom have experienced. To allow the boy or girl to win all the games will give him or her a misleading foundation for self-evaluation and lay the basis of overreaction in competition with peers and others. Rather, the careful gradualness of success in the course of the group's functioning should serve to slowly build up self-confidence and aid in the acquisition of skills that give reality to the improved feeling of "self."

On the other hand, some children are overassertive and overconfident, which makes them abrasive and boastful. These characteristics are behind their social maladjustment and interpersonal problems in their environment. We have recommended that therapists consistently defeat these children in the games, with the exception of the last one. The strategy of allowing them to win the last game is intended to cushion the impact of their failure, prevent too great injury to their egos and the possible onset of depression. As these children slough off their overevaluation of themselves and moderate their attitudes and conduct in therapy, they are slowly allowed to increase their winnings.

Therapist's Lateness

It is of the utmost importance that patients do not foregather in hallways or on the street before the therapist's arrival to unlock the door to the treatment room. The antecedent attitudes—hilarity, or hostility and/or rivalries generated before entering the room—set the mood for the group not rooted in the real attitudes and feelings with which they come to the group session. AGT addresses itself to correcting the latter conditions. When, because a therapist is late, waiting children are placed in a position of dissipating feelings generated by daily stresses, or significantly altering them by free-for-all acting out in an unconditioned environment of a hallway or a street, the group loses much of its therapeutic effect. The process no longer is addressed to the state in which the patients came for treatment. The emotions aroused during the period of waiting for the therapist come into focus, rather than those generated in their daily living which require correction. The therapist, therefore, must arrive in advance of the time set for the sessions. This punctuality not only has the advantage that he can put the room in order, should the preceding group fail to do so, but also has educational value in fostering responsibility.

Therapist's Absences

It is of the utmost importance that therapists do not absent themselves from group sessions. (For obvious reasons no substitutes can be used.) Should this be unavoidable, the group members must be informed sufficiently in advance to prevent disappointment and consequent resentment. Should the time be too short even for "special delivery" mail, the telephone can be used. No matter what the reason for the therapist's absence may be, the only explanation that can be given in the notifications is illness of the therapist. Any other reason, no matter how urgent it may be for the adult, will convey to the children that other matters are more important to him than the "club." Only illness, which all have experienced, is acceptable.

Prevention of Physical Injury

The provision that therapists abstain from replicating the role of the parents and teachers by allowing each child to find his own way in the group has only one exception. This is the use of linoleum block carving gouges. Adults, and more so children, tend to place the free hand quite naturally in front of the gouge to prevent the block from slipping. In case of slips, which constantly occur, the very sharp tools cut into the hand and cause deep gashes. The therapist must observe the child who launches such a project and as soon as he places the free hand to hold

161

down the linoleum block, he should go over and, without a word, either nail a small strip of wood in front of the block, or set two nails to hold the block in place, thus making it unnecessary to use the free hand.

A similar strategy may be employed also when a child attempts to cut a board with the wrong saw—a rip saw instead of a cross-cut or vice versa—or when he grips the saw inappropriately. The therapist may place the proper saw on the bench in the child's immediate vicinity in the hope that the combination of his frustration and visual suggestion will activate him to try the proper saw. If this does not transpire, the therapist should go over and quietly say, "I think the other saw is better," and at once return to work on his own project.

Preventing Vandalism

At times a member of a group may commit an act that may be regarded on the surface as an act of vandalism, though it may be nothing more than an oversight, unawareness, or home or community habituation. One such situation arises when a child sets out to paint an object of his own production or a piece of furniture—usually a chair—without protecting the surrounding floor or table areas from defilement by paint droppings. In such an instance the therapist excuses himself as he raises the object being painted and spreads newspapers under it, also under the can of paint and on the immediate surrounding area, and then walks off without any comment.

Another instance is a child's setting out to drill a hole in the floor of the room or a table top. The impulse to engage in such an activity may have varying meanings, one of which is sexual, but the nature of the act is blatantly destructive and constitutes a challenge to the adult. Instead of prohibiting it, even with an obviously reasonable explanation about damaging the room or the table, the therapist places a chunk of wood under the bit (drill) by wordlessly lifting it from the floor or table; after doing so, he returns to his own occupation.

An even more direct assailment against the therapist as the representative of the "repressive" societal culture is painting graffiti on the walls of the treatment room, which few groups fail to do during early sessions. The psychology of graffiti is a fascinating one, but it would be out of place to enter into it here. What we are concerned with is how its manifestation should be dealt with in AGT. The therapist in this instance does nothing, but stays behind after the children leave (or returns a short time later if conditions demand his leaving with them) and paints over the defacements with paint of the same color as the walls (a can of which and a brush must always be kept available, stashed away from the children's sight).

The strategies suggested here are graphic illustrations of the principle of *acceptance of the child, but not of his behavior.*

Readmitting a Locked-out Patient

A most common symbolic group manifestation of sibling rivalry invariably occurring in early sessions of groups is locking a fellow member out, by one or a few of the group's constituents, and refusing to readmit him. The act of "locking out" also serves the scapegoating propensities of groups and is the first step toward their cooperation and whatever rudimentary cohesiveness may appear later.

However, it presents the therapist with a dilemma: to allow permanent or extended exclusion of the victim will generate in him resentful alienation from the therapist for not coming to his aid, but to unlock the door or remove the barricade may turn the other boy's wrath against him. A compromise strategy which both pleases the victim and prevents resentment from the aggressors is for the therapist to take up the trash basket and, under the pretense of emptying it, open the door and walk out with it, thus providing the exiled child reentrance into the room.

Borrowing Money

One of the unmistakable evidences of young patients' acceptance of the therapist *in loco parentis*—in addition to their desire and fantasies of visiting him in his home and his going to theirs—is that at a certain stage in the relation a few may ask him for money. While this maneuver is never widespread, it does occur in some groups, with potential negative outcomes. When it does occur, the request is made for a loan of a specific small sum, a nickel or a dime. We suspect that the real motivation is most often ascertaining the genuineness of the therapist's apparent benevolence and interest in his charges. It is thus one of the tests—and in the eyes of children a severe one at that—to which patients in AGT subject the therapist. He must pass this pivotal test with flying colors if he is to maintain his good standing with his young patients. There is only one course open to him, namely, to comply.

While doing so, he also opens a Pandora's box, for the same child may make a practice of it without repaying his debt and thus become an "exploitative parasite," in addition to being conditioned in dishonesty. Of further import, the practice may spread to others and even to all the members of a group. We found that most often the debts are scrupulously repaid at the following group session, usually in a bombastic manner with appropriate pronouncements. This may terminate the money-borrowing practice, as the other children are made party to the transaction. However, when a child does not return the loan, we found two methods effective to deal with the problem.

Depending upon the personality structure of a particular borrower, the therapist may calmly, almost inadvertently, ask the child whether he remembered the debt and brought money to repay it. Or, better still, he may overlook one or two instances, as isolated events, but when the child, or others following his example, continues asking for money, the therapist withdraws from his pocket the small change and proclaims that he happens to have only enough for his own fare home. *But he cannot do so unless it is really true.* He must come to the group with only that amount, leaving other money behind him in his office or elsewhere. After a few weeks of this, the practice disappears.

Dealing with Stealing

Stealing occurs rarely in AGT, partially because of the intake policy of not admitting overt delinquents, but more because of the permissive climate of the group and the children's attitude toward the therapist. As already indicated, group members are free to take materials home to work with (as well as their finished and unfinished projects). This policy reduces the need and temptation to purloin them.

We have had only two incidents of stealing in our experience. In one instance stealing in a group was a part of an extended syndrome of a boy's violent and destructive conduct, in and out of sessions, which led to a restudy of the case. He was found to be psychopathic, and this finding necessitated his withdrawal from the group, with other arrangements for his rehabilitation.[6]

Dealing with Requests for Special Materials

Sometimes children request new materials that are not part of the regular supplies. This may be attributed to one or more of the following reasons: a realistic need for a special item to complete a project, e.g., hinges for a shoeshine box; the child's need to test the genuineness of the therapist; rivalry with another child; an immature dependency need; an expressed group need, following a discussion.

The therapist should fulfill all such needs, except when it is counterindicated, as in the case of an oral, infantile child who persistently asks for special items. To accede to all his requests will merely fortify his oral dependency and create the problem of the spread of unreasonable demands by other group members. However, when supplying requested materials is indicated, delay must be avoided at all costs. The desired object must be provided at the very next session, whenever possible. For emotionally disturbed children especially, who may in the past have had their wishes ignored or neglected, the therapist's prompt attention has dramatic psychological impact. The children need such tangible evidences of the therapist's interest in them.

THE MATTER OF PERSONAL GARB

The therapist, as the symbolic representative of external reality, should be cautious in his dress. Some degree of individuality and divergence from the rigidities of fashion is permissible, but too "far out" garb, uncleanliness, and general sloppiness are taboo. Serving willy-nilly as an identification model, the therapist

[6] This case is detailed in *The Practice of Group Therapy* (Slavson, 1947).

165

should strive to set an example for personal orderliness, a modicum of neatness, and respectability. This is part of the educational influence of our groups. Priestly garb is also taboo for an activity group therapist, and we have always advised priests to wear sports clothes, which they are permitted to do. The clerical garb by itself tends to inhibit young patients from maximal action catharsis, which limits the effectiveness of the group as a therapeutic agent. It is inadvisable for groups in which the membership is recruited from different religious, racial, and ethnic sources and especially where the children are of the same religion as the therapist. Such garb may intensify provocative trends in some children of different religious persuasions.

PROFESSIONAL AND OTHER "STIGMATA"

The principle of the therapist's neutral personality extends beyond his conduct and responses delineated in many connections in preceding pages. He must also be free of peculiarities in his conduct, physical appearance, and manner of speaking. Even when the therapist is a physician in clinical practice, the fact should be withheld from the group. This is achieved by having therapists introduce themselves without Mr. or Miss or Reverend or Father. All correspondence to the children is also signed without special identifying titles. We once had many difficulties when an office clerk attached a note to the door of the treatment room addressing the therapist, who was a psychiatric intern, as "Doctor." As already indicated, the group must remain a "club" to the children to prevent abashment and resistance to a medical connotation.

PRIVATE PRACTICE

In private (noninstitutional) practice of AGT, it becomes less feasible for the therapist to introduce the group in terms of "club." Nevertheless, to the extent that it is possible, the therapist should avoid emphasizing his professional identity and describe the group to prospective candidates as one in which boys (or girls, as the case may be) meet as a "group" (not a club) to make things as they wish, have refreshments, go on trips, and make friends. All clinical references are omitted in the introduction. When a therapist refers a patient to a group conducted by another practitioner, he follows the same lines of initiation, so that the newcomer will not tell the others in the group of its clinical intent.

EMPHASIZING PATIENTS' RESPONSIBILITIES

Not infrequently a child who feels disturbed or is frightened by violent playfulness of a group (which can reach high crescendos of mobility and emotion) approaches the therapist complaining and requesting that he stop the turmoil (see Chapter I). The therapist's appropriate reply to this should be, "This is the boys' club and it is up to them." This statement, which is not lost on those who hear it, usually has a profound effect on the participants and may become the subject of deliberations at the refreshment table in which the therapist must in no way participate. It is thus brought patently and emphatically to the boys that they are responsible for their "club" and not the therapist.

PREVENTING APPEARANCES OF PREFERENCE
(COUNTERTRANSFERENCE)

The neutrality of the therapist demands that he maintain emotional objectivity with regard to all his patients. His equalitarian conduct toward them must be as genuine as is humanly possible. To achieve such detachment and objectivity is no easy matter, but it is essential in preventing jealousy among the young patients and thus avoiding negative consequences that may ensue from partiality. The therapist has to work on his feelings studiously until he achieves the desired detachment. Inevitably certain traits, appearances, and mannerisms of one child appeal more to him than do qualities of others, but the group therapist must be aware of his attitudes and work them through within himself.

Often a group member is overly dependent, or is drawn to and gravitates toward the therapist, and unless the therapist exercises caution in his responses, he may create the impression that the child is his favorite. As a consequence, other members of the group, some of whom have been defeated in sibling rivalry, transfer their hostilities from their siblings upon the clinging fellow group member, who then becomes the target of persecution and the object of scapegoating. In addition, the aggressives may turn upon the therapist as a parent substitute, and inaugurate individual or group action with a view of provoking or irritating him.

One of the critical situations in which misunderstanding can be easily created is when one child and the therapist leave the premises together on the way home after the sessions because of their common travel facilities. This fact, unknown to the others (and even when it is known), cannot but arouse resentment in children whose problems stem from parental discrimination. The therapist should devise some strategy to prevent this eventuality. Discovering the direction the child in question takes, the therapist bids the child good-bye and turns in the opposite direction, even when this takes him away from his destination. Or he can join the majority of the members for a short period and then turn off to resume his own direction.

Another strategy is for the therapist to announce to the child in the hearing of the group that he has some business in a store or a building which he enters briefly, to emerge as the child disappears. Another procedure is for the therapist to remain in the room occupied in setting it in order and leave alone some minutes later. The problem is not as great when the therapist departs with two or more children who travel in the same direction.

THE SIGNIFICANCE OF "PABLUM" THERAPY AND THE THERAPIST'S ROLE

Among the peak therapeutic experiences of AGT is the refreshment period at the concluding thirty minutes of the two-hour sessions. The significances of being fed by the therapist are many, and the services of the repast in the context of the therapeutic dynamics are extremely important. On the empirical side, the therapist's first steps in the preparation and setting out of the food signal the ending of the work and play activities, which obviates the necessity of his terminating them by fiat. This prevents placing him in the position of authority. At the same time, it further reinforces his image of a provider, which supplying of materials has established. Especially after a noisy and disruptive session the children cannot but be impressed by the fact that, despite it all, he retains his accepting posture rather than becoming punitive as other adults in their experience have been. The oral gratification that the food yields further enhances the therapist's image of benevolence.

As the time for refreshment approaches, the therapist leaves his project and proceeds to clear the room of the debris and strewn tools and materials, sweeps the floor, and prepares the refreshment table by washing and covering it with cloth and setting out plates, cups, saucers, cutlery, and napkins in their appropriate places. From the very outset, the therapist consistently demonstrates proper social procedures by laying out these utensils. This formality may appear incongruous in the contrived setting of an AGT room, especially where "proper" behavior is not imposed. However, these proprieties are purposive and are meaningfully related to the reeducation process. The therapist's acting in a socially regulated manner in no way abrogates his permissiveness; nor is it a mandate to the children that orderly behavior is expected of them, for they are not accountable should they not adopt the manners demonstrated by him.

The acquisition of social amenities serves as an ego-integrating force contributing to the improvement of the patients' personalities. In line with this, the therapist always washes his hands before handling the food and the implements he uses in its preparation and serving. He makes a point of this by either washing or drying them within the sight of the children.

After he has set the table and the group is seated, even though there may be some stragglers who for varying reasons delay joining the others at the table, the therapist wordlessly passes the serving plate to the child nearest him, who helps himself and passes it on. The therapist waits until all the children have helped themselves to the food and is last in line. (The therapist also makes a point of placing the napkin on his lap, and sets the example by using the proper items of cutlery.) He thus, step by step, demonstrates socially approved table manners but makes no comment if children do not adhere to them. In time they all modify their table deportment, partly by copying the therapist as a model and partly under pressure from others in the group. Many years of experience have demonstrated that children are significantly impressed by the manner in which the therapist discharges his role in preparing and serving food when later they take over these chores. This is particularly true of children who came from families which lack social amenities because of cultural and economic deprivations.

A variety of foods are served over the period of a group's existence, since children like variety. However, the staple foods are usually "treat" or dessert types: cake, fruit, cookies, soda, milk, syrup-flavored milk, ice cream, hot chocolate, frankfurters. As the group progresses, the members request foods for succeeding sessions such as crackers and jam or peanut butter sandwiches and hot soup.

When we first introduced what later became AGT during the depression early in the 1930s, the children came from economically deprived homes, and more substantial food, such as canned spaghetti and meatballs, was served. This is no longer necessary. The therapist meets special requests if at all possible, and if not, suitable and convincing reasons should be offered at the appropriate time and in the prescribed manner. (The practical consideration of preparing more complex food items is no real problem today, since a great variety of precooked foods are obtainable.)

In the beginning, the therapist purchases food on the way to the treatment center and, as indicated, sets the table and attends to all incidental chores, including clearing the table and washing the dishes and utensils. In time group members take over these chores voluntarily, except, of course, purchasing the food. Later the therapist stops bringing food and some of the children volunteer to take over responsibility by going to nearby stores, usually in twos or threes, as the others continue their work.

The choice of food for the following session becomes a subject for intragroup interaction that frequently results in argument, discussions, and disagreements at the refreshment table as to who will do the purchasing, what should be bought, and other related problems. In all these episodes the therapist remains completely uninvolved. All he does is place money on a table, and the group is left to resolve its problems on its own.

CHANGING THERAPISTS IN MIDYEAR

It is advantageous to have the same person work with a group throughout its existence, which is two school years. This creates no problem in private practice. However, in child guidance clinics this is at times not possible because of staff turnover or some other unavoidable eventualities. A break in continuity and in whatever transferential feelings the children may have established may prove a serious deterrent. To minimize or prevent its effect, the group must be prepared for the change.

The procedure we have evolved is to have the replacement therapist visit the group session for a period of a half hour or so as a visitor (adult visitors are otherwise strictly barred) and leave as the group prepares for refreshments. By this time he (or she), having been introduced to the group by the therapist, has attempted to make contact with some of the group members. At the next session, the visitor appears about a half hour before the refreshments are to be served. As preparations are being made for the repast, the therapist invites the visitor loudly enough for the children to hear to join the group at the table.

The current therapist involves the prospective therapist in the ensuing conversation at the table. Both adults remain in the room as the children leave. At the session that follows, the therapist tells the children that the "office" gave him a new assignment (not that he leaves for another job, even if this is the case) and has asked (naming the new therapist by first name and surname) to lead the club. The new therapist appears for the third time shortly before the refreshments are served. This done, the retiring therapist says "So long" to the children and leaves the new "leader" to proceed at the refreshment table.

THE SKILLS OF THE THERAPIST

It is clear from the foregoing, expressed and implied, that an activity group therapist needs to master many skills in addition to having psychologic judgments and perspicacity. He or she—each according to suitability to the gender of the young patients—will fail to meet needs of children unless each has a working knowledge of the various arts and crafts skills and proficiency in the ordinary games that are part of the children's life in their specific culture and subcultures.

The manifest abilities and interests of the adult in areas in which children are interested, especially those that are culturally invested with affect and importance such as baseball and current news for boys, and fashions, and also sewing and cooking, for girls, generate a commonness and a closeness between them. This basic commonality "breaks the ice" that has built up between the generations in the home and community and lays the foundation for empathy and psycho-interpenetration. Our adage has always been that the psychotherapist (with all ages and varieties of patients) must know everything, or nearly everything. We have been accused of requiring supermen in our work. We do not; we expect them to be only superior men and women.

IX

Interpretation of Group
Protocol in Chapter I[1]

The condensed anamneses of the boys constituting the group described in Chapter I make it seem surcharged with pathology, some of which is theoretically inaccessible by AGT. The neurotic reactions (not psychoneuroses) of a few of the boys, the severity of character and behavior patterns in a number of them would render the group difficult to reach by nontransferential, nonverbal therapy, which AGT is. But because of our belief in the flexibility and malleability of children's personalities and the absence of full-blown and fixed symptomology in the boys chosen for the group (except in one or two cases), we experimentally proceeded with it.

Certainly, if the group hyperactivity manifested in the protocol continued indefinitely, nothing but harm to the patients (and the therapist) would result. Under such circumstances the therapist (and his consultant or supervisor, if there is one) would have to reassess the constitution of the group and identify the boy (or boys) who is, or are, the true center (this may differ from the apparent) of infection and eliminate him. We have done this only once in our experience, notably, in the group we filmed, to which references have been made elsewhere in this volume. This was not necessary in the group under consideration here.

The following are comments on some of the major develop-

[1] In order to profit fully from these interpretations, the reader is advised to read lettered sections of this chapter in conjunction with the correspondingly lettered sections of Chapter I.

ments in the group identified by corresponding alphabetical letters here and in Chapter I.

(A) The therapist made a point of purchasing both beverages because two boys asked for them. Had he brought either one, the other boy would have felt rejected. By remembering and fulfilling the requests, he demonstrates equal interest in both boys, thus preventing (sibling) rivalry. Arthur has isolated himself from the other boys in the past, and this is only the second time that he has played with another boy.

(B) This may have been a step on Paul's part to ingratiate himself with the therapist. The therapist, however, does not acknowledge it, thereby conveying that such maneuvers are not necessary for maintaining their relation.

(C) The therapist turns his attention to the children's needs first, before his own. At the same time they can start work instead of idling, during which they may become playful again.

(D) The therapist does not pick up the coats at once, for reasons indicated in the preceding chapter.

(E) The therapist fails to demonstrate responsibility by not spreading old newspapers under the chair to protect the room. Arthur begins to act out against the setting (therapist). It is interesting that he chooses to do so by painting furniture, and does so sloppily. His mother is an artist and is seductive to him, which is a source of his anxiety. By allowing Arthur to paint the furniture, the therapist demonstrates the extent of his permissiveness.

(F) Paul usually arrives first to the sessions, which may signify a need to be the "only one", or the first in the attention of the therapist. It will be remembered that Paul feels intensely jealous of his sibling and has lately become friendlier with the therapist. At the moment he is hostile because the therapist's attention is being solicited by others. Sol always seemed to know what to do at previous sessions. His present indecision may be related to his feelings about his older brother, who dominates him and escorts him to and from the center. Sol's manner throughout this session is quite significant in the light of his basic problem. In this incident his complaining is equivalent to a small child's whining to get attention from an adult. He also displaces anger against his sibling by criticizing Arthur. He is to do much of this during this session toward other boys as well. By the therapist's correctly ignoring Sol's announcement he aids the child to move toward self-reliance and demonstrates his own neutrality.

(G) The therapist had placed himself on the periphery of the group; this is the correct position. By engaging concentratedly on work, he both sets an example for the boys and becomes less accessible. Sol continues restless, but is able to stand up against Paul, an aggressive boy. (At the time of referral, Sol played only with younger children. His caseworker reported that since he has attended the group he has become more communicative, having been inaccessible before. Such improvement in individual therapy through AGT is not unusual in latency patients, who are otherwise notably resistive to individual treatment.)

(H) Ronald's father is a strict, overpowering man, who often beats him. Ronald's interest in pugilistic display probably stems from his fantasies of physical strength. It is also interesting that he lisps (infantile speech) with adults but not when speaking with children.

(I) In his state of anxiety, Sol is easily distracted. He, Arthur, and Paul display rivalry in asking for special materials. For Arthur this is particularly good, because he is able to displace the jealousy he harbors against his sister on a substitute sibling, which helps him overcome his fear of expressing it at home.

(J) Morris is usually late. Morris, though dependent, is ambivalent in his feelings toward the therapist. He reveals these confused feelings in his seeking out the therapist and asking for help unnecessarily. Morris, to recall, lost his father when he was five years old, hates his only sister, older than himself, and gets little comfort from a dominating mother. Morris's need for relationship with a male adult is reflected in his dependence on the therapist, his seeking physical proximity to him, and his need to "confess" (explain) the reasons for his absence. The therapist is careful to fulfill the boy's needs, but he also does not support his overdependence. Note how he manages to separate himself from the boy. Group activities and social stimulation are extremely important for this child, for they counteract his tendency to withdraw from his contemporaries and to steep himself in fantasy to an extent that at times he seems almost "as if he were in a stupor." The advisability of the second move away from Morris by the therapist can be questioned. At this point the meaning of the boy's seeking out the therapist again is not clear and, therefore, such drastic action should not have been taken. There are two major possibilities for the boy's seeking physical proximity with the adult male: (1) attachment to a father substitute as replacement for his deceased father, or (2) fear of the other boys. The cardinal rule in AGT² is, *say nothing, do nothing, when in doubt, don't,* for it is easier to correct an oversight in the future then to undo an error.

(K) Paul's criticism of Arthur may be an attempt to ingratiate himself with the therapist, another example of his sibling rivalry feelings. Because he was not admonished or punished for the messing, Arthur responds by helping move the chairs. But what is more significant is that for the first time, probably in gratitude to the therapist, he replaces his working tools in the closet. It may also be an indication of a budding superego which his family climate failed to help him establish.

(L) Sol continues to shift from place to place, discharging his anger and rivalry against the boys, probably a displacement from his older brother who tries to assume in the family the role of the missing father. Sol has usually avoided fights in the past, but now wrestles with Robert, who is quite aggressive. Sol can now give overt expression to his hostility: he struggles with Robert, makes a clay face and smashes it, probably a symbolic destruction of his brother. The fact that he calls the therapist's attention to this is an indication of the emotional significance of this act and his growing freedom in discharging hostility.

(M) Paul has been withdrawing from contact with the therapist and involves himself more frequently with Ronald. This is a change in *supportive ego* relationship: at first the therapist was the person with whom Paul had this basic relation. Note how Sol again reenacts his aggressive feelings toward the older brother, and perhaps toward the absent father, when he competes with the therapist, as he tells Morris that he will show him the right

---

²And perhaps in life generally.

way to carve the linoleum block when Morris requests help of the therapist.

(N) Robert provokes the boys. Such behavior is what got him into difficulties at school and was one of the reasons for his referral. The aggressive play that follows, and which eventually involves all but one of the boys, was ignored by the therapist. (This is typical of the degree of permissiveness allowed in AGT.) Given the necessary psychological balance due to proper grouping, the aggressive interaction is maintained within bounds tolerable to the protagonists. Thus, despite the tensions and fears that are mobilized in some of them, the therapist can feel secure in allowing such behavior to continue. The frightened group members themselves make accommodations to situations that threaten them. Morris and Arthur, for example, who were at first anxious about what was going on, protected themselves by continuing with their crafts work. Arthur's increased banging is probably a sign of his agitation, as are Morris's more frequent consultations with the therapist and his asking the latter to do some of his work. The influence of "neutralizers" (contrainstigators) resolves the problem, as we shall presently see.

(O) The "game" changes in character as the hostile element is intensified. Sol scapegoats by directing the others against Robert, urging them to push Robert out of the room. There is probably some relatedness here to the older brother (who is expected to take Sol home later). Paul, who is also extremely rivalrous with his sibling, is having a royal time exercising power, which he cannot do at home.

(P) Robert is aware of the fact that the small pieces of wood belong to the therapist, yet he peremptorily takes possession of some of them, and were it not for the emergency he was in, it could be interpreted as defiance. Robert who was really being pushed very hard by now, struck back and hurt Paul. The boys are startled by this development but are allowed by the therapist to experience the full impact of their boisterousness and lack of control. But with characteristic resilience, the boys find justification for their treatment of Robert. The therapist's response at this point is meaningful: he properly attends to Paul to see if he is injured, a demonstration of concern and sympathy. Yet, by not commenting or imposing limits, the therapist relieves Robert of his anxiety (who shouted, "I told you to stop!") by accepting him, even though he obviously does not at this stage accept or approve his own behavior.

(Q) It is the therapist's responses that restore a measure of "peace" to the battle game. While it did continue, it did so at least for awhile with less impetus.

(R) Note how free the boys feel about using the setting: standing on the table; building a barricade (and doing it more extensively later). Arthur is now involved actively. While he still could not initiate aggression, he was now mobilized to participate, sharing it with others.

(S) Now Arthur is really drawn into the fray and is more vigorously wrestling with Robert, even threatening him with a hammer. The therapist made no move to interfere, for he was confident that Arthur would not use it. (Such decisions, which must be made instantaneously, are not idly arrived at. They are based on understanding of each child's essential personality and propensities, and the therapist's perception and estimation of the gravity of the situation.) Once more we wee the boys' assurance of the therapist's acceptance when Robert accidentally breaks one of the large plaster boards and greatly messes the floor.

(T) Morris's anxiety about aggression surfaced when he asked the therapist directly to stop what the boys were doing. For him it proved "too much." This is neurotic anxiety and part of Morris's many fears. The tumult and violence of the game threatened his defenses. The therapist, however, seems for the most part to have correctly estimated Morris's tolerance. He felt that this experience was a critical event for this boy. This assessment is validated when, shortly after, Morris "breaks through" and joins the action. Later in the session he again becomes anxious, but his participation in such aggressive play does, in fact, decathect the fears that underlie his latent aggression.

(U) Paul takes on the role of instigator to manage the struggle. However, the notable development in the stream of the group's activity is that, goaded by him, it backs down in its destructiveness and the boys on their own begin to undo the damage they have wrought, proceeding to clean up the room. Because the therapist did not prohibit or control their vandalism, the boys' guilts set in, and what may be termed a *group superego* is aroused, touched off by Paul's stance. (It is by these means that AGT not only strengthens the patients' egos, but also corrects their superegos. However, these salutary results can be achieved only when the choice and grouping of patients make them possible. For were there psychopathic or uncontrollably aggressive children among them, Paul's call for a truce would have gone unheeded.) Arthur, who was reported as having difficulties in relations with peers, seemed to enjoy the hilarity and participated in it minimally. He now assumes the lead in drawing up "peace regulations." His remark, "except in certain times we shall have war," is significant; it betrays his basic ambivalence. Following the adult political model, the boys inaugurate election procedures.

(V) These developments illustrate how in a suitably conditioned (not controlled) environment interpersonal conflicts and tensions can yield to autogenerated moderating influences and how a feeling of *groupism* can evolve. Elections, rules, limits, and other such *self-evolving* and *self-formulated* procedures are the roots of individual and group identity. It is also most significant that Morris, who stayed out of the melee, was elected to the presidency. Morris now finds that he can safely enter the situation, as the hostile edge of the interaction has been eliminated. Morris seemed pleased by the recognition, and the therapist's responsive smile was appropriate, as it conveyed much meaning to the boy.

(W) Apparently the boys were not ready for organizational controls, probably largely because of the (sibling) jealousy of the elevation of some of their numbers to positions of prestige, and the peace plan is readily scrapped.[3] The pleasure principle outweighs the reality, however, and the boys resume the "war." But it is now a game, not a hostile scapegoating of one of their number. Even the very brief interlude of "peace" brings a feeling of togetherness and playfulness, eliminating hostility.

(X) There is understandable competition in the light of sibling

---

[3] We have had several instances when boys organized "clubs" with officers. We have suggested that the therapists ignore these events in subsequent sessions. In all cases the boys completely dropped their plans, never even mentioning them.

rivalry for preferred seating next to the therapist. Paul's helping to set the table is the beginning of the boys' later taking over this chore, which extended in later sessions to their selecting and going out to purchase the food. Paul continues in the role of leadership, i.e., as the instigator, which is a reaction to his rivalrous feelings against his older brother. Throughout the session he acted out this problem in dominating the group as his brother dominated him. Arthur's lagging after the others to come to the table may be acting out passive defiance and testing of the therapist.

(Y) The interaction which preceded the refreshments has brought all the boys into animated conversation. The refreshment table is a focal point at which the events of a group session often become integrated into their conversations. The boys seemed relaxed and happy; they were now close to the person of the therapist, who had patiently tolerated the ebb and flow of their emotions, frustrations, and anxieties, while at the same time supporting them in time of need. They feel a part of the group and the group a part of them. They suggest kinds of foods and materials. They take an interest in the group as such in various ways. The therapist makes the error of promising (by implication) to obtain wet clay, which cannot be used in AGT because of its messiness. He should have said, "I'll ask the office to get it." He can then blame the office when it does not arrive or can receive a letter of refusal.

When Morris asks the therapist where the absentee member is, the therapist erroneously replies that he attended the previous session. This is not what he was asked. The reply should have been, "I don't know. I guess he couldn't come today." A therapist must be scrupulous in answering appropriately all questions, neither evasively nor circumlocutionally. Of striking significance is Robert's tying up the group with home. In his fantasy he wishes the same acceptance and comfort in his own home he experiences in the group. The therapist becomes a good parent.

(Z) When the boys play the game of hiding Robert's hat and coat, Paul confides in the therapist. This has a combination of meanings: Paul seeks forgiveness for his behavior by being now a "good" boy and also shows trust in the therapist by letting him "in" on the game. Morris becomes frightened again and verbalizes his anxiety even more emphatically than earlier. Again the therapist listens; and again he does not respond, which he should have done. He should have said, "This is the boys' club. It's up to them." Morris once more hovers close for safety. Nonetheless the therapist does convey to Morris that he (the therapist) is not concerned about the disorder, and that he feels Morris can handle it. This supports the boy as he experiments tentatively at first through marginal participation in the aggressive games. In this way he will be enabled to tap some of his blocked hostility, and will learn that anger and aggression can be discharged safely and without danger. The therapist planfully separates from Morris in the street. This is proper technique.

Note: Hyperactivity following the refreshment period is normal for children. The young of all animal species display it in the form of play and feeding. Unlike the old, including man, who become drowsy after meals, the young become stimulated. The fact that Robert again becomes the scapegoat requires examination of his suitability for AGT or temporary transfer to a group of younger boys.

This treatment group continued for another year, during which its progress and improvement of individual boys continued.

X

Evidences of Group and Individual Improvement[1]

In Chapters I and IX a protocol of the fourteenth session of a boy's activity therapy group with an analysis of the significant elements of individual behavior and group dynamics was presented. The protocol was chosen to convey to the student the process and climate of a group at one point in its development characterized by maximal acting out. This stage, which we identify as *supernodal*, is critical in the life of an activity therapy group. Following a period of rather slow acclimatization, lasting about seven sessions, during which time the boys were adjusting to the permissive setting, they relaxed and their behavior became more spontaneous. During the ninth session of this group, for example, transient subgroupings arose with aggressive alignments of one such small group against another, which took the form of thinly disguised, aggressive "war" games. By the twelfth session even more open conflicts took place among several boys, as a few others grew frightened by the intensified aggression.

The fourteenth session typifies the level of hyperactivity that an activity therapy group can reach when its members shed their distrust of the therapist and feel more comfortable with each other. The idiosyncratic qualities of each are now clearly in evidence, including the respective role each plays in the group, their relationships with each other and with the therapist.

---

[1]As in Chapters I and IX, we suggest that the student read the first part of this chapter and then turn to the correspondingly lettered section in the past part.

The following abstracts from later sessions trace further developments of the same group. Portions of the records of sessions 17, 18, 20, and 29 have been extrapolated in an attempt to give a sense of continuity and record obvious changes in individual group members and in the group as a whole. The last session, the twenty-ninth, was an "excursion" before the sessions were temporarily suspended for the summer vacation. One boy was added in the interim. His anamnesis in a highly condensed form follows.

Norman

Diagnosis: neurosis with possible schizoid trends; excessive fantasy; depressive features; "silly behavior" on which other boys comment. Norman was initially treated individually, then referred for cooperative individual and group treatment.

Abstract from Session 17

Paul went to the supply closet, took out materials, and began to carve a linoleum block. The therapist was straightening out the closet shelves. Norman (new member) stood in the corner, watching them and appearing quite ill at ease and frightened. He shifted back and forth from one foot to the other, constantly looking around. Several times Paul asked Norman, "Why don't you make something?" Norman did not reply.

A few minutes after the time set for the "meeting" Ronald walked in and greeted Paul and the therapist. He took off his coat and placed it on the radiator, then came over to the therapist in a rather embarrassed manner and said he had missed the last session because he had to be at a wedding, and next week he would again be absent because of another wedding. Paul now said that he, too, had been absent because he was sick, and described some details. Ronald watched Paul work on the linoleum. Paul was unsuccessful, because the printing ink kept smearing. Paul again said to Norman, "Why don't you make something?" Again Norman did not reply. Paul then said to Ronald, "Did you meet him?" When Ronald shook his head, Paul said, "Ronald, this is Norman; Norman, this is Ronald."[2]

---

[2]Ordinarily, this function should be exercised by the therapist.

Ronald walked over to where Norman was standing with his hands behind his back, still seemingly frightened. When Ronald extended his hand in greeting, he got no response. He then made a motion as if to shove Norman, who reacted fearfully. Ronald laughed and said, "Hello." Norman then shook hands with him (A). Ronald busied himself looking at the supplies. Paul gave up the linoleum work *and replaced* the materials in the supply cabinet. Norman had finally taken some plasticine (material of low resistivity) and began to knead it. Paul found a long, round stick which he announced was a javelin and approached Ronald threateningly. Both boys chased each other playfully. Paul made a gesture with the stick toward Norman, who reacted with fear.

Ronald told Paul to paint some "blood" at the end of the stick. Paul thought it a good idea but used blue paint. Sol entered the room late, and his facial expression turned sour as he noted the others. He came directly to the therapist and asked whether the boat models were received. When told that they had not yet arrived, Sol looked displeased. A few minutes later, however, when Sol began to make a ring, the therapist heard him complain to Ronald that there were plenty of other stores that sold models and there was no reason for waiting.

Arthur, who had arrived a few minutes before, also asked for the models; the therapist gave him the same information. Arthur made no comment.[3] Instead, he found the copper disks which he had requested several weeks before and said, "I see that these came in," and began working on one to make an ashtray. Paul followed suit. They both pounded the disks rhythmically, enjoying themselves. Ronald found the lanyard material and asked the therapist to start one for him. The therapist said he was not sure how but would try.[4] As he attempted it, Sol looked on for a moment and then said that *he* knew how to do it very well, except that he did not know how to start it. He added that he had a friend who knew how to start it as well as do it. He

---

[3] Note the difference in the reactions to frustration in the two boys. This event also emphasizes the importance of obtaining, on time, the wherewithal for children's activities.

[4] This was the therapist's first group. Obviously, he was poorly prepared for this handicraft, and he should not have volunteered.

wandered away. When he came back later, he made another remark about the therapist's not having procured the airplanes or the boat (B).

Morris (who had come in earlier) was looking at Norman, and then whispered to each of the other boys in turn, obviously about Norman.[5] They responded by giggling. Norman was molding the clay into a ruglike shape. Morris enticed Norman into a "game." He led him outside the partition wall and slammed the door. Norman, now outside the room proper, made no response; no sound was heard from him. Arthur, meanwhile, picked up Norman's clay work and threw it. It failed to go over the partition, which was his intention, but stuck to it instead. Arthur unstuck it, crumbled it, and placed it on the worktable.

Soon after, the boys lost interest in Norman and invited him back into the room. Norman said, almost nonchalantly, "Is that what you call a game?" and walked over to his clay work, saw it was ruined, picked it up, seated himself again *at the isolate table,* and again started to work on it. While the therapist worked on Ronald's lanyard, Morris kept reminding him that his turn was next. When the therapist moved to work on Morris's lanyard, Sol kept reminding him about his request for help in an infantile, whining manner. As the therapist moved from helping one boy to another, some would return to ask for instructions. The boys would question: "Al, are you finished yet?" The therapist always responded to the effect: "Not yet, but I'll get to you as soon as I finish this part." Sol was quite boastful toward the others about his work on the lanyard. Ronald finally learned how to make the weaving stitch which had earlier confounded him. He came to the therapist and said, "I don't know why, Al, I've always tried to learn how to do this, and this is the first time I was able to." Ten minutes later he came again to the therapist to show his progress, and repeated the same remark.

The period of interest in lanyard making was interspersed briefly at times by the boys playfully chasing around the room after each other, with all participating except Norman and Ronald. Paul always took the initiative in this. There were also moments of

[5] The therapist again failed to introduce a newcomer.

loud debate over sports, with Morris and Ronald the loudest participants (C).

Abstract from Session 18

A moment after the boys entered, Arthur asked the therapist if he got the boat or airplane models. The therapist replied that he had boats—all destroyer models. As the therapist unwrapped the large package he had brought, all the boys stood around, watching excitedly. Paul rapidly *replaced* in the cabinet most of the tools with which he had already begun to work. Everyone marveled as they opened the individual boxes containing the models. Arthur exclaimed, "A real destroyer!" Norman took his away and sat down at the refreshment table with it. While the therapist was trying to open the bottle of glue which one of the boys had brought him because the cap stuck, Sol entered the room, again with an annoyed expression on his face. Since Sol had said nothing, the therapist said, "Hello." Sol returned the greeting.

Noticing the boats the boys were working on, Sol came running over to ask if the boats came in and whether there were two kinds, since there had been two models of airplanes on another such occasion. The therapist replied that there was only a destroyer model and handed Sol a box with his name on it. Sol looked at it, said it was nice, then immediately criticized the way the therapist was trying to open the glue bottle. A little later the therapist finally succeeded and placed it on the table for the boys to use. For about an hour all worked steadily. There was constant and animated discussion among them.

Arthur worked most deliberately, examining the plans, consulting the therapist at each step. He did not ask for the therapist's help until it was clear that others were doing so. After awhile, Sol said quite loudly that he knew nothing about making boats. He said he would let the therapist help him with it and show him all about it. There was something very infantile in the way he spoke. Norman also said he knew nothing about it either. Norman was making errors in the simplest steps. He then asked the therapist for help, who directed him. Norman, however, continued to make errors; he seemed to have no conception of what a ship was like or its spatial arrangements. Thus, each step he made, he called the therapist over to verify it. The therapist would say, "It might be a little better over here," gluing the part in the correct position so that the ship gradually took the same shape as those of the other boys (D).

At one point Morris called to the therapist, asking whether they could finish the ping-pong game they had started at an earlier session. The therapist said he would as soon as he finished (helping Sol). Morris meanwhile went to look for a ping-pong ball but could not find one and finally said they would have to finish the game the following week. He also said he could not remember the score, so they would have to start a new game. Sol said, "Al [the therapist] let you get ahead in the score. *He can beat anyone here in anything.*" At one point, while measuring the mast for his boat, Arthur said it was 11 inches long, therefore, he would call his boat "11 incher." Later he changed this, saying he was going to name it for his sister (E).

The therapist was washing paint off his hands when Sol came to ask whether the "club" could go to see another movie. The therapist replied that it was all right if that is what "the club" wanted. Sol then ran to the other boys to ask if they wanted to see a movie. Arthur said there were nicer things to do. Norman exclaimed, "Oh boy!" Paul: "A movie — or anything is good." Arthur asked the therapist if there was somewhere else the group could go. The therapist suggested the Museum of Science and Industry. Arthur said that would be swell and Sol said it was all right with him. The others concurred. Sol announced that the majority was in favor of the museum. The therapist said he would arrange for the trip and that he would notify the boys by mail about the details. Sol said, "You send all of us letters. We are going next Sunday" (F).

The boys resumed working, except for Paul, who batted the shuttlecock around with one of the boys. After the discussion about the trip, Sol began to hum a song from a current movie. Paul and others joined in. Sol then began to parody the song, singing, "Mammy, mammy, how I *hate* you!" Paul and Morris marched about singing other songs from the same movie. They placed stools on the large worktable, sat on them, continued singing. Sol, who was making frequent demands for help with his boat, now finished it rapidly and joined Paul and Morris. They all sat on stools singing hilariously, now rocking the table back and forth. Arthur, who was far behind in work on his boat, made threatening gestures at them (perhaps because he was frustrated in his work). Paul said to the others, "Let's get him."

They jumped off the table and began to push Arthur through the partition door. Norman left his work to join them. He laughed happily in a sort of infantile manner. Sol told Norman, "Get out of here." Norman stood aside, but still enjoyed the tussle. Arthur was now shoved outside, and Sol locked the door. Arthur began to knock on the partition, demanding to be let in. A small duster was thrown over the partition. One of the boys held up a stool, as if to toss it over, but Norman said reasonably, "Don't do that. You might just happen to crack his skull."

Arthur was now striking the partition rhythmically, and Norman said excitedly, "It's like a song; let's dance to it!" and began to skip around the room. The boys paid no attention to Arthur's knocking. He demanded that they take the coats off the hooks on the partition wall, so that he could climb over it. The boys did not accede. Arthur now called to the therapist to open the door, but Paul and others asked him not to. The therapist continued with his work, as if he had not heard either request. The boys now climbed back on the stools on the table, rocking back and forth and laughing at Arthur's efforts to get back in.[6]

Norman took a folding chair, put it on the same table, climbed up on it awkwardly, and joined the others in rocking. Arthur threw the duster back over the partition. Morris picked it up to throw it back, but the therapist asked for it, saying he needed it to clean up, a process he had started shortly before. Meanwhile, one of the boys had quietly unlatched the partition door. Arthur obviously did not know this, because he was climbing over it.

One of the boys yelled to him that the door was unlocked; so Arthur dropped to the floor and entered by the door. For a few moments Arthur wrestled with Paul and Morris. Then there was a general chasing about the room, with the boys now attempting to lock Arthur in the lavatory. Sol said, "Let's get him [Norman]." They pushed Norman outside the partition. He put up

---

[6]The therapist was too inexperienced to use the strategy of emptying the basket.

no resistance. The boys quickly lost interest in this. Norman reentered and returned to working on his boat, as did Arthur (G).

The boys were now standing around the electric hotplate, watching the frankfurters being cooked. The therapist was washing and drying the dishes. When he finished, Paul placed them on the table, each in front of a chair, and asked the therapist where he was going to sit. The therapist indicated his usual seat. Paul claimed the chair next to it, announcing it to the others. Sol claimed the chair on the other side of the therapist. When the therapist went to the washroom to wash the cups, Sol came over and asked if he wanted him to carry them. The therapist said he could. Toward the end of the session, Sol asked whether the boys who were finished could make a second boat. The therapist said that all the boys had asked for boat models and that he had ordered one for each and had to save the remaining ones for the boys who were absent. Sol said nothing further about this.

Prior to sitting down for refreshments, Sol said to the therapist, "You know, Al, I would like a submarine or a plane next week." The therapist replied that he would try to get them. He added that he was not sure that the "office" could make them available because they were quite expensive, and the office had already bought a number of models.[7] Sol said, quietly, "I hope you can get them. Next week when the others [absent ones] work on their boats some of the boys might be angry if they don't have any to work on." Later, when Morris asked the therapist if he could bring more models, the therapist replied that he would try to get them.

When the frankfurters were ready, the therapist served them. The boys poured soda, and the therapist noticed that someone had provided for him. The therapist passed the dish of frankfurters to Paul on his left, who took his share and passed on the serving plate. There was a fair distribution. Everybody was eating with seeming enjoyment. There was a relaxed discussion about camp experiences.

While the therapist washed the dishes, Sol again came to ask

[7] The explanation was unnecessary.

whether he wanted him to carry them. Again the therapist told him he could, and Sol replaced them properly in the cupboard. He then returned to the therapist to ask the time and proceeded to put on his coat; the others followed suit. Arthur said, "You can't get my hat today—I didn't wear any." Paul said it had taken Arthur a long time to get it back last week. The boys proudly carried their finished boats. As they were walking down the stairs, Paul said, "Let's all go down the street together and all the people will see our boats." The boys said "good-bye" in a happy mood, Sol adding, "Send us a letter if there is a trip" (H).

Abstract from Session 20

Arthur was first to arrive and as he walked in said, "Hello." The therapist returned the greeting. Arthur immediately asked whether the supplies had come. The therapist showed him the ashtray materials which he had brought. Arthur took some, saying he was going to make one. He asked for something that could be used to make designs on the metal, and the therapist gave him the proper tool. When Arthur began to work, Norman came over to watch, asking questions to which Arthur did not respond (I). Sol walked in a few moments later and said, "Hello." The therapist replied. Sol asked the therapist whether he had got the tracing paper he had requested. The therapist procured it and handed it to Sol.

Sol became dissatisfied with his work after several attempts, and asked the therapist to do it for him. When the therapist completed the lettering, Sol said, "How nice you do it." Later he asked the therapist to do the same thing, this time on linoleum. Sol said to the other boys, "Look how nice Al does it. I can't." He kept calling for help later in a whining fashion. Norman, working at the far table in the corner, rolled clay into long rolls and made markings on them with a file. He giggled as he made a series of these, doing and undoing them. He made several penis-like objects and smashed them with a file. He then made the face of a man and called the therapist over to show it to him. When the therapist came over to look, Norman smashed the clay face with the file. He giggled in a silly way as he announced, "I'm doing clay work" (J).

Robert walked in, about fifteen minutes late, came up to the

191

therapist, said he was on time this week, and added that he had come too late to go on the trip the previous week. (This was the trip requested by the boys in session 18.) The therapist replied that they were all sorry that Robert had missed the trip. Robert asked if there was lumber. The therapist reminded him about a letter recently received from the office to the effect that the group would get no more lumber. (The boys had used an enormous quantity of lumber wastefully, and the group therapy department — "the office" — imposed this *realistic* limit.) Sometime later Robert saw several boxes of models in the cabinet and asked the therapist what they were for. The therapist explained that they had been requested by some of the boys and that these were for the boys who had been absent. One was for Robert. Robert became excited over this. He opened his box and proceeded to work on the model.

Arthur was attempting to mark cork with the pyropencil (electric woodburner) and commented on the odor. Sol, who was watching him, said, "Do you want to burn it? I have matches." Arthur agreed. Norman left his work to watch. The therapist continued what he was doing. Ronald and Robert worked on their boat models. Sol ignited a piece of cork with a match. Arthur jumped about excitedly, saying that if they had a microscope they could see the charcoal. He then came to the therapist and asked if a microscope was available, but as though he did not expect a reply, returned to the fire game.

The cork was now burning brightly, and Arthur asked the therapist if he had some of the fire-extinguishing materials they had seen at the science exhibit on their trip. At this, Ronald and Robert looked up from their work. Robert said, "You dopes." Ronald exclaimed, "Put it out!" Sol turned around, the burning cork in his hand, to show it to everybody. As the flame got larger, Arthur moved away, uneasily. Sol was also becoming a bit uncomfortable and began to blow at it. Finally, when the fire was almost out, Arthur came closer again to the boys and began to laugh (K).

After observing the fire play, Norman returned to his clay work, but soon left it to play ping-pong all by himself. He stood at one end of the ping-pong table and said, "Now watch this swift serve." After several missed attempts, he managed to hit one

over the net, in awkward fashion. Then he chased after the ball
to do the same thing from the other end. He "talked" the game
aloud, several times expressing dissatisfaction and occasionally
showing pleasure: "Oh gosh" or "That wasn't so good" or "Watch
that swift one." In the meantime, Sol took the pot to the sink,
emptied its contents, washed it, and put fresh water in to boil in
preparation for cooking frankfurters. He then took the package
of frankfurters and rolls and counted them. Norman left the
ping-pong table, picked up the deck of Old Maid, began to turn
over the cards, showing everybody the funny pictures. He asked if
anyone wanted to play. Ronald joined him, followed by Robert.
Norman acted in a silly fashion, calling various people "Old
Maid" (L).

When the game of Old Maid was finished, the boys began to
chase each other around the room with all the boys participating.
Norman skipped clumsily, his hands clasped, as if he were having
a "chicken fight," as he had seen others do before. Arthur pushed
him a few times, then lost interest. Robert wrestled briefly, first
with Ronald, then with Arthur. Arthur wrestled briefly with
Ronald. Everybody was laughing. During the chasing about, Robert jumped on the refreshment table. Sol told him to get off because that table was used for eating. Robert argued, "You don't
eat on a table." However, he did come down.

An argument arose over possession of the broom, everybody
joining in, which ended when the therapist approached the table
with the refreshments. Prior to that the therapist had washed the
table. Arthur started a conversation about a trip by asking if the
group could go to the circus. Some of the others were interested
in this, and the therapist said he could find out from the "office."
Robert was less interested in the circus because he thought his
family was planning to go. Ronald felt the same way and wondered about a boat ride up the Hudson River. The idea of a ball
game also came up. Norman had no opinion; he was enthused
by every idea.

During the repast Robert and Arthur became involved in conversation with suggestive sexual connotations. Robert picked up
his frankfurter roll and pointing to the pointed end stated that he
had "one" and, therefore, did not need a frankfurter. Arthur
picked up the edge of his roll, pulling it back and forth, stating,

"Mine goes in and out." He laughed as the others giggled.[8] One of the boys spoke of "Bubonic plague" which Arthur changed to "Boolaphant" plague, causing everyone to laugh. Norman distorted the word even further, and everyone thought it hilarious. Arthur said if he got that (plague), his nose would fall off (M).

Abstract from Session 29 (Trip to Central Park)

The therapist met the group in front of the building at 12:30, and left the boys at 6, when the trip was over. It took about fifteen minutes for the boys to assemble. During this time there was discussion about what to do, since the ball game they were to have seen had been postponed because of rain the night before; the field was still wet. The boys decided to go to Central Park instead. The group stopped to buy some rubber balls, then went by subway to the park. The major activities during this trip were punchball games, visiting the zoo, exploring, playing on the grass, and refreshments.

On the way to the subway, Norman walked a short distance behind the others, even though Morris invited him in a friendly way to join the group. The therapist also made several attempts to involve Norman in conversation with the others. During the subway ride, there was much conversation about summer camp plans and other vacation activities. The boys were full of enthusiasm when they reached the park. They settled on a grassy plot where they could play punchball. As the group approached this spot, Norman commented to the therapist about how hot he was and asked if he could look for a cool spot. The therapist said he could if he so wished.

Robert and Paul took the lead in making up the teams. When they chose Norman, placing three on each team, Norman said he did not want to play. Morris particularly encouraged him, but Norman asked the therapist if he could climb on the "mountain," referring to a large rock. Again the therapist told him he could. Morris asked the therapist if he would play instead, and the therapist replied that he would if the boys wished it. Morris continued to talk boastfully about his prowess, but actually did

[8] Obvious references to penises and coitus.

not do well in the game. Several times during the game Norman returned to tell the therapist that he had climbed the "mountain" and had chased the "penguins" (pigeons). The boys corrected him several times, but he continued to call them "penguins" (N).

Everyone rested after the punchball game. Morris and Robert had also brought sandwiches. Morris began to eat his, but after taking a few bites did not want to eat them, referring to them as his "mother's eggs." He fed part of them to the pigeons and threw the rest away. Paul had candy, some of which he offered to the therapist. The group proceeded to the zoo, where the therapist gave each boy money for refreshments. Everyone had orange drink. The boys ran around periodically as they walked, Norman and Morris participating only a little in this.

Norman spoke at length to the therapist about the presidents of the United States (as he had done also at a previous session) and quoted many bits of historical information. While Norman was expostulating on the presidents, Morris, who was walking on the other side of the therapist, kept talking about sports and boasted about his feats in the punchball game just ended. Neither boy seemed to expect responses from the therapist, and each ignored the other. Both spoke at once and for a good length of time. The therapist listened to both boys sympathetically and from time to time made appropriate comments.

Paul and Robert.were extremely active; Sol sometimes accompanied them. All the boys seemed to be having a good time. The boys lost interest in the animals after a short time. Norman commented that the Bronx Zoo was much larger. Whenever there was an opportunity to play "catch" with the ball, Robert and Paul took advantage of it. A suggestion was made that they have another game of punchball. All agreed. Sol remarked that he was hungry, and the therapist suggested that it was a good time to go to the cafeteria. He gave each boy additional money to make his own purchase.

The boys sat around, enjoying their food. Norman enjoyed his drink; he made a point of buying the same iced drink the therapist had selected for himself. He asked the therapist if it was all right to suck the ice. When told it was, he did so slowly, mentioning several times that he liked it, adding that he used to think ice was poison. During the course of refreshments, there was general conversation. Morris, as usual, talked about sports, with Robert interrupting from time to time. Norman again discussed presidents. Morris discovered that Robert's mother was going to be a counselor at the same camp where Morris's sister was going to work. It was then established that Morris's sister actually knew Robert and his mother. They spoke of mutual acquaintances during the remainder of the afternoon and exchanged summer addresses, promising to write to each other.

Sol was eating quietly. He learned that the therapist was going to pay the carfare on the way home, as he had in coming. Sol, therefore, decided he could afford to buy another frankfurter, using part of his own funds (O). Robert and Paul were particularly eager to get some place where the group could again play ball. This time they wanted to play touch football. Morris asked Norman to play, stating that he was needed for equal sides. The therapist had been asked to play but avoided doing so this time, saying that he was too heavy for them in a football game. This excuse was readily accepted. Paul also encouraged Norman to play. Norman finally said he "might" play. The boys said they were counting on him to do so.

En route to a field, Morris told the therapist that he hoped he would continue to be the "leader" of the "club" next year, and everybody chimed in, agreeing. Robert said, "We all like you," and wondered if it couldn't be arranged. Morris asked the therapist to "please tell the office." At this point the therapist reminded the boys that this was the last time they would meet until the fall, when they would hear from the office. All the boys made it clear that they wanted to be in the group, including Norman, who usually did not join in such conversations.

At one point the boys had to walk on rocks over a small stream, and Norman slipped into the water with one foot. It was then that he seemed to change his mind about playing football. The boys managed to form teams without him and played energetically, calling to the therapist several times for decisions. Norman sat near the therapist, still chattering about presidents. Occasionally the others urged him to join the football game, but he refused.

After awhile, he moved some distance from the therapist and began to roll down a grassy slope. He called to the therapist and the other boys, who had sat down for a brief rest, to observe him.

Robert referred to Norman as "Fatso." Paul joined Norman in rolling. Paul then wanted to finish the football game, but Robert and Sol objected. Paul, however, insisted and they gave in. When the game ended, Robert and Sol threw Norman's jacket around, but Morris and Paul retrieved it; they were protective of Norman (P).

It was time to leave. As the group left Central Park, Norman waved to the therapist, calling out playfully that he was going to stay. The therapist waved back, smiling as he did so to support Norman's pretense. Norman followed the group at some distance and finally rejoined it when the boys stopped at a drinking fountain. There was some horseplay and throwing the ball back and forth while on the way to the subway.

The subway train was crowded, and some of the boys began shoving. Several passengers complained about their behavior. The therapist told the boys it was "too crowded for shoving." All stopped. Robert and Morris again spoke in a friendly way about writing to each other during the summer. Robert reminded the therapist that the boys all wanted him for the "leader" next year. Morris repeated it, and the others chimed in emphatically. Morris asked the therapist if he would visit Camp R.(the agency's camp). Sol also asked the therapist if he would. The therapist replied that he would try to visit on both camp "trips." When the group reached its destination, the boys parted. Morris said to the therapist, "Thanks for everything." Again he reminded the therapist to try to visit him at camp. Paul said to the therapist, "I'll see you next year." Robert asked where he could write to the therapist during the summer. Sol said he hoped they would have the "club" next year (Q).

Interpretation: Session 17

(A) The new member's extraordinary insecurity is seen here. While Paul—and later Ronald—act in what appears to be a friendly manner, it is deceptive. A treatment group in its early development does not take kindly to new members. The design of an AGT treatment room is justified when Norman, frightened, retreats to the safety of the isolate table. Ronald sees fit to explain his prior absence because he received a letter from the therapist, which is a regular procedure when members are absent.

197

Of interest is Paul's voluntary remark about his own absence, which had occurred two sessions earlier. This is indicative of rivalry. At this stage a positive relationship to the therapist is very important to Paul. His need to ingratiate himself with the therapist was seen in session 14. Rivalry for the therapist's attention, which varies in degree depending on the nature of a client's personality and problems, is not uncommon at this stage of AGT.

(B) Norman finally responds, occupying himself with plasticine. His choice of material is of interest, since no other boy is using it. Norman is immature, and his idle squeezing of clay, a material of low resistivity, is typical of the regressive occupation such children engage in at first and in which Norman was to continue for many sessions. It should be noted, however, that his starting an activity in this session is in response to his perception of what the other boys are doing. Paul demonstrates the aggressiveness which typifies his behavior and which was seen so forcefully in the fourteenth session. However, his aggression in this instance is more reasonable in degree and less hostile in quality. Also, it is expressed in more sublimated ways. Ronald's remark about "blood" is related to his real concern and fear of aggression. He is physically beaten by his father and has held in repression his own hostile impulses. Now he is able to reveal this more openly; heretofore he could only boast about his prowess, as in session 14, when he spoke about the "small man who beats the big man with judo."

Sol's negativism is transparent: he belittles the therapist when he criticizes him to another group member because the supplies were not yet available. Sol is not only critical of the therapist for not providing the boats or airplanes, but he actually tries to show that he can do things better than the therapist. The therapist is partially at fault here, because he professes being unable to use a basic material—lanyard lacing. As already stated, therapists should be competent with all crafts media provided in AGT. Actually Sol is displacing his anger toward his father, who abandoned him when he was three years old.

Sol's behavior is in contrast to Arthur's, who also asked about the boats, but who could tolerate frustration better, substituting other crafts materials instead. Arthur could express his gratification because the therapist did remember to bring the other materials. Note that he and Paul enjoy themselves at work. This is a shared quality through creative work, which is observable in AGT as patients begin to respond to the corrective experiences of a therapeutic group. Abrasiveness and aggressive acting out begin to diminish as creative work and social group participation gradually supplant earlier behavior.

(C) Morris's aggressive provocation of Norman, the new member, is significant when it is recalled how ambivalent and anxious he was in a similar incident during session 14 when some of the group ganged up on Robert. The goals in Morris's treatment are to foster male identification and to help him discharge aggression. Of course, his picking on Norman also indicates his own and the group's resistance to a new member. The fact that this resentment was easily worked through in a few sessions was indicative of growth. Arthur, who was also at first fearful of his peers, acts aggressively toward Norman, destroying his clay work. This represented a rather exceptional venture into aggression for Arthur.

The therapist's neutral and fulfilling role is well exemplified as the boys compete for his attention and help. Paul, who is probably the most rivalrous for the attention of the therapist, may have initiated the active chasing game to draw the boys away from the therapist. Sol, despite his negative transference behavior, still reveals his immature dependence on the therapist, who satisfies the boy's dependency needs while, at the same time, he does not react to his negativism. This accepting behavior of the therapist illustrates one of the primary, change-inducing elements of AGT. Ronald, who was once so fearful, and who had a diminished self-image, is greatly fortified by his conquest of the lanyard weaving, which he has learned to do "for the first time." Again, this illustrates the ego-strengthening effects of work activity. Morris and Ronald avoid the active chasing game in this session, although they do occasionally participate in such games. However, being still insecure, they intellectualize their aggression this time through boastful argumentation.

Interpretation: Session 18

(D) Just as had been promised by the therapist, the boat models arrived. Such fulfillment is basic to the therapist's func-

199

tioning. The boys learn that he is a dependable person; that he can be trusted; that he is truly concerned with their needs. Sol is again annoyed on entrance, probably because he is working through significant emotional feelings in the transference. When other boys arrive at the treatment room before him, as in this instance, it is tantamount in Sol's mind to their being preferred. His marked ambivalence is again shown when he first expresses satisfaction with the model that the therapist has put aside for him, then criticizes the therapist's efforts to open the jar. Such freedom to discharge anger, unconsciously intended for the father who left the family, is the therapeutic force that relieves him of much tension. Sol's emotional dependence on the therapist is basic, despite his ambivalence, and it is again revealed and tests the therapist when he announces that he knows nothing about boats and that the therapist will do it for him. Norman knows even less than Sol about craft work, but he at least attempts it. The therapist corrects each step in Norman's faulty work without emphasizing his lack of skill.

(E) The treatment process is successfully changing Morris. He is now interested in sports and is identifying himself more and more with the therapist. AGT is an effective instrument for modifying character structure of boys with defective masculine identifications. This is a nuclear element of Morris's problem, for since the death of his father when he was five years old, he had been raised in an entirely female-oriented environment. With respect to Sol, the positive transference to the therapist and the diminishing negativeness are revealed when he announces that the therapist can "beat anyone here *in anything*."

(F) The group has recently gone to a movie, as a substitute for one of the regular sessions. Such trips are part of the treatment program. The therapist responds to Sol's request correctly by referring him to the group for its decision. However, he then responds incorrectly by suggesting only one possible choice for the group. The proper technique is to offer several choices without demonstrating preference. This gives the group a chance to discuss alternatives and make a decision. It is conceivable that the therapist was reacting in countertransference to Sol, who had really been extremely demanding and at times hostile in manner toward him, despite evidences of latent positive transference. This ambivalence of Sol's was seen when he challenged the therapist, who has just told the group he would notify them by mail about arrangements. Sol peremptorily ends the discussion about the trip with: "We are going next Sunday."

(G) The manner in which a therapy group comes to look upon and to use the treatment setting as theirs with freedom is typified in the boys' sitting on the table and using the partition in the game of locking Arthur out. Arthur, who may be neurotically disturbed (anxiety hysteria, possibly schizoid) does not take frustration well. Since his boat construction was moving slowly (he had worked at it in a typically compulsive, exact manner), he became annoyed with the rocking and singing of the other boys. Such reactions in a child usually reflect a neurotic type of frustration which can be partially corrected only in an ego-level form of treatment. The boys actually punish him for interfering with their fun by locking him out.

Norman's participation in such aggressive play is a very important development. For the first time he is now able, even though in a minimal, timid fashion, to manifest aggression. He still exhibits a quality of effeminacy (which was not noted in the referral material) when he begins to dance and skip under the exhilarating influence of the game. This points up one value of AGT in making differential diagnoses.

Several times during this episode, Sol manages to behave aggressively but only by using Paul and others as supportive egos, urging them first against Arthur and later against Norman. Such behavior is not atypical for truly frightened children, who thus express their aggressions vicariously. The therapist did not interfere, because Arthur was not really frightened now. The episode was aggressive in tone but enacted as a game and in a much different manner from a similar episode during session 14 and others.

(H) Paul seeks to ingratiate himself with the therapist by helping with the dishes. He also announces to the group that he has the preferred seating position, next to the therapist. As noted earlier, for Paul the positive transference to the therapist is very meaningful. In his family, his father's remoteness exposed Paul to the anxiety-producing behavior of his overly solicitous, anxious mother, who still helped him dress himself. Paul's tension was being discharged through impulsive, aggressive behavior outside the home which got him into trouble in school. In the relation with the therapist Paul benefits from identification with a *responsive* and supportive male, which was lacking in his family, and serves to reduce the anxiety generated by his parents' behavior toward him.

It is significant that Paul's bid for the therapist induces Sol to act similarly. Sol also has much need for relationship with a father figure, since his own father left the home and visits only infrequently. Sol was also exposed to the influence of destructive mothering, perhaps more so than Paul, since Sol's mother acted in an aggressive, castrating manner. Sol's great need for preferred status drives him to ask for special considerations, such as the other boat models. The therapist's response is here again incorrect as he tells Sol that he might "not be able to get the models from the office." At this point the proper response—which, by the way, he did make when Morris asked the same question—was to say that he would try to get them. (Was the difference countertransferential?) In fact, if he could not supply them, a letter from the "office" would have been the proper procedure. As a matter of fact it was important to grant Sol's request at this time.

Refreshment time was pleasant. There was no squabbling over food, which had taken place in earlier sessions. Conversation was free, with all boys participating. The refreshment periods were becoming more pleasant. It represents a "coming together" despite any conflictual episodes that may have preceded it such as the teasing of Arthur and Norman and the instances of competitiveness and rivalry. The generally happier mood is reflected in the way in which the boys carried their finished boats and in Paul's comments about going down to the street "together," so that people could see "our boats."

Interpretation: Session 20

(I) The therapist still consistently fulfills the boy's needs. Increasingly, Norman is drawn into social contact and work activities. Because of certain bizarre mannerisms he has, members of the group have come to treat him in a special way—sometimes with amused tolerance, at other times by mild teasing, and finally, as in this instance, by ignoring him. Yet, for Norman, AGT is a most valuable treatment method, because it actually draws him from what was entrenched isolationism into social contacts. Children like Norman also gain immeasurably as their motor skills are developed through physical activities and crafts work.

(J) Sol continues to test the therapist, and the therapist meets his needs. Now there is a significant change in Sol's behavior toward the therapist. In earlier episodes Sol acted out hostility and general negativistic feelings toward him and at times even tended to denigrate him. Several times he even intimated that he could do things better than the therapist. Now, Sol spontaneously praises the therapist, even telling the group how proficient the therapist is. This is not entirely an ingratiating strategy. Sol, now, is rather acting out positive transference feelings toward the therapist, and responding to the therapist more. Norman now enacts what represents for him an altogether new emotion. From idle play with rolling clay "penises," which caused his giggling, he performs a symbolic homicide.

The fact that he first called the therapist over to demonstrate it directly is very significant. In so doing Norman is unconsciously indicating that he is now able to express anger which has heretofore been entirely suppressed and which is massive in its degree. The referral information from the caseworker (Norman was in conjoint individual and group treatment) indicated that Norman's fantasy play involved killing women. Norman occasionally also expressed negative feelings toward his maternal grandmother, with whom he stayed while his mother was at work. Because of Norman's symbolic homicide of using the clay figure, the supervising consultant of AGT raised the question of possible psychotic tendencies. Here again it is seen how AGT serves as a clinical tool for differential diagnosis, because it provides more latitude for expressive behavior for children than does individual treatment.

(K) The therapist conveys his and the group's concern for Robert's coming too late for the trip. This, and the fact that the therapist remembered to save a boat model for him, is immensely reassuring to the boy. Robert has suffered severe rejection from his mother, who barely concealed her disappointment in the child she had not wanted. The therapist erred in asking Robert why he wanted the lumber. The question was gratuitous, serving no purpose, since the fact that there was no lumber had already been stated. Some of the boys experiment with fire; the therapist does not interfere. This freedom to engage in an activity, though dangerous but fraught with special meanings, promotes confidence in children despite initial anxiety, as witness Arthur's reactions. Sol, who was referred as infantile and fearful of the dark, and who is generally a frightened boy, feels quite potent with his successful "conquest" of fire.

(L) In the short time of approximately a month and a half that he has been a member of the therapy group, Norman has shown impressive progress, despite the serious nature of his disorder. He is more actively seeking contact with others, and despite his extremely awkward and uncoordinated movements, he attempts activities he has observed others participating in and with success. As is customarily the case in AGT, the boys are tolerant of his bizarre manners. AGT is proving to be a valuable adjunct to individual therapy for Norman in that it is extending and reinforcing his ego capacities. Sol assumes the responsibility for preparing the refreshments at this session, and the group as a whole is now also beginning to assume responsibilities for some of the chores.

(M) It may have been the fire play earlier in the session that stimulated the boys toward the energetic running about. This should be compared to the episode reported in session 14, when the group also ran around. However, at that time, there was much more polarized aggression and even hostility of one boy against another, or of a subgroup ganging up against one boy, and actual destructiveness. In addition, in that session, some of the boys—Morris and Arthur particularly—really became frightened. In that session Paul acted out his strong hostility that had been anticipated on referral. In the present session, the tone of the hilarity is quite different: the boys *enjoy* themselves, and no one is fearful.

Such changes take place in AGT as individual needs of patients are fulfilled and a group identity begins to emerge. Of course, arguments and conflicts still arise, but they are more easily resolved. Robert, for instance, jumps on the refreshment table, which is rarely so abused because it is, as Sol says, "a place for eating," to which Robert responds. Robert's act of jumping on the table was undoubtedly an unconscious displacement of defiance of his rejecting mother. The therapist does not serve food until he washes the table surface. In this way he fulfills one of his functions: to act in ways that are socially acceptable, thus demonstrating social practices patients can learn.

The therapist makes no critical references to Robert's acting out. Nor does he do so a short time later under other circumstances, when Robert and Arthur make almost blatant sexual comments. This is a formidable test put to the therapist. The group is conscious of it, as shown by the suppressed giggling on the part of some. By not reacting to such flagrant, challenging conduct the therapist further demonstrates his permissiveness. It is interesting that anxiety over sexual matters becomes reflected in the interchanges, despite the muted hilarity. They speak of disease — Bubonic plague — and Arthur reveals castration anxiety — viz., his nose "would fall off" if he got "that." In Arthur's case, this is neurotic-type anxiety, and its genesis with Arthur lies in the fact that he occasionally still sleeps with his mother when his father works at night. He also has sleep disturbances.

Interpretation: Session 29

(N) The boys accommodate well to the disappointment of the cancelled baseball game which they were to have attended. Their discussion and decision about a substitute activity is a measure of growth and indicates an improved ability to tolerate frustration. Norman, who has become more confident, is less so when removed from the familiar treatment setting. Morris tries to support him, and even the therapist attempts to involve Norman in conversation with the others. This is a departure from the therapist's usual role, but in this instance it is justifiable, as it would be in other cases when special considerations indicate that a therapist modify his role to meet exceptional needs. The therapist sensed that this trip represented a special trial for Norman, not only because of the nature of his problems, but because he had less experience with trips since he had been in group treatment a short time.

Norman evades participation in a competitive game which would expose his athletic ineptness. Paul's predominating role in the group's activities is again demonstrated. He characteristically takes a leadership (instigator) position in discussions and in or-

205

ganizing activities. Because Norman withdrew, the teams would have been uneven without the therapist's participation. Yet he does not offer to join without the invitation of the group. Norman becomes an "explorer," separating himself from the group to climb the "mountain," though he still needs to return periodically to the therapist for reassurance. Since he had separation anxiety and fears, this self-testing experience was valuable for him.

(O) One of the purposes of trips in AGT is to expand experiential horizons. Emotionally disturbed children, with a few exceptions, are characteristically fearful of traveling to places removed from their immediate and familiar neighborhoods. During trips, the therapist takes advantage of every opportunity to enhance the confidence of the children and to foster independent functioning. On trips to Central Park, therapy groups have also included bicycle riding and rowing.

Instead of purchasing food for the boys, the therapist gives each money to do so for himself. He gives them the opportunity to explore and decide for themselves, being always on the alert as to where they go and what they're doing. Paul and Robert, for instance, have run off from time to time to play independently. Norman and Morris are less confident, and on the way to the zoo, practically attach themselves to the therapist, vying for his attention.

The fact that Morris and Robert have discovered at this late date that they have common acquaintances is interesting. In the beginning of treatment, almost all children are self-preoccupied, despite the interactions among them. As individual problems are diminished by therapy, awareness of others is increased. It has been noted that prior to this development, the self-centeredness is such that patients even forget the names of their group mates. Now there is growing spirit of camaraderie evident as the boys communicate during the refreshment period, despite idiosyncratic differences in the conversational content of several, viz., Norman with his obsessive preoccupation with presidents; Morris's constant reference to sports activities and his exaggerated portrayals of his ability, which, as has been described, is a compensatory device.

(P) The therapist avoids joining the football game, because Norman tentatively agreed to play in response to the pressure of most of the group. Norman is becoming increasingly daring as he separates from the therapist and undertakes a new game. He is so emboldened by the experience that he wants everyone to take notice of him. The trip has obviously had much strengthening effect on him. The group as a whole expresses its liking for the therapist and their desire that he continue with them in the fall.

(Q) Norman becomes increasingly bolder as time passes. His game of pretending to leave the group is an infantile form of testing his growing self-confidence. The trip has served to begin to crystallize in him the growth experiences which have been taking place in the treatment room. Careful observation of Norman by the therapist seems to confirm the suspicion of pathology. Nevertheless, there has been improvement in his social adaptation. One of the effects of trips is to promote a sense of group unity. This is a group-polarizing effect which is brought about when the group moves from the security of the treatment room to unfamiliar settings and the group's integration is reinforced.

On the subway train the therapist tells the boys not to shove, and they respond. This limit is necessary outside the treatment room to reeducate the boys to reality demands. They respond favorably in this instance because they have matured, and they accept reasonable limits from the adult whom they like and respect. Therapy groups in their earlier stages do not necessarily behave so well on trips, and the group members may then draw upon themselves annoyed and angry responses of other passengers. The therapist allows the children to face the full brunt of their annoying behavior until some untoward act from other passengers is threatened. Then he steps forward and announces, "These boys are with me." Though this may lead to the therapist's becoming the recipient of criticism, it does fortify his role as a protector in the eyes of his group members. Also, the group members feel chastised and contrite by the fact that they have caused the therapist embarrassment, a momentous moral experience.

The fact that the boys again remind the therapist to visit camp, and also, their comments about meeting "next year" is an indication of their *separation* grief. They need reassurance that the experience which has become meaningful to them will continue. It was inadvisable for the therapist to imply that he might visit some of the boys at camp, because he may not be in a position to visit all of them, and thus would show preference.

207

PATIENTS' IMPROVEMENT

The partial records of the foregoing four sessions depict the evolution of an activity group over a period of time. Changes can be detected on two levels: first, in the nature of behavior of individual group members; second, in the quality of group interactions. The twenty-ninth session is dramatically different from the fourteenth, which was characterized by much diffuse aggression, acting out, and fear in group members.

Four times during a treatment year, evaluations are routinely made of each patient's progress. Clinical planning may have to be modified in some cases according to the observations made by the therapist and on the basis of information from additional sources —psychological findings, psychiatric examinations and evaluations, school and summer camp reports, parents' statements, and the information gleaned from follow-up studies, counseling, and/ or treatment of parents. What follows is a highly condensed statement on each member of the group from these evaluative studies:

Morris

In conjoint individual and AGT, following two years of ineffective individual therapy, the caseworker reported that Morris has become more outgoing since joining AGT. He now speaks directly about problems, whereas formerly he used to be evasive and would talk impersonally. He ventilates more freely, saying that he "hates women" and that his family tried to make a "sissy" out of him. He also has begun to speak of his anxiety about being short of stature, of not growing up to be tall. His mother reported that Morris improved in many ways, but that rivalry still persisted with the sibling. The therapy group has become very important to Morris, she said. He has chosen to come to sessions rather than to other activities, including attending a professional ball game as arranged by his parochial school. Morris expressed some fear about the group not having the same "leader" next year. In general, it was felt that Morris was becoming better able to mobilize and discharge his aggressions. The recommendation was that he continue in exclusive AGT.

Paul

Treated exclusively in AGT. There had been initial concern as to whether Paul could be managed in a group because of his aggressiveness. The basis of this was his strong sibling rivalry with an older brother, who had a cardiac condition and who had as a result received preferred treatment because of it. Paul did act aggressively in the group, but at no time did it become an excessive threat to the group's psychological balance. He gradually assumed a leadership role. Even though he yelled a good deal and acted boisterously, he revealed "pleasing qualities." The other members liked him and considered him capable. The relationship with the therapist was important in his improvement. At the beginning, he was somewhat dependent on this relationship and sought special privileges, but he gradually grew free of it. It was decided to continue him in exclusive AGT.

Arthur

Treated exclusively in AGT. There were many indications in the developmental history and in the referral material of anxiety, apparently aroused by a seductive mother. The tentative diagnosis was that of a "psychoneurosis." The nervous mannerisms and awkwardness described at referral have been dissipated. He has become decidedly more relaxed. In the group he moved about easily and frequently hummed as he worked. It was felt that AGT has strengthened his ego to *deal better* with his anxieties. In addition, his sexual identification has greatly improved through the group. Enuresis has completely disappeared, behavior in school improved, and a number of neurotic traits have been sloughed off. AGT has been beneficial, but because of continuing anxiety, consideration is to be given to possibly initiating individual treatment in addition to AGT. Arthur's mother was to be continued in treatment.

Sol

Treated conjointly in individual and AGT. Referred because he was resisting individual treatment, Sol was initially ingratiating toward the group therapist and behaved in a very "proper" fash-

209

ion. His behavior has grown freer and more assertive and his attitude toward the therapist markedly ambivalent. He has been at times complainingly dependent, then very negativistic. This ambivalence has noticeably lessened in time, and a more positive relationship with the therapist has taken its place. Sol's sexual identification has become less of a problem, as demonstrated by his participation with the other boys in aggressive play and sports, and his having recently spoken of having a "girl friend." In individual treatment Sol still attempted to deny any difficulties. However, he grew friendlier toward his female caseworker when, on the recommendation of the group therapy department, she altered her approach from one of probing for conflict areas to emphasizing a corrective relation with the boy. Sol's mother reported that his behavior at home and at school "greatly improved." His relations with other children were better and he now had friends and is at ease with them. Sol is to be continued in cooperative treatment.

Ronald

Transferred to exclusive AGT because of implacable resistance to individual treatment, Ronald has become very happy in the group. While he is essentially insecure and compensates for this by boasting about his athletic prowess, the group experience has helped him discover his ability to get along with peers. Ronald has also been helped by the group to externalize his hitherto suppressed aggression. His stammer has improved, but he still tends to stammer or lisp when he gets excited and attempts to speak rapidly. He is particularly concerned with receiving approval from the therapist. Ronald is to be continued in group treatment.

Robert

Treated exclusively in AGT. Initially Robert acted aggressively toward the other group members. He argued with them and depreciated their work. While he still tends to be "bossy" Robert has become more integrated into the group. He is accepted, but is not popular. Robert persistently tested the therapist's permissiveness, but eventually became convinced of the latter's sincerity when he relaxed and communicated more freely with him. This was an important change for Robert, because much of his original suspiciousness and negativism stemmed from the traumatic rejection he had experienced from his mother. The improvement, which became evident in the treatment group, was reflected also in reports of his behavior at home and school. Robert is to be continued in AGT.

Norman

Norman was a cooperative case in individual and in AGT. Norman was added to the group in mid-year. The group considered him strange and bizarre. He was called "crazy" several times. Although they occasionally ridiculed and teased him, the boys tolerated him and never subjected him to excessive provocation. On the contrary, there always seemed to be someone who protected him.

From a beginning position of social isolation and fear of others, Norman moved into group contacts. He demonstrated real *social hunger* by trying to do the things in which he saw others involved. His craft-work efforts were awkward, but he did pursue them. There was much fantasy preoccupation, with symbolic and direct references to sexuality. There were several episodes in which he revealed an underlying hostility with homicidal undertones. The changes in Norman were all on an ego level, but they represented significant alterations from the almost encapsulated state of isolation which typified his behavior at the start.

His nuclear problem of poor sexual identification was quite evident in his conduct. We thought that some aspects of his conduct in the group reflected the possibility of deeper pathology than had been suspected on initial diagnosis. An additional effect of AGT on this boy was to make him more communicative in individual treatment, where he now began to speak of the content of his fantasies and his destructive feelings toward women. It was decided to continue Norman in both forms of treatment, with further reevaluation of the diagnosis and the treatment plans for him.

GLOBAL VALUES OF AGT

Most noteworthy are the alterations in the total climate of the

211

group and in the attitudes of its members toward the group and toward each other. In later sessions their mood continued to grow in constructiveness; they found interests and satisfactions in activities beyond playful hilarity and thinly disguised discharge of hostile acting out. The boys grew sufficiently relaxed and innerly gratified so that they acted protectively toward Norman, whose pathology they empathically perceived, though hardly understood. If it can justifiably be said that the civilizability an individual achieves can be measured by his capacity to identify with his fellow men, the boys in their treatment of Norman have been on the way to being civilized.

The group members have also moved in the direction of cooperative activity and feelings, allotropic in relation to their individualistic centeredness and strivings with which they came to us, as revealed in their life histories and in their initial conduct in the group. Because of the freedom they found in the setting and the unconditional acceptance (love) consistently demonstrated by the therapist, each grew able to relate to others with comparative benevolence and positive feelings. The two years in the group, the microcosm in which humanization of personality has been occurring, were in great contrast to the world from which they came and to which they unfortunately would return. "Man is nothing without the works of man," the ancient Greeks averred. There is little doubt that whatever is human in us is given us by other humans. Human bestiality is the heritage from our prehuman ancestry. It took eons to decondition us only partially, and periodically men return, and being basically also moral, cover it up by various rationalizations. Because in the earlier lives of our patients humanizing influences were almost nil, they required corrective treatment. An activity therapy group is an arena in which such treatment is eminently possible to selected children.

The plans the boys later made encompassed the group, rather than being limited to themselves as individuals, and it is noteworthy that in the short span of only about seven months a sense of responsibility for the group and for its chores began to emerge spontaneously. The boys achieved a "we" feeling. The unmistakable increase in frustration tolerance toward the end of the second year in activity group treatment was striking compared with the egocentric and unsocial responses with which they came to us.

The group setting awakened in them latent affection and loyalty to an adult, the therapist, perhaps the first experience of its kind for all of them. This was not only touching, but also highly constructive in generating humanistic feelings and social values. The affectional capacities of an individual are outgrowths of wholesome affectional ties in childhood, which are denied in one way or another to countless children who require subliminal roots for the almost vanished humanism in human relations.

XI

Transitional Groups

PROBLEMS OF TERMINATION

Terminating therapy is a perennial problem for all psychotherapists. To determine with any degree of certainty when a patient is ready to set out on his own to deal with the complexities and stresses of the modern urban world without regression requires reliable judgment as well as keen intuitional perceptiveness. There are no definitive objective tests on which to base determinations, and the therapist's judgment is still the best criterion.

Freud was aware of the risks in making such judgments and stipulated that his patients and pupils submit periodically to reanalysis. Although prevention of regression was not the only reason for this proviso—among the others being the cropping up of new intrapsychic problems during the former patient's interactions with the world of actuality—it was nonetheless the main aim. Adult patients in less intensive therapies than psychoanalysis are even more likely to slough off their improvements in therapy in the course of time and return to their more entrenched, more deeply imprinted, earlier characterological and neurotic patterns. This phenomenon is even more likely to occur in adult patients who have received solely group therapy.

It is for this reason, among others, that terminating *all* patients in a group simultaneously should be avoided. Closings in all forms of therapy should be made strictly on the indications of the needs of patients, based on a thorough study of each case. If properly and objectively carried out, with consideration of each patient's past, his current state, the ego strengths he acquired during therapy, and the total or partial dissolution of his former noxious feelings and responses, these studies result in a different plan for each member of a group.

215

While most latency children who are treated in AGT are probably ready for (conditional) termination at the end of two years, some individuals require varying provisions for continuing in AGT, tapering-off experiences or more intensive treatment. Among these may be transfer to another, advanced therapy group, individual psychotherapy, or membership in a neighborhood center for general (nonclinical) social participation or for specialized creative interests.

The reconditioning and relearning involving neuronic engrams that seem to appear by the end of two years may prove illusory under the impact of the demands and stresses that a world tailored for adults makes upon a child. The imprinting during the earlier formative periods is often too deeply ensconced to give way to short-lived superficial modifications. Even at the end of such a seemingly long course of treatment, there are some children who have been so deeply traumatized that they do not fully overcome the early damage, nor do they completely slough off characterological or neurotic syndromes. They, too, like their older counterparts, require extended reformative and/or corrective repetitive experiences; they, too, require differential plans to achieve desirable ends.

RESIDUES

In planning termination, the therapeutic team needs to consider pathologic and pathogenic *residues* even after symptoms seemingly disappear. AGT, for example, may remove certain behavioral anomalies without affecting significantly neurotic components which may be reactivated after termination, causing the patient to regress to his original condition. These neurotic residues require continuing therapy on an individual or suitable group basis.[1] On the other hand, some children in analytically oriented groups may overcome neurotic traits but remain with characterologically conditioned reflex behavioral patterns that can cause them difficulties in interpersonal relations and again lead to social maladjustment. These characterological residues must receive the attention of the responsible therapist.

[1] These are analogous to "the return of the repressed," but differ psychodynamically.

Even so thoroughgoing a treatment modality for full-blown psychoneuroses as classical psychoanalysis leaves many patients with character idiosyncracies that interfere with adequate social adjustment. Some of the more receptive analysts, therefore, suggest group experiences to their patients as a tapering-off medium. A group may also serve as an arena for reality testing, but its greater value, in some cases, lies in the reconditioning of old responses and relearning of new, more socially suitable interpersonal conduct. Therapeutic schools which advocate reconditioning measures initially and as a sole therapy modality, have, certainly in cases of true psychoneuroses, not only put the cart before the horse, but omitted the horse altogether.

Values of Transitional Groups

In treatment of children in groups, we have employed what we term *transitional groups.* The term transitional is intended in this connection to suggest the idea that even children who do not require extended postgroup therapy may need an attenuated group experience that will facilitate their transition from the conditioned environment of a therapy group to the climate of ordinary groups in the community. Termination of a therapy group should be timed to coincide with the end of the school year or thereabouts, after plans had been made for each patient according to his needs. Those few who are unready to make an adequate adjustment on their own and require a transitional group experience are reinvited at the beginning of the following school year. The others are dropped without any communication, except for one explanatory conference with each parent. Children whose adjustments at school, in the home, and with peers present minimal or no problems within the bounds of "normality" but who, because of their youth and inexperience, may not be able or may feel unready to adjust on their own, need to be helped to make their way into the wider community through a transitional group. The important elements in this tapering-off procedure are (1) the therapist now becomes a *club leader,* and (2) the locale of the *meetings* is changed to a neighborhood center or a "Y." The membership of a transitional group may include children from several former therapy groups.

In the event that initiating a transitional group is impossible or for some reason inadvisable, the therapist should arrange to take the children to the nearest community center in the fall and by prearrangement introduce them to the club or special activities directors or both.

THE PATTERN OF A TRANSITIONAL GROUP

After briefly gathering in a room assigned at the first session of a transitional group, the group is taken by their "leader" (erstwhile therapist) on a tour of the various activities in the center by prearrangement with its director or other appropriate staff member. The objective is to expose the children to interest possibilities from which they can make individual choices. After they have briefly observed the various shops, arts and crafts activities, dramatic groups, the gymnasium, swimming pool, and have fleetingly visited a few club discussions, the group returns to its own room, where the leader asks for the group's reactions to what they have seen and which activities they liked most. Invariably, each verbalizes his views, stating some activity of his preference. The leader then asks the group what they would like to do now. On the basis of what they have seen, the usual response is that they would like to form "a club." This the leader follows up with a query as to what steps should be taken to set one in motion. The natural response is that "officers" be elected. Which officers? President, secretary, and treasurer are always enumerated or, if necessary, suggested by the new "leader."

On the leader's suggestion, nominations are duly made, and when the officers are elected, he yields "the chair" to the president and the other officers, but remains up front at the table with the three boys or girls. He does not abandon the group to its own resources before its members have tried their wings at conducting a traditional meeting. His visible presence helps overcome insecurities and feelings of being abandoned.

At the suggestion of the president, or the leader if it is not forthcoming from that newly elected and inexperienced official, the group sets certain details for its deliberations, such as a club name, a constitution, and plans for activities. The leader encourages the president to involve the members in the discussion of these plans and formulations. If he is too inexperienced or for other reasons is unable to do so on his own, the leader quietly coaches him in taking the next steps toward laying plans.

Among the decisions that should ensue from this first meeting are, or course, the meeting time, amount of dues, and whether youngsters other than the original group members are acceptable to the newly constituted organization. If the decision favors the latter, the staff of the center are apprised of it and are asked to refer children of appropriate ages to the club a month or six weeks later, thus giving the organization time to cohere. The question of external membership may be better introduced after the club has functioned for the period indicated, since this may be less threatening to the uninitiated in procedural matters and group planning.

At the second or third meeting the leader, who is now seated among the membership, yields active guidance of the club to the president, but may ask for the floor and make suggestions at appropriate points with a view of helping the president as any other club member would, not as a person in authority. The program of activities may include discussions of topics which the members suggest, such as school and sports, matters relevant to their lives, and plans for trips. But as far as possible, and with the cooperation of the center staff, the club should be involved in the center's overall programs and activities.

The center administration should invite the new club to elect a representative to the council of clubs (of their own age), to parties, exhibits, bazaars, movies, sports contests, lectures, and all other educational and recreational affairs arranged by the boys' or girls' councils or by the center officials. Club members may be asked to bring or make objects for exhibits or for sale to raise funds for center or community and charitable enterprises. The club's secretary should be required to present to the meetings not only minutes of its proceedings, but also communications from the center's administration and the "club council." Such activities, and many others in an active community center, expand the social reality of the children's world and help each to find his special interests. Of even greater value, these activities enhance the maturity of the children by awakening allotropic interests beyond themselves and train them in social participation and discharging responsibilities.

SUITABILITY OF PROGRAMS

To have such meanings, the activities and the responsibilities must be commensurate with the age and maturity of participants, and they must enter into them willingly. Because of these requirements, a psychologically literate person, such as a trained psychotherapist, can be entrusted with the early steps of initiating erstwhile child patients into the broader arena of the world in which they are to live and of which they have to become a part.

Members in transitional groups have to be, for a time, guarded against the customary crudity with which they are treated in schools and community recreational facilities until they can build up inner strengths not to be hurt or crushed by the practices in these institutions. It is the function of the transitional groups to make this *transition* from the protected therapy groups, where they have been respected, to the abrasiveness of the outside world. In a sense these groups are also "protected groups" through the months that the therapist remains with the club. His efforts are bent on helping each of his charges to find a meaningful, sustaining interest from those offered by the center. Such interests may persist later in life or may be only transient. In either case they are the essentials of personality growth, character formation, and the degree of mental health possible under the rigors of modern living. Imprints of these idiosyncratic ties to life and interests, and the group experiences and interactions, form the warp and woof of a healthy personality.[2]

INVOLVING THE CENTER STAFF

To achieve salutary results in the social reeducation of former young patients, it is necessary to involve the regular activities staff of the center. The former therapist maintains frequent contacts with them, giving specific suggestions as to easement procedures for individual children in developing ties to the community within the center and, when appropriate, to the larger community, within the scope and understanding of children of their ages.

After three or four months of thus "nursing" along the group,

---

[2] Content and procedures had been covered in considerable detail in *Creative Group Education* (Slavson, 1937) and *Character Education in a Democracy* (Slavson, 1939).

the therapist may find it advisable to relinquish his functions and turn his responsibilities over to a suitable member of the regular group-work staff of the institution. This must be done with caution so as not to create a feeling of rejection or abandonment in the children, and gradual preparation for the break will be required.

One effective procedure is to have the prospective club leader attend a few meetings and introduce him to the children as someone who will help with the work of the club. The newcomer, who may be resented at first, should have the personality, warmth, and skill to insinuate himself by his outgoingness and enthusiasm to draw the children toward himself. After a few such sessions, the therapist can announce that the visitor will take over the club as its leader.

The probability is that attendance will drop sharply. Only the members who live in the neighborhood or who have found genuine recreational or creative interests may remain loyal to the club. The others drop away. This exigency is unavoidable and would occur eventually even if the therapist continued.

Bases for Group Coherence

It must be kept in mind that "social clubs" of children are formed, and their members are attracted to them, by the factors of mutual identity and propinquity. One of the striking characteristics of an activity therapy group (not so in the interview groups) is that most of the children do not even know each other's names, often after two years of co-membership. This is especially so in the case of boys. When they inquire about an absent boy, which they seldom do, they describe him by his special features, such as "the fat kid with glasses," because in contacts with each other, being activity and minimally verbal, they do not learn each other's names. This is not so in the neighborhood or at school, where the interactions require direct verbal communication.

Members of all types of children's therapy groups never establish lasting friendships in the groups that carry over beyond the treatment rooms. This is probably due to lack of daily or at least frequent contacts that occur in neighborhoods and schools where companionships naturally arise. The neighborhood peer group plays a vastly larger role with children in establishing friendships and more or less lasting natural play groups than is possible in congregate therapy groups.

Our experience with a comparatively small number of congregate transitional and large numbers of natural groups leads us to the tentative conclusion that one of the major values of transitional groups lies in the children's discovery, through exposure, of individual activity interests in the new setting which they are able to pursue spontaneously at their convenience. In time, most of the original members in our transitional groups dropped out, but some continued in the special interest groups offered by the center; others joined existing clubs in their own neighborhood centers. In a way, they closed themselves out as they felt ready to participate. Those who clung to the original club and were favorably located geographically were integrated by the center staff into one of the ongoing clubs.

However, it was felt that the experience, as brief as it was, in participating in a directly interacting and cooperative group was beneficial as both a reality-testing situation and a more directly socializing experience, which served in good stead as the youngsters entered adolescence, when group associations become major modalities in personality development and maturity.

XII

Activity Group Therapy in a Residential Setting

SYNCRETISM BETWEEN FREEDOM AND DISCIPLINE

Activity group therapy was used effectively in residential treatment for delinquent boys at Children's Village in New York State under the direction of one of the authors (S.R.S.) during 1957-1960. This was a radical departure from previous applications of this form of treatment in child guidance out-patient clinics, and it initially posed many new questions.

Because AGT allows its young patients an unusual degree of freedom for acting out, it had been restricted to specific types of patients in urban settings where delinquents were scrupulously barred. Children who reached a degree of maladjustment that required commitment could be expected to act out their delinquencies and vandalism in a milieu free of external controls, thereby preventing the emergence of the essential therapeutic climate. Consideration had to be given also to the implications of such freedom in an institutional setting for a large number of delinquent boys, where routines and order are of the essence to prevent violence and chaos. An institutional setting of this nature can function and survive only when accommodations by the residents to group living, to discipline, and cooperation at different areas are made in the residential cottages, in the academic school, in recreational activities, and in other groups that evolve in a large community of this nature. There also arose the question of how boys accustomed to destructive and rowdy behavior would respond to the permissiveness of the therapy group.

PSYCHOMALIGNANCIES OF PATIENTS' BACKGROUNDS

These and similar questions came to the fore because it was the extreme conduct of the prospective activity group members that led to their commitment to the institution through courts or by direct application from various community agencies. Their behavior was highly aggressive, impulsive, defiant, and socially destructive. The personality characteristics that typified many of the boys were tough, pervasive narcissistic qualities, propensities for indulging in fantasy and a belief in magic, a basic sense of alienation from themselves and society, oral fixations, defective self-images and defective perceptions of reality, sexual perversions, confused and nonexistent identifications as a result of pernicious relations with parents (or the absence of these) and siblings, or with foster parents (multiple, in many cases), temporary guardians, step-parents and siblings, and other relations either by consanguinity or by welfare agency arrangements.

A prominent feature of their early life experiences was deprivation of nurturance during infancy and early childhood. Basic developmental needs were aborted by interruptions and inconsistencies during these most important phases of personality and character development. In addition, they had experienced much shifting and alteration in primary group constellations; much moving from one living quarter to another with transfers between schools, the latter making already difficult educational experiences even more so. There also was an extraordinary degree of pervasive distrust of, and hostility toward, adults and antagonism to all forms of authority accompanied by defiance, vandalism, and delinquent behavior in the "home," school, and community — which led to commitment.

Clinical examinations after placement at the Village disclosed a good deal of neurotic and psychopathic content and a high degree of infantilism in the psyche of most of the boys. The emotional disabilities all pointed to the personality primitivism characteristic of early childhood.

While all persons, including children, have in varying degrees negative emotions associated with their early lives, they are adequately repressed, suppressed, or controlled where the ego adaptation is adequate. It is this difference in ego adaptation, which has origins in childhood, that distinguishes the "normal" from the problem personality. In the former, the controls, defenses, and a capacity for reality testing, as slight as they may be, are present even in children. Where there is complete absence of these there is psychosis, but where they are present, but inadequate in relation to age and responsibilities, character disorders and especially infantile personality (which underlie delinquency and crime) result.

THE ENVISAGED RISKS

As we have seen, the essential clinical requirement for AGT is freedom of action. To boys whose life experiences during their formative years were highly psychotraumatic, such freedom would present opportunities to act out their unbridled infantile urges and would provide avenues of discharging accumulated resentments and rage. It was, therefore, necessary to speculate as to what degree freeing boys to discharge hostilities and impulsivity not only would prove dangerous, but might also serve to diminish further their already meager ego resources. The most important hazard, as we saw it at the time, was the risk that the boys would carry over the acting out permitted in the group to the residential cottages and school classrooms, which would cause much disturbance, increase repressive measures from the staff, and bring disrepute to our project, and also to the para-analytic groups with older adolescents which were our major concern (Slavson, 1965). Another important question to consider was the more or less essential institutional regimen and the attitudes and values of the professional, para and nonprofessional staff members toward the permissiveness of AGT that might prove antithetical to established practices and personal values and attitudes.

Despite the multitude and serious nature of the problems inherent in the project as well as in the nature of the boys' personalities (despite the institution's liberal and progressive policies and some of its practices), it was considered that the clinical indications of the younger residents warranted the attempt to test the AGT method on an experimental basis, but with alert caution. We felt that if we could demonstrate that humane attitudes can prove effective in reclaiming even delinquent pubertal boys, a dramatic and giant step would be made in the direction of humanistic, reeducative, and corrective treatment of children who, through no fault of their own, had suffered marked emotional deprivations in infancy and early childhood.[1]

EXPERIMENT WITH PUBERTAL-AGE BOYS

The ages of the boys with whom we were concerned ranged between 11.6 and 13 years. While some of them were chronologically already in the pubertal stage, the prominent infantile features of their personalities, their behavior and psychological development were essentially retarded, and they could have been considered psychologically prepubertal. In fact, in most instances they were in the pregenital stage, so that their chronological ages were not in themselves counterindications for inclusion in AGT. Stress factors associated with the pubertal stage are subordinated and secondary to emotional problems in children so emotionally and otherwise deprived.

As we have seen in preceding sections of this volume, AGT is an effective procedure in maturing of children with habit and character disorders arising from deprivation and neglect. The fact that the boys in the activity groups at the Village made impressive and often dramatic progress in their total development is only another indication that their presenting problems had to do with character and ego development. Objective observers among the institutional staff repeatedly remarked that the younger boys in AGT showed greater improvement than did the sixteen-to eighteen-year-olds treated in "verbal" therapy by the same therapist and supervisor.

The activity group selected for presentation here met for two hours weekly for a total of thirty-nine sessions. At all other times the boys participated in the regular life of the institution, living in cottages with cottage parents (couples) and other boys, carrying on various imposed chores, attending academic school, and participating in recreational and other school community activities.

CONTRAST BETWEEN *in Situ* AND RESIDENTIAL REPONSES

Seven boys were included in the group on whom we focus attention here. Among those selected and combined in accordance

---

[1]A first step in this direction had been made in 1935. See Slavson (1954).

with the principle of *group balance* were aggressive, acting out, as well as more withdrawn children; one was a latent schizophrenic. Almost immediately after the start of the group it was apparent that the qualities of the boys' responses were appreciably different from those of the children treated in AGT *in situ*. This was evidenced by the types of work projects they engaged in, their distractability, intensity of oral anxiety, and the "childish" patterns with which they related to one another. It seemed as though these boys had to act out and live *ab nova* earlier stages in development which they missed because of pressures from parents or their substitutes and/or their rebelliousness against those they had rejected because of the pain and anxiety they had caused.

Healthy growth of personality can occur only when each stage in the differential unfoldment of powers and capabilities occurs in a biopsychological order genetically inherent in each individual. When voids in development occur because of physical and especially affectional deprivation, the personality, as a totality, grows defective and the individual is personally and socially maladjusted. Corrective effort must therefore contain restitutive elements of which the child was originally deprived. While this principle operates in all forms of child therapy (as well as in those adults suffering from affect hunger) and is predominant in AGT, we have counted on it most in the treatment of the "totally rejected" children in the institution, and we have repeatedly emphasized this point to the therapist. We were convinced that, more than in any other therapeutic situation, helping the boys here to establish affectional ties would be the acme of the therapeutic armamentarium.

Absolute Freedom an Essential

One of the principles we established *a priori* was absolute freedom of movement, which was of necessity controlled and restricted in the institutional setting, but had to be allowed these boys in the course of treatment. They were therefore free *during the hours they were in the group* to peregrinate to and from the outdoors and otherwise freely utilize the total environment.[2] As a

[2] This is rather an important point, since after the termination of our demonstration, the casework director ordered the door to the outdoors locked to prevent boys from leaving the room.

result, there was a good deal of movement in and out of the treatment room. Each boy was free to act according to his idiosyncratic needs at the moment. Thus, the conduct of the boys was viewed in the dimensions of *being*, of time, and of place. This would please the "existential therapist."

It would be both difficult and prohibitive in the confines of this text to enter into exhaustive descriptions of the backgrounds of each boy and the dynamics of the therapy group, or to trace meanings and significances of activities as correctives in ego strengthening and personality integration. We can only call attention to the special climate of this institutional activity group in which each individual was made to feel free to act in accordance with his existing level of maturity regardless of the risks to the children and inconvenience to the staff. In addition to the more general information already given here about the character problems and backgrounds of boys in the institution, brief glimpses of each boy included in the group are given below.

THE GROUP PERSONNEL

Jose was a boy with "deeply rooted hostility." He had had great difficulty relating to peer groups prior to his coming to the Village. These difficulties continued in his cottage and in the academic school. He was often moody and sullen and usually isolated himself from the other boys and the staff in the cottage, in school, and in other activities. Because of the seriousness of his problem, he received psychotherapy from a psychiatrist which was continued while he was in AGT. The psychiatrist later reported, "Boy more available for individual therapy as a result of group treatment." Formerly Jose had stubbornly resisted it. His teacher indicated that "Jose is less isolated."

Robert, who was diagnosed as an "oral character," was "babyish in appearance, and seemed to babble rather than talk." He often withdrew into fantasy as he removed himself from contact with peers and adults. On the rare occasions when he did relate to others, he assumed the role of an infant, seeking gratifications without giving anything in return. His caseworker, who treated him for about a year prior to his being placed in AGT, reported also "poor sexual identification." As his membership in the group extended, Robert changed from a shy and reticent to a friendly outgoing boy. He formed meaningful relationships with peers on a more mature level. His behavior in the group, where he seemed to have found a milieu in which he could test himself against other boys and made the discovery that expressing anger would not be devastating, released his potentials for growth. Through his newly found security with the therapist and his own status in the group, Robert discovered that it was not necessary to ingratiate himself with the staff and that he could function safely by being a boy of his age rather than a "cute baby." He seemed to have also discovered that there were gains in interacting with peers. The psychiatrist stated, "Robert has far more ease with adults." His caseworker also saw much change, "Robert is more verbal and assertive; tremendous change from original infantile, passive behavior; dramatic change." In class his teacher noted parallel improvement, "Robert now functions like a normal boy."

William was described as "hyperactive, nervous, at times presenting peculiar behavior" in the referral summary submitted by his caseworker. He came to the Village after a series of destructive experiences in six foster home placements beginning in infancy. Some of his behavior, the caseworker reported, had an autistic quality, and his sexual identification was defective. The initial diagnostic "impression" of the psychiatrist who examined him at the Village, based on William's hypermotility, periods of seeming dissociations, autism, depressions, and fantasy, was "incipient schizophrenia." Another psychiatrist who examined William about a year after group treatment concluded that the boy "was now less given to fantasy, less depressed and responded to reality much more appropriately." The activities in the group, work with tangible materials, and close interaction with the other boys produced in William more "purposeful responses." Whereas formerly he had been bewildered and sometimes immobilized by a cavalcade of events about him, the group supplied him with an appropriate tangible reality with which, supported by the therapist, he was able to cope. A still later psychiatric report stated: "William was considered schizophrenic; group helped him reach out to peers; he is far less infantile; neater in dress and appearance; William used to roll on the floor at the beginning of treatment." The child-care supervisor observed, "This boy really grew up; growth occurred while he was a member of the group; William learned to move on own behalf; at end of therapy group he joined a singing group at Community Center; also joined dramatic group." The teacher found him more motivated, "Boy stopped making excuses that he cannot do work."[3]

Rafael was referred for AGT because casework therapy had had no impact whatever on him. The boy was given only to whining and complaining. His pattern of dealing with people was that of manipulation and trickery. His gains during his stay at the Village were marginal. However, his relationships with the cottage parents improved to some degree as a result of his group experience, and "he became less fearful of boys." The changed attitude of the cottage parents toward Rafael, following some interviews with them by the "cottage life supervisor" instigated by the group therapy supervisory-consultant (S.R.S.), greatly helped in achieving the changes that took place in this boy.

The caseworker was able to report that the group effected changes in Rafael's treatment, "Rafael now expresses anger; also expresses guilt about masturbation and homosexual activity." Rafael's teacher, on the other hand, still considered him to be "a very infantile boy." The cottage father saw the influence of the group in that "Rafael is less clinging to the cottage mother; less fearful of older boys."

John was described as extremely impulsive and aggressive and was rejected by his cottage mates and all other boys in the school community with whom he had come in contact, probably because of his highly unpredictable behavior, which vacillated between depressive uncommunicativeness and provocative teasing. He tended to be manipulative as he contrived ways of obtaining favors from others, usually by bribery. While he presented himself to adults in a manner that he felt they expected of him, this was considered a veneer covering up massive hostility and rage. In the group he was initially uncommunicative, markedly ambivalent in his feelings toward the therapist. The freedom of the group even-

---

[3] The outcome in this case supports the hypothesis of "induced schizophrenia," which in this instance was the result of the inescapable inconsistencies and deprivations in the foster homes beginning at a very young age. See Slavson, 1964, pp. 507-547.

tually relaxed him, and he once verbalized that he wished it could continue meeting "forever." As a result of the calming group experience, where relations were more benign, the boy became considerably more accepted by other boys as his defensive bullying of them diminished. His caseworker reported, "Boy is more realistic, more available to discuss feelings." While his behavior improved, there were no marked changes in his basic character as a result of the brief experience in the group.

Philip, the biggest, roughest, and toughest boy in the group, was well known in the institutional community. He moved into the activity group as he did in all other groups, trying to take over. Group therapy had a significant impact on this boy, however. Perhaps for the first time in his life he was enabled to be comfortable "playing second fiddle," which helped him to substitute reasoning for fighting to attain his ends. He even admitted during one refreshment conversation that the boys in the Village now "stood up" to him, that they did not accept his bullying any more. Though in the group he was physically the strongest, he seemed to have discovered that there was no advantage in his beating up boys and that there were other bases for leadership besides triumphing with fists. The school teachers reported that since he had attended the group his reading improved, he began to express himself verbally with greater facility, was reaching out toward his teachers, and acted less aggressively toward his classmates. The psychiatrist observed, "The group helped Philip to respond well to peer group pressure."

Louis attended only a few sessions before he was discharged after a very short stay at the Village.

The Treatment Room

The room used for the activity group was a rearranged, completely isolated basement room at the rear of a staff residence cottage. Physically, the room left much to be desired. Among the many problems it presented was that the entrance door to the room opened directly to the outdoors and on the level with it, which encouraged the boys to run in and out. This movement occurred most often on sunny days during spring and fall. However, this disadvantage was not totally without benefit, since it was a means of siphoning off tensions that inevitably generated during the group sessions. Contrary to expectations, events proved that this ready escape into the open was not an impediment to resolutions of conflicts and tensions or to the boys' emotional improvement. As a matter of fact, the proximity of the field edged by a nearby forest provided both privacy and freedom for locomotion, play, and exploration, which to these young denizens of crowded ghettos must have been a great delight.

From the very outset the room assumed a special meaning to the boys. Because of its physical detachment from all other buildings at the rear of the large campus and out of sight of the areas of activity of the school's population, it quickly became the place where the boys could take off their masks of conformity and act out their true selves. In this room they could do and say whatever they pleased without fear of adult disapproval and only too ready punishment. Habituated elsewhere by staff impositions to do chores, the boys from the very start swept the room at the end of each session (perhaps to please and ingratiate themselves with the therapist). Feeling the freedom of the group and the acceptance by the therapist, they soon abandoned this. However, months later, out of an inner feeling of wishing to keep "their" room clean, they resumed it voluntarily and, by their own arrangement, took turns at it in an organized fashion.

Synopsis of First Nine Sessions

The first session was notable by reason of all the boys' dependency and submissiveness to the therapist as they kept seeking permission from him to use tools, to eat, to leave the room, etc. There was an obsequious, conforming quality throughout the session. Although the therapist was engaged in his own projects and observed the group unobtrusively, everyone was acutely aware of his presence, much more so than in urban groups. The majority sought his praise and approval. The boys seemed to *expect* control and admonition. When the boys, for example, asked whether they could make lanyards and were told that they could "make whatever they liked," they seemed uncomfortable; they did not quite believe what they had heard. There was something different about this place, and in their anxiety, they grouped together while working as though they sought safety in numbers (A).[4]

As the sessions progressed, things began to change. When one boy suggested ice cream for the next refreshment period, the therapist, to emphasize his nonauthoritarian role, turned the request to the group: what do the other boys think about having ice cream? The practice of asking the group for their consideration and decisions was continued by the therapist for some weeks, when one of the boys, instead of turning to the therapist, asked the others directly whether they wanted a special food item. As the group agreed to the suggestion, it was transmitted to the therapist.

Out of a feeling of discomfort in the strangeness of being allowed to make decisions for themselves, the boys would giggle nervously; then, becoming assured of the permissiveness and the genuine attitude of the therapist, Philip, the toughest boy in the group, attempted to impose his will upon the others, sometimes directly and at other times in the guise of holding a perfunctory sort of voting. Gradually, as the others grew bolder, the decisions began to reflect the group's choice rather than the wishes of any one boy (B).

By the fifth session, the boys referred to themselves as the "Wednesday Club," marking the day of the week when the sessions were held after school hours. Throughout the thirty-nine sessions no serious fight ever occurred. There were numerous threats and ephemeral pugilistic posturing, but they never culminated in real fisticuffs. As might be expected, such fights among the "ghetto toughies" were not uncommon elsewhere on the campus. Impulsive, aggressive delinquents are prone to such physical combat, but it never culminated in the quieting and secure climate of the activity group. Because the therapist, as a representative of the adult world, did not frustrate or anger them, they did not displace feelings on each other. Once the boys sensed that the therapist would not intervene, their own feeble ego controls acted as deterrents. Moreover, as all the boys began to feel their growing ego strengths, the group, as a whole, assumed a progressively more social character (C).

---

[4] As in earlier chapters, these letters are keyed to the interpretation that begins on page 243.

Another remarkable phenomenon was that on no occasion was a tool ever purloined. John and Jose sometimes borrowed tools to continue their work at their cottages between sessions, but they always returned them the following week. On one occasion when Jose had not done so, it was because one of his cottage mates had taken it from him, but Jose finally retrieved it and returned it to the group a week later.[5] Practically every boy, at some time or other, felt free to take tools out of the room for use in the nearby woods during the sessions, or to work on some project evenings in their cottages, but they always returned them.

The following incident palpably demonstrated the boys' growing social awareness. At times, during the sessions, it was necessary to store some of the refreshments, such as ice cream, in the staff refrigerator, which was on another floor of the cottage. As the boys began to share in the preparation of the refreshments, the therapist would go up to fetch the food. At first, some of them would accompany him, but later boys volunteered to take over this chore completely.

One day a staff member reported a few eggs were missing from the refrigerator. At a supervision conference, we suggested that the therapist mention this complaint to the group at the refreshment table and then find some excuse for leaving the room for a brief period, thus giving the boys an opportunity to discuss the matter among themselves. He did so. Upon his return, Jose, acting as spokesman, told him the boys talked it over and suggested that whenever one of them went upstairs he, the therapist, should search him upon his return to the clubroom. This was a customary procedure in the Village. The therapist reacted to this suggestion with the statement that he would never search anyone, he *trusted them*; if they said such an incident would never occur again, it was good enough for him. As if a single person, the group promised it would never happen. It never did (D).

Full Protocol of Group Session 10

This session started promptly at 3 P.M. When the therapist arrived, he found Louis and Rafael already waiting outside the door. Louis immediately took note of the package the therapist

[5] It was possible to allow such borrowings here, since no other group met in the room.

was carrying and asked if it was the ice cream he had promised to buy for them the week before. The therapist said it was. Louis seemed worried about how it would be kept from melting. The therapist told him he would put it into the refrigerator in the cottage. He left to do so; when he returned in a few minutes he found all the boys waiting. John and William stood together. The therapist unlocked the door, and the boys rushed into the room. In the room, Philip came over to John, and they had a whispered conversation. Then Philip picked up a long wood dowel and proceeded to fashion an arrow while William impulsively grabbed the food, examined it, and annouced that at this "meeting" he would take charge of setting up the table and distributing the food (E) .

Rafael, who had been working on a candy dish at the preceding session, immediately set out to continue his work on it. Robert had a bird in his hand and came up to the therapist to show it to him, explaining that it was a bluejay. The bird seemed injured, and Robert handled it very tenderly, while Louis just wandered about. (Louis left the Village shortly thereafter.) Robert did not bring the box on which he had been working during previous sessions. For a time he seemed more interested in observing what the other boys were doing, and then remained with Philip, who was now making a bow for his arrow.

Robert came up to where the therapist was working and asked for some string. Since none was available, the therapist suggested that he could use lanyard (leather) string material. Robert added that he wanted to tie the bird's leg in order to teach it "to do tricks." The therapist could not quite envisage how he would do this, but making no comment, gave him the lanyard material. At this point a boy, not a member of the group, entered the room. He had with him a makeshift birdcage. It developed that the bird Robert had actually belonged to that boy. He and Robert now walked through the room holding a long stick with the bird perched on it. Since its feet were tied, the bird could not walk on the stick, which was what they were attempting to get it to do. Louis, who was observing the two boys with the bird, suddenly burst out, "The bird will not die." His voice seemed to quiver as if he were frightened and was asking for reassurance that the bird would live (F) .

Jose, who at this time was still very withdrawn, surprisingly came over to William and offered to help him set the table, which, even more surprisingly, William allowed him to do.[6] As Jose and William were so engaged, Jose began to hum a song. William picked up the tune, and the two hummed together. At one point William put down the food and broke into what appeared to be a calypso dance, as Jose continued to hum the tune for him. Throughout the larger part of the session, these two conversed with each other, acting as *supportive egos* to each other. The conversation had to do with the differences between white and colored boys. (William is black, Jose is Puerto Rican.) At times Jose would twist his body in an effeminate manner as he talked with William (G).

Although he had begun to work on the candy dish again, carving it from a block of wood, Rafael did not seem particularly interested in it. He seemed undecided, which may have had something to do with the last session when William, with what appeared to be a disguised purpose, broke Rafael's dish. Very listlessly, Rafael was trying to gouge out a new one. The therapist placed a more appropriate chisel near where Rafael was working, but Rafael did not pick it up, apparently preferring to go about his job in his own way. In the meantime, Philip, who had run out of the room, came back with a "flint" (flat stone) for the head of his arrow. He then proceeded to make a wedge in the thin piece of wood into which he intended to insert the "flint" (H).

John stood around watching Philip. The therapist noted that every so often the two boys would engage in conversation. At one point Louis walked over and joined in. They now spoke of going out to a certain tree. Suddenly most of the boys ran out of the room, leaving William with Jose helping him set the table. Rafael stood just outside the doorway for a while and soon returned to working on his piece of wood while the others ran into the woods nearby. He called out to William that he would later make a

---

[6] This is a most important episode for a diffident, self-encapsulated boy like Jose, in overcoming his fears. We consider his first move toward a relationship as a *projection of emotional pseudopods*. When encouraged, the patient will continue to move out of his shell, but when rebuffed, he will again withdraw into himself. This was also a "critical event" in Jose's therapy.

sword. William seemed very happy: he was the "boss" and Jose his helper was in no way threatening his position of power (I).

Robert returned without the bird and walked toward William. Suddenly the two boys began wrestling. The therapist could not determine who started it. Robert tried to hold his ground, but being unable to do so, attempted to run away from William. As he did so, William literally leaped upon his back, almost throwing him to the floor. Robert, now in a fury, turned and shouted, "Get the hell out of here, you bastard!" and, in a rage, walked out of the room. William laughed uproariously and received laughing encouragement from Jose, who had been watching the struggle, giggling (J).

The boy who remained most in the background throughout the session was John, who seemed undecided about what to do. Except for the conversations with Philip that preceded their leaving the room, he had engaged in very little else. John was out of the room until the time the group sat down for refreshments.

William and Jose continued to talk about "white and black boys." More was said on the subject at a later refreshment table. Robert had returned alone and proclaimed affirmatively that he was "ready to eat." William asked the therapist to fetch the ice cream from the refrigerator upstairs while Rafael, on his own, left to call the other boys. He soon returned, announcing that he could not find them, and went out again. William offered to cut the ice cream block into slices as Robert and Jose offered to help him do it. Although Jose seemed to want to cut the large block of ice cream, he apparently was undecided and gave the knife to William, pointing out how it should be done. William was more assured and said it should be cut "into small pieces." At this point Rafael and Louis ran into the room and took their seats. Louis sat in the seat next to the one the therapist usually occupied.

William served a rather small piece of ice cream to Rafael. Rafael complained about the flavor he got. He said he preferred vanilla and butterscotch to chocolate. He also complained about the small piece given him, and William assured him that all the boys would be getting small pieces. Louis, speaking excitedly, said that he wanted "only chocolate." Jose suggested that he would share the chocolate with him. There was only one brick of chocolate ice cream, and William cut it in two, giving a rather large piece to Jose and the other piece to Louis. At this point Rafael again objected, saying he was being "gypped." Once more, William assured him that he would "take care" of him.

The boys had taken their usual seats. Robert made a very careful tour of inspection and, looking around at the share of cookies and ice cream that the others had, said to William, "You're not going to cheat me this week." Rafael complained that his piece of ice cream was small and insisted threateningly that William give him a larger piece. This William appeared to be reluctant to do, preferring to tease Rafael as to the amount of ice cream he was going to get. Rafael demanded another piece, but all the boys in concert turned against him and said that he had "enough." Rafael appeared stuck and impotent. He did not seem able to stand up against all the boys and looked on quietly at the distribution of the food. Whatever his feelings were, he carefully concealed them.

Before the group sat down to eat, Rafael had cut his finger with one of the wood-gouging chisels. After rummaging around for the first-aid kit, with all the boys being concerned about Rafael's injury, the therapist went out and borrowed a Band-Aid from a staff member, and after washing the finger very carefully and attentively he applied it. Rafael looked pleased at this attention, and kept assuring the therapist that it would "be all right." He "can take it" (K).

During the refreshment period Philip and John threw furtive glances at the therapist. They seemed to be up to something, which they soon revealed when John asked the therapist in a very timid voice whether the therapist would go "hunting rats" with him. The therapist, who was otherwise engaged at the moment, did not respond. John rather feebly reiterated his request. When the therapist finally turned to him, the boy did not repeat it, however. Since he did not persist, the subject was dropped.

John turned to the other boys and began talking about all the rats they were catching. He said he used a stick while he was outside and had beaten one to death. Philip confirmed John's claim. Jose expressed a lively interest in this, asking, "Where did you find the rats, and how big were they?" John acted the "king at the table," as he described, with gesticulations, the huge rats with huge, gnawing teeth and how "they eat baby rats and mice." Robert laughed with glee at this characterization and said that after he finished eating, he would join them in hunting rats. Louis looked interested, but said nothing as Rafael, the timid one, was watching the boys. Since he had the smallest portion, he had finished his ice cream first. At this point he piped up and demanded more ice cream, but again the boys, almost as one, turned against him, refusing it. With this, Rafael got up from the table, walked over to the workbench, picked up some wood that was lying there, and began fashioning a sword, going outdoors to whittle on it. Later, with a great deal of energy, using both hands, Rafael feverishly sawed the wood. He had not finished making his candy dish.

Meanwhile, John continued talking about the rats. Some of the other boys seemed to have lost interest in the subject, but his interest did not seem to wane. It seemed that the rats, as a symbol, were, for some reason, important to the boys, even though it was evident that the subject was not the pleasantest for a dinner conversation. John, however, grandiloquently continued to try to hold the boys' interest, obviously as a status-seeking device. William disrupted the conversation by jumping up, getting the jar of Bosco, and walking around the table, putting chocolate syrup on each boy's ice cream.

When William reached Louis, he felt that he did not get enough, demanding more. William told him that "the club had to save it." Louis said, "Man, what the hell you talking about? You can get all the chocolate syrup you want in this club. All you have to do is ask Mr. Ellery." William seemed to be unsure whether they should or should not ask the therapist. However, Louis said to him, "Hey, you know they don't want us to be juvenile delinquents, and if they don't want us to be juvenile delinquents, *they* got to do everything to suit us." No one responded to this; instead, John suggested to all the boys that they now wash their hands. Philip quickly got up and said, "Yeah, you guys, let's wash hands. You've all been throwing rocks and your hands are filthy."

John, Philip, Robert, and Jose washed their hands, although Jose was not with the boys who played outdoors. After the hand-washing, John, Philip, and Robert again ran out. Louis, Jose,

William, and the therapist remained sitting at the table while Rafael continued to work on his sword (L).

Louis looked at Jose and asked him in the tone of an inquisitor, "Hey, what the hell are you up at the Village for, anyway?" Jose said that he had no home and that he was at the Village "for only one thing—running away." William laughed at this and said that he was up for something like that, too; he was in a lot of places (foster homes) "and then they put me up here." Jose listened rather attentively. William then asked him again why he was at the Village, but this time Jose did not answer. William asked whether Jose had any family. Louis replied, "You know Jose doesn't have any family." Jose then said that when his mother died, they put him in a hospital first, then sent him to "another place," and then they sent him to the Village. Louis listened attentively, but did not reveal anything about himself.

At this point, Louis got up and left the room, leaving William and Jose. Jose walked over to William and began to play with his hair, making fun of William's hair, saying that his hair "was kinky." Jose spoke deprecatingly of kinky hair. William asked Jose if he was Spanish. Jose denied it vehemently, but William insisted that Jose was Spanish. Again Jose denied it. Jose rubbed his own head and then rubbed William's head and said that his own hair was nicer. Taking a comb out of his pocket, he began to comb William's hair. There was an effeminate quality in the way Jose manipulated William's hair. As he did this, Jose twisted his body in a girlish fashion (M).

Rafael, who persisted in working on his sword, gradually appeared to be losing interest in it. It was almost as if continuing it served to wear off his rage. At this point, William (the schizophrenic boy) tapped the therapist on the shoulder and, obviously not remembering his name, said, "Hey, would you help me make a sword? I never made one." (William actually had never made anything in the group, although he had done extremely well personally, and derived a great deal of satisfaction in managing the refreshments.)

William picked up a few pieces of wood and asked whether it was possible to make a sword out of them. He finally found an appropriate piece and as he started working on it asked the therapist to draw a point on it. This the therapist did. As the therapist began helping him, William was almost trembling with fear and anticipation and had to reassure himself many times that the therapist would be at his side to support him. He asked what kind of sword he could make and was given a limited number of alternatives, since the therapist did not feel the boy could cope with too many ideas at one time. William wanted to know the kind of saw he should use. The therapist gave him one. He then asked that the therapist start cutting for him. *After a few strokes,* William took over and proceeded on his own. He was "all thumbs" in manipulating the coping saw. But as he began to feel more reassured in using it, his strokes became a little bolder. However, he still worked gingerly, as though the wood would split or the saw would break, and appeared very fearful.

When Louis saw William at work, he, too, picked up a piece of board and rapidly drew what appeared to be a saber. He began work on it energetically, as if in competition with William. Rafael was at this point walking around on the lawn outside the room and soon walked away. The therapist became concerned as to what his role with Rafael should be. Rafael appeared to need help, but this could not be offered without confirming the boy's feelings of impotence and weakness and at the same time arousing the resentment of the other boys. The boy was obviously trying to venture forth, but was having a rough time of it.

Most of the therapist's time during the remainder of the session was taken up with William constantly asking him what kind of file to use, how to manipulate the file, how to use the plane — all of which he showed him. He said that he hoped he would finish the sword before the end of the session, because he wanted to take it with him. He also wished he would have enough time to make a leather sheath for the sword. Now he seemed to be bubbling inside. The therapist assured him that he would be ready to help him and did so every time William asked for help. Only basic strokes were shown him, after which William would take over. Surprisingly, he was able to pick up rather quickly, and although inept at the beginning, he grew more and more confident to do things by himself. At many points he came to ask whether the sword was finished. The therapist commented that it looked very nice but suggested that he could sand it down a little, if he wanted to. William would generally accept suggestions and work on them. (The therapist avoided being too directive, however, but felt it was necessary for the boy to feel supported in his

241

beginning efforts to work at something substantial with tools, which he had never done before (N).

While the excitement around the sword making was in progress, Rafael returned to the room and to working on his weapon. The blade of his coping saw snapped, and he did not know what to do. The therapist offered to help him replace it. While the therapist was so engaged, Rafael reached for another coping saw which was lying nearby. At the same time Louis also reached for it. Rafael was first to clutch it, but Louis demanded that he give it up. Adamantly, Rafael refused. The two fell to wrestling and Louis finally succeeded in pulling it away. The therapist was loath to distract Louis at this point, since he might have caught on to the significance of the act, namely, to protect Rafael, and probably would then have continued the struggle with even more determination.

When the therapist gave Rafael the coping saw that he had put to rights, Rafael did not use it. He took the crosscut saw instead. As usual, for him, he concealed his feelings of hurt and resentment against Louis and perhaps also against the therapist for not being protected. (The therapist felt that somehow he was not getting through to the boy in trying to protect him, and perhaps at this point Rafael was being victimized by the other members of the group because they were all physically larger than he, except for Jose and Robert. Out of the therapist's feelings for Rafael, he runs the risk by seeming to expect too much from the boy.) (O)

William finally finished the sword and did a pretty good job of it, considering that it was his first try. He then asked help with making a sheath. The therapist and William fetched leather from the supply closet, and he was shown how to proceed. He asked for help with punching the holes. The therapist punched *a few holes* when William volunteered to take the punching tool. He continued on his own and found that he was successful at making the holes by himself. Meanwhile, Louis was working hard on his sword and by the end of the session had pretty much completed it. He had done a fairly good job. Later, at the end of the session when the group was leaving, Louis came along for the first time in some weeks without stalling or announcing that he needed "ten more minutes" for his work, making everybody wait for him.

Before the end, all the boys had gathered in the room. Robert was now in the center of the group showing the boys twenty empty cartridge shells he had picked up in the woods. Philip also had a batch of them in his pockets. The therapist did not know where the boys had been and where they could have found the cartridges. Once the "souvenirs" were displayed there arose a flurry of excitement. Philip, John, and Robert grabbed pieces of wood and were busily engaged in making swords, which they finished in short order. None of the boys seemed to pay attention as to how well the swords came out, as they had done also with their other projects at previous sessions.

Amid all this excitement, Jose came over to ask whether the therapist could get him a combination lock. As soon as Louis and Rafael heard it, they, too, joined in and before long, everyone in the room wanted a combination lock. Since the therapist felt that this might run into quite an expense, he said that he would have to ask the Club Department whether they could supply the locks. The boys agreed to wait. Louis then said that the therapist should ask the Club Department whether the "club could have two meetings a week instead of one." He would like to come twice a week, he said. Louis then wondered whether the same boys would be in the group next year. The therapist said that as far as he knew they would. Louis, Philip, and Rafael exclaimed, "Yippee! We want to come back!"

After the swords were finished, the boys ran out. Only William was left behind, trying his best to finish his project. He came up to the therapist asking for help in lacing the leather sheath. The therapist *started,* and William, quickly perceiving the process, finished it, expressing great satisfaction with it. He said, "You know, this is the first sword I ever made. Boy, I never thought I would be a guy who could make a sword!" Thereupon he ran off, but soon returned momentarily to say, "Hey, Mr. Whatchama-call-it, so long. I'll see you next week"(P).

Interpretation of the Records

(A) As in all activity therapy groups the boys here, too, are going through a period of acclimatization, which extends for several sessions. In this group the period was more extensive than in an urban out-patient clinic because these boys had been cowed before their commitment and to some extent also by the institutional regime and by some of the staff and teachers. Children in all groups accept the therapist's permissiveness, neutrality, and tolerance only after a period of testing and experiencing; but patients *in situ* accept these more readily than the boys did in the institution. The shock reaction that bewilders patients at first wears off much more easily in urban children than it did in these boys, because their past experiences with adults and authority were more traumatic. They start with caution, obsequiousness, and ingratiation. The permissive climate of AGT represented an apotheosis of all past social authority to them, even though the climate and the staff of the Children's Village were immeasurably more humane than in most institutions of this genre.

(B) The therapist is aware of the suspicion the boys entertain about the freedom he extends to them. He, therefore, consistently refers all matters affecting the boys for the group's decision. It is as if he were saying, repetitively, "Believe it; I do trust you." The suspicion and disbelief of the youngsters are reflected in their tense giggling. Finally, as uncertainty diminishes, the real characters of the boys begin to show through: Philip, a tough boy, acts according to his usual pattern but this time takes refuge in a false facade of "democracy," rather than fighting it out when things get tough for him. However, the other boys have assimilated the therapist's implicit message that they are, in fact, autonomous, so that they are now able to take steps against one who tries to dominate them.

(C) A sense of *groupism* emerged more rapidly here than it ordinarily does in urban clinic groups. This can be accounted for by the fact that the members know and are on intimate terms with each other. Even though most came from different cottages, they had antecedent contact in the various school and leisure time activities. Another reason is that homeless children such as these, who have been, in effect, deprived materially, emotionally, and socially tend to band together for comfort and protection, which is the etiology of gangs in ghettos. Groups serve them as substitute for, or as supplements to, the primary family groups that in many ways failed to foster essential affectional ties and security.

The remarkable absence of violent outbreaks and fights was not fortuitous. It came about also from the proper selection of patients and careful psychological balancing, both of which are only too often overlooked in forming all types of therapy groups.

Rudimentary social (group) restraints arose in this group more readily than in any of our urban groups. At this stage, this can be attributed to the restraining cultural climate of the institution.

(D) There is no need here to validate the obvious; in the disadvantaged circumstances and social mores from which these boys came, stealing is so common that it is not considered atypical or amoral. Yet, the impressive fact is that in the therapy group where the very setting was the easiest to steal from, this never became a problem. One does not have to steal "love" when it is freely given. When the therapist posed the situation of the purloining of the eggs, the group's anxiety was greatly in evidence. Undoubtedly the anxiety arose from guilt at having been disloyal and treacherous to the therapist, who had treated them so generously and humanely. This is a major leverage in making patients aware of transgressions without resorting to blame, chastisement, or punishment.

When children are treated badly by adults, they find in it justification for delinquencies and vandalism, consciously, but most often quite unconsciously, as retributional acts. But when they receive consideration and respect, as exercised by an AGT worker, even their rudimentary superegos — "fairness" — generate the change in their sense of values and of self. The fact that the therapist refused to search the boys and his assertion that he trusted them could not but have startling impact on these youngsters. No adult in their experience or imagination would have acted with such generosity! We have found in our work with verbal or para-analytic group therapy with older delinquents intense preoccupation with being "trusted." This wish and their chagrin at not being trusted repeatedly arose during the discussions. It was our impression that being trusted somehow represented, in fantasy, being accepted and loved. This is a major reason why egocentric and psychopathic patients cannot be reached by AGT. The therapist's forbearance to them would be perceived as foolhardiness or weakness.

(E) While there are many differences between the behavioral responses of these boys and children in activity groups elsewhere, the psychological mechanisms and interpersonal dynamics are identical. For instance, in all activity groups, the children are emotionally impacted by the consistent, giving therapist: his remembering their special requests, for example. Bringing the ice cream requested at the previous session is typical. Also, in all activity groups the youngsters show their eagerness to "get started." Even though a full week has passed between sessions, group members often burst into the treatment room, and most resume the activities they were engaged in before, sometimes conveying the feeling that only a day had elapsed. This may be symptomatic of the pleasure the boys had been deriving from past sessions; in others it may be a reenactment of sibling rivalry.

(F) Robert, originally selected for the group because of his extreme babyishness and his dependent manner of soliciting attention, according to the "cottage life" staff and others, has been making progress: his contacts with other boys have become more mature and are now on a "give and take" basis. He is also more aggressively direct, which is manifested in the protocol record. Note that the therapist supports him in this growth and does not interfere with his "experiment," even though the therapist considered the stated objective palpably unrealistic. This is part of the neutrality and noninterference, which fosters individual autonomy in children and real learning through discovery and experience.

Louis' spontaneous reaction (where he expresses fear of death by denying it) is understandable in the light of his background. Louis, as is the case with other boys in the group and in the institution, has been exposed in his early life to the most trying and threatening disasters: separation anxiety caused by repeated family disruptions, desertions, divorces, multiple foster homes, multiple "parents." For young children these are all equivalent to traumatic losses: feelings about disease, injury, and death are thus experienced as forms of psychological separation. Hence, Louis' anxious and seemingly dissociated response to a fettered, injured bird.

(G) Jose was defensive in his withdrawal, but not especially frightened of others. The group has begun to help him reach out, and he is beginning to relate better. Here he is reaching out for a *supportive ego* relationship with another boy. He does not seek out the therapist as others did, which may be an indication of his discomfort with or hostility toward adults or, perhaps, fear of them. The happiness both boys experience, so different from any other area in their lives, is demonstrated by their humming together, and not surprisingly, in William's spontaneous dance. The therapist's observation of effeminacy in Jose's movements poses another question having to do with the boy's sexual identification.

AGT provides a natural setting for differential diagnosis and clinical observations often overlooked on referral. The conversation about difference in race and color recurred several times during this session. It is therapeutically and sociologically very helpful for even youngsters to bring their subsurface feelings about race into the open. However, note should be taken that both boys stem from minority groups; one is black and the other is Puerto Rican.

(H) The therapist's placing of an appropriate tool within the area of vision was the correct procedure, but apparently it did not work. Rafael, ordinarily a manipulative, complaining youngster, resisted close relationships despite his seeming pattern of seeking them out. He may have become embarrassed by having aroused attention to himself for using a wrong tool. It may also be an act of defiance on his part toward adults. Philip's project is meaningful to him in the light of his aggressiveness and bullying in the community and in the therapy group.

(I) The boys feel free to leave the room. The nice weather and the pastoral setting are added factors to this. The countryside offered tempting space, natural interests, and opportunities for exploration and discovery. At first the youngsters experienced the freedom of leaving the room without permission, which violated one of the rigid rules of the institution and was a test of the therapist's forbearance. We felt that the games and activities outside the confinement of the room had for these regimented children meaningful significance, and they were therefore allowed even though rules set by the administration were being transgressed.

After some time, it became clear that these spontaneous excursions, the rummaging about, observations, and discoveries were not escapes from the treatment setting, but rather had the effect of expanding it. This impression was validated when the boys brought the "outside" back to their "home base," as, for example, when one boy brought evergreens to decorate the dingy, half-dark treatment room, or when others brought in cartridges and turtles at other times, or when Robert brought the bluejay to "train."

William, however, was not tempted to leave the room. What was happening to him is extremely significant. William, who was somewhat autistic and at times behaved "peculiarly," grew increasingly reactive to the stimulation of interpersonal contacts in the therapy group. The effect of these was to revitalize him, to make him more appropriately responsive to others. By taking over the responsibility for the refreshment table, he enjoyed the social status it afforded him. This is furthered by the fact that he uses Jose as a helper. But as he is helped, he also helps Jose in return. The supportive ego relationship acts for their mutual benefit and aids their social development.

(J) This is extraordinary behavior for Robert, without regard to whether he provoked the fight or not. In comparison to his original dependence and diffidence, this open manifestation of anger, cursing, and physical aggression is a sign of growth. He has already discovered that he can achieve status not only in babylike fashion but by acting as his peers did. As for William, this minor "fight" is psychologically significant because it represents externalization of aggression. However, the therapist had learned that William could easily fragment as his anger was tapped, and he was alert to the possibility of having to use indirect limits to help William control his anger if it threatened to become severe. Every alteration in William's ego functioning in a direction that involved him in more meaningful interpersonal situations, even the mildly aggressive incident with Robert, acted to diminish his pathology.

(K) While it is customary in AGT to have refreshments near the end of a session, thus suggesting its termination, the therapist responds if the group requests to eat earlier. By gratifying the youngsters' request on demand, the therapist continues to demonstrate respect for the children and his flexibility. Note he withdraws completely from preparing and serving food, now that the boys show willingness to do it themselves. They now feel the group is theirs and they are a part of it. Of further note is the fact that when there was arguing over portions, the therapist did not interfere.

Routinely, when there is conflict over food, the therapist continues to eat calmly so that he is not drawn into the argument. In this way a group and the individuals involved are forced to resolve their own problems. This is what was happening here.

Rafael incurs the group's displeasure, and they deny him a second helping. Later on in the session, Rafael, who was unmotivated when he tentatively worked on his candy dish because his earlier attempt was destroyed, now decides to make a sword and does so, working at it vigorously. This is an obvious displacement of his anger toward William and the others.

Rafael had cut his finger. Without much verbalization, but with concern and care, the therapist applies himself fo "fixing it up." This is proper technique when children have scrapes or minor cuts. It represents personal attention (love), and with youngsters who have been emotionally deprived, the therapist's response at such times is very heartwarming. However, not having first-aid supplies on hand is a serious oversight. These must be part of the initial equipment of an activity therapy room and must be replenished immediately.

(L) It is interesting that John and Philip ask the therapist to go hunting rats with them. They are the most aggressive and "toughest" boys in the group. They are probably referring to field mice, which were common in the meadows around the campus. Philip's working on his bow and arrow was probably to use in hunting rats. What may seem like an unusual interest in rats has a reality basis for children who have lived in tenements in urban slums.

It will be noted here, once again, that the refreshment table is a focal place in AGT. It is a time for coming together, not only for a repast, but to share ideas and experiences, and to assimilate emotionally some of the interpersonal episodes that transpired during the earlier part of the session. For example, John has an opportunity to be in the social limelight as he declaims his expertness about rats; again, Robert is able to identify *with* his peers — instead of using them to satisfy his earlier infantile demands, he now joins with the others to hunt rats. William continues to fortify his food-dispensing leadership role by distributing syrup and deciding against Louis' demand for more because the "group" had to save it.

Louis speaks inferentially but dramatically of the therapeutic climate of the group when he states unequivocally that in "this club you can get all the syrup you want!" He is quite serious when he refers to the need to gratify the boys if the adults don't want them to be delinquent. The probable implicit meaning of this remark is that delinquency is a symptomatic behavioral response to parental and social neglect.

Rafael is having a hard time as the scapegoat of the group. It is not always possible to determine the reasons for a group's choice of a scapegoat and is particularly difficult in this group where attitudes to a specific member can be shaped outside the group, in the community, in the cottage, or in the academic school. These are carried over into the group. The situation as it presented itself here is very trying for the therapist. His sense of justice is seriously assailed, as is also his compassion for the victim of the group's seemingly unjustified cruelty. He must now watch out for his countertransferential feelings and control them, hoping that as Rafael gains in ego strength through the group, either he will be able to deal with the situation himself or the group will abate automatically as it recognizes his powers.

(M) Several of the boys became interested in each other's backgrounds. Louis, who first raises the subject, is reluctant to speak of his own family, although he is interested in knowing about how the others came to the Village. At this time, and in subsequent sessions, there was an exchange of personal experiences between the boys. This type of communication, in which children share knowledge of common antecedent experiences, helps weld a group. There is a quality of shared identity in the exchange between Jose and William, even though there was some good-natured spoofing about differences.

Earlier, Jose and William had conversed about white and black boys. There seemed to be two elements involved in this content: Jose, a Puerto Rican boy, seems to be struggling with his image of himself (identity); is he white or is he black? William, a black, with whom he has at present a supportive relationship, also arouses in him some anxiety on this score. Also, the homoerotic trends in Jose, which had been observed in earlier sessions directed toward Robert, were now transferred to William when the former strokes his hair.

It is noteworthy, in our experience, that only in the institutional groups have patients explored their backgrounds and personal difficulties. None of the hundreds of outside groups have ever broached these subjects. Doing so, of course, has many positive therapeutic potentials and can serve to turn activity groups into verbal, perhaps para-analytic groups. However, we have not attempted this because of the age of the members and the *primary group code,* namely, that the contents of the groups are motoric activities on the one hand, and unrestricted freedom on the other. All the residents in the Village had been assigned to caseworkers for counseling or therapy and, in serious cases, to psychiatrists for treatment. The reason for the institutional boys' interest in each other's histories may be that they know each other intimately from living in the same closed community, or in the same cottages and even more so because of their awareness of their own problems. The urban groups were viewed by the boys and girls merely as "clubs."

Jose's character is strongly stamped by female identification, which can be altered only by reidentification with males, and when this is the case, the reidentification is best achieved with child models. We have had a number of effeminate boys, in all of whom the identifications have been corrected in AGT. The fact that Jose transferred his attachment from Robert, the most infantile boy, to William, the strongest boy in the group, as his supportive ego can be viewed as the first step in the direction of corrective sexual reidentification. A classical case of this is Ivor Brown, who carried over his feminine identification of hiring himself to do housecleaning, making artificial flowers, wearing aprons, and avoiding boys and their activities. As a result of his two-year AGT experiences, Ivor abandoned all his feminine occupations, joined neighborhood boys in their games, and *resigned* from the group because he was "too busy playing baseball" (Slavson, 1945, pp. 259-273).

Another rather soft, plump boy of eleven in another urban group, with distinct and very exaggerated feminine walk, body movements, and mannerisms that "disgusted" a female member of the clinic staff who had observed the group through a one-way screen, changed so in the two years of AGT that she was "startled" on seeing him. Later he was reported to participate in all boys' activities in his neighborhood and school and "even had a girl friend."

We also find in this portion of the protocol how Rafael's anger becomes dissipated through activity, and the ego is called into action. Work in AGT serves in various ways to control strong emotions and prevents them from exploding into open outbursts, which is ultimately carried over into daily living. In some instances, the work is libido-binding; in other cases, particularly when resistive materials such as wood are used, strong emotions can be sublimated through discharge of energy in motoric pathways. Finding sublimations for antisocial inner pressures is one of the five objectives of psychotherapy.

(N) William's interest in making something and his involvement in the various processes in working with wood, plus the tangible outcome of his labors, constitute a *critical event* in his treatment. It should be kept in mind that a critical event integrates prior successes or is a resolution of the major intrapsychic difficulty in a patient, i.e., his nuclear problem. This becomes clear when it is remembered that William is clinically a borderline (probably induced) schizophrenic. He struggles between indecision and fear about whether he is really capable of making the sword and an overpowering need to do so.

The therapist, sensing the importance of having William succeed, carefully but surely helps the boy toward successful fruition of his effort. Yet, he measures his assistance sensitively, so that William is not robbed of the sense of self-fulfillment. So great is William's need for success that he insists that the project has to be completed at this session. Because of this need for successful completion of projects within the space of one session, as stated elsewhere, materials provided are of a type that lend themselves to projects that can be readily completed. Children like William, who have been deeply frustrated and defeated, need successes, however small. The therapist's continuous attention to William seems to arouse jealousy in Louis, who takes up a project like William's.

(O) Rafael is still generally at odds. He is restless, moving in and out of the room and from one activity to another, being apparently unable to stay with anything for long. The "hassle" over the food during refreshments seemed to aggravate his preexisting unhappy mood. A degree of anxiety is detectable in the therapist's reactions to Rafael. This may have originated with Rafael's earlier rejection of assistance from the therapist and, once again, at the point when he refuses the coping saw. Some of the therapist's ministrations and concern for Rafael are overdetermined and are, perhaps, countertransference responses based on denial of his own anger aroused by Rafael's behavior.

(P) The "rat hunters" return again. One gets the feeling as though very young children, who have become secure enough to "explore" interesting areas beyond home boundaries, are returning periodically to the haven of security, their home. (The cartridge shells were undoubtedly dropped by hunters who hunt small game in that area.) Despite the excitement of this "find," they seem to take in instantaneously what has been going on in their absence and also start to fabricate swords. Once again, his typical oral quality is manifested when Jose, followed by Louis and Rafael, and then by all the others, ask for combination locks. The therapist, undecided as to whether he can, in fact, meet this request, prepares them for the possible denial by introducing an outside denier, the Club Department.

William speaks the last word, in its own context a simple assertion with dramatic overtones: "Boy, I never thought I would be a guy who could make a sword!" The seeming impersonal appellation "Mr. Whatchma-call-it" which William used in addressing the therapist is far from being that. For a schizophrenic boy it represents a step in ego integration, especially when he adds, "So long. I'll see you next week!" William has been gradually becoming involved in affective, emotional attitudes toward the therapist, who is now a significant affectional object for him, as are also some of the other boys. Louis, leaving with the group without his customary delay, indicates his strengthened ego and improved self-image, no longer requiring to focus attention on himself and vicariously dominating the group. These improvements are a result of his new-found interest in manual work and his success with it at this session.

The significance of the group to the youngsters is revealed in their request for more frequent "meetings" and the "guarantee" that it will continue next year with the same complement.

DISCUSSION

In the protocol of the tenth session, we see how the boys struggle to find means for cooperating and forming friendships through numerous experimental and transitory relationships, from which later in the year emerged a moderately cohesive group and individuals with more mature attitudes and behavior. We are also impressed with the conquest of fear in a borderline schizophrenic boy like William and his significant discovery that he possesses powers of which he was not aware when he exclaims that he never thought he could make a sword. This was the beginning of very impressive growth in this boy.

Equally significant is the growth of the boys' capacities for object relations and the beginnings of social attitudes, as they are revealed in their interest in one another when they inquire about each other's backgrounds, nationality, family, and the reasons for being placed in the Village. The conflicts that arose in the setting of the table for refreshments, discovering ways of dealing with one another in the matters of food and sharing tools and materials, observing each other's work, criticizing and helping one another, participating together in hilarity and pleasantries — are all steps that dissolve emotional isolation and promote relatedness. The need for each other and acquiring the means of expressing this need in action soon followed, and more mature, socially constructive personalities emerged. The unconscious feelings of fulfillment are revealed by the boys in their desire to meet together more frequently and to make certain that they will all continue in the group.

Finally, if we take even a cursory look at the function of the therapist, the many forms it assumes become clear. He helps some, withholds help from others, spends a great deal of time with a weak boy, and stays away from another because of awareness that the latter would be either mistrustful or too antagonistic to accept help. He praises the boys' achievements with discrimination, and he is aware of his own countertransference feelings. Although he does not directly look, he sees everything that each boy does and feels. He does not chastise or admonish in the episode of the purloined eggs, but creates an opportunity for them, as a group, to deal with it. Thus is the superego repaired and feelings of responsibility emerge.

The student of this volume cannot overlook the difference in the content and character in the urban and the institutional groups. The members of the latter are obviously less mature, and there is more real childishness in their behavior and remarks. This is more or less characteristic of children who have been sequestered physically, others psychologically, from their original communities because of their vandalism, disobedience, and delinquencies. Our study in depth of delinquents (and this is possibly true also of adult criminals) impressed us with their basic immaturity, the evidence for which we have suggested in another work (Slavson, 1965).

Perhaps it is this very arrested development and their suppressed potentials and psycho-organic readiness for broader emotional and intellectual functions that propelled the institutional children into so much more meaningful and growth-producing activities and interpersonal interactions. It is not surprising, therefore, that the boys in the activity groups gained more than the older boys in para-analytic therapy, whose characters and defenses had grown more rigid and their inner turmoil more intense and complicated by sex urges and fantasies. Several decades ago, a prominent South American psychiatrist, after learning about and observing our urban activity therapy groups, declared in an article that these groups have great potentials for "delinquency prevention." It may well be.

EVALUATION OF AGT AT CHILDREN'S VILLAGE

Three activity therapy groups were conducted from 1957 to 1960, each for a period of one school year with an average of about forty sessions per group. The groups, initially composed of twenty-eight youngsters, were diminished by five, who were either discharged from Children's Village or dropped.

No attempt was made to assess the therapeutic effectiveness of AGT upon individual youngsters in a structured residential, authoritarian environment, since these groups were short-lived. The three experimental groups were set up as an aside to the central project of "para-analytic group psychotherapy and the inversion technique" with older teen-age adolescents.

The aim of the AGT project was to test out the capacity of both the institution and the residents involved to tolerate a permissive treatment. Information on the changes in the boys was incidental; the interactional manifestations between the permissiveness of the groups and all the other centers of the institution such as life in the cottages, changes in behavior in the academic school, in recreational activities, and on the campus generally were the foci of interest. All staff evaluated the project favorably. The statistical table that follows was compiled on the basis of re-

255

sponses of the staffs who operated these various centers and activities. (1) The project unequivocally demonstrated that AGT, despite its permissiveness and the therapist's passivity, can in good hands be integrated into a setting for preadolescent youngsters in residential treatment. (2) The institutional personnel not only proved accepting of the freedom accorded their charges but actually expressed enthusiasm for its effects upon them. (3) As shown in Table 1, based on reports from staff, one may hypothesize that AGT can be as effective in institutional settings as it is with out-patients in urban communities.

TABLE 1

INCIDENCE OF IMPROVEMENT IN ACTIVITY GROUPS

Group Number	1	2	3	Totals
Significant improvement	1	4	4	9
Partial improvement	5	3	4	12
No improvement	1	1*	0	2

* Placed in session 30; attended only 13 sessions.

XIII

Some Administrative Aspects of Activity Group Therapy

INVITING CHILDREN TO A GROUP

The initial invitation to an activity therapy group is made by the referring persons, most often social workers, psychologists, or psychiatrists in child guidance agencies. The therapy group is described to the prospective patient as a "club" with activities such as arts and crafts, games, and trips to places of interest. No mention is made at this time of refreshments, which should come as an unexpected and pleasant surprise at the first session. Referring persons should avoid extended conversation about the nature of the group and its activities, and they should not describe the therapist.

An unusually shy youngster may need support in making the initial move toward attending a therapy group, and either the referring person, a parent, or a social worker may have to accompany him to the therapy room for the first session. Most often a parent accompanies the child. Often social work aides or social work students are available for this task. The accompanying adult should separate from the child at the entrance door, leaving the child and the group therapist to "break the ice," as it were.

The first letter of invitation is sent from the "office" addressed to the patient. The following is a sample:

Dear Thomas:

Miss Smith [the child therapist or intake worker] suggested that you would like to join a club of boys [girls] in

257

your neighborhood. This club will meet at 5509 Andersen Street, near Drayton Avenue, on Tuesday, September 29th, at 4 o'clock.

The boys [girls] work with all kinds of materials like wood, paints, and metals, play games, and go on picnics and trips.

The leader of the club is George Kelly, and he will be expecting you.

> Yours truly,
> Anna Johnson
> Club Department

The group therapist sends reminder notes of the following nature in an envelope for the first three sessions:

Dear Thomas:

Our club will meet again this Tuesday at 4 o'clock at the same place, 5509 Andersen Street. The other boys [girls] and I are looking forward to seeing you. I hope you will come.

> Yours truly,
> George Kelly

These reminder notes are then discontinued, but not before the therapist mentions at the fourth session during refreshments that the club will meet again every week at the same time, and asks the children whether they need further reminders or will they remember? If they decide to continue receiving them, the therapist (or office) complies and raises the question a month later.

NOTES TO ABSENTEES

To members who are absent from a session, the therapist throughout the life of the group sends a note to this effect:

Dear Thomas:

I am sorry you were not able to come to our meeting last Tuesday. The boys [girls] and I missed you, and we all hope you can come this week. We had a very nice time at the meeting.

Looking forward to seeing you,

> Yours truly,
> George Kelly

Letters such as the foregoing (rather than post cards) have telling significance to children deprived of recognition. The fact that letters are addressed to them in person and the statement that they have been "missed" promote a sense of worth. Some children proudly announce on arrival at the group, "I got a letter!"

In the case of preschool, young children, who are always accompanied by an adult, all correspondence should be addressed to the mother.

PROBLEM OF POSTED MONEY

Where families are unable to meet the traveling expenses of children, our practice has been to mail the fare addressed to the children and timed so that it reaches them the day before the session. When a child who has been receiving such aid absents himself from the session, only a reminding letter should be mailed to him but no funds, thus preventing the temptation of exploiting the agency.

LENGTH AND TIMING OF GROUP SESSIONS

The length of the treatment year is almost coincidental with the school year, starting in September and extending to the beginning of the summer school vacation, except that the group sessions start two weeks after the opening of school to avoid the need for children to cope with two diverse adjustments simultaneously.

A group session of AGT lasts two hours—ninety minutes of activities and thirty minutes for refreshments—although there are occasional modifications in this due to circumstances arising at some sessions. Termination of a session is usually signaled after refreshments, when the therapist proceeds to clean up, following which he dons his jacket or coat and stands near the door. The therapist *never tells* the group to leave.

Note Taking, Reporting

Recording of what transpires at each session of AGT is essential to help the therapist become aware in retrospect of the significance of events. Records are also essential to the supervisory process. They should be, preferably, dictated into a recording machine and transcribed by a typist in time for the supervisor to read them before the supervisory session. It is of utmost importance that note taking at the AGT session be eschewed, as it would give it a reportorial character.

Referral Summary

Pertinent information must be presented by the referring source for each child under consideration to determine his suitability for group treatment. The typed referral summary should include a condensed anamnesis, including the observations and findings of any special examinations or tests that would contribute to establishing a tentative diagnosis, such as intelligence and projective tests, physical examination if any, psychological and psychiatric reports. While not essential, information from schools, camps, and settlement houses may prove valuable in providing a perspective of the child in the context of his intrapsychic problems and social adjustment. If a child is, or has been, in individual therapy, a summary statement of the course and current status of treatment should be included.

Outlines of Reports for AGT

Referral Summary

Referrals of children to analytically oriented groups follow the outlines of referral to individual therapy, which include the child's individual adjustment.

Date	Referred by
Name of client	Office
Address	Father's name and age
Birth date	Mother's name and age
I.Q.	Siblings and ages
Grade in school	

1. *Family Background and Economic Situation.* Describe the main points of the family maladjustment. What is the economic status of the family? Will the patient be able to supply carfare, or shall the agency provide this?

2. *Physical Description.* Give as full a description of the child's physical appearance as possible. Is he oversized or underdeveloped for his age? Does he appear undernourished? Does he dress neatly or shabbily? Has he any visible physical defects? Any speech defects?

3. *Patient's Personality.* Describe as fully as practical the problem for which the child is being referred. A description of his personality should give an insight into his emotional difficulties and help in assigning him to an appropriate group. It is necessary, for example, to know whether the child is aggressive or withdrawing; whether he is infantile or oversophisticated; hostile or submissive; and how these characterisitcs exhibit themselves in his behavior.

4. *School Adjustment.*

5. *Adjustment to Other Children.* What recreational resources are being used by the patient at present? Is he a member of a gang or other unorganized play groups in the neighborhood? Does he belong to a neighborhood center? What are his hobbies and leisure-time interests? How does he get along with other children?

6. *Adjustment at Camp.* Has the child attended camp? If possible, attach a copy of a camp report or give a short description of this adjustment.

7. *Diagnostic Statement on the Client, If Any.*

8. *Reason for Referral to the Therapy Group.*

The foregoing outline is used by the referring person as an aid in summarizing the history of the patient with a view to pointing up the particular problems and difficulties which may be treated in a group. It is not essential to follow the outline exactly as it stands, if the necessary information is given in the body of the summary.

First Impressions Report

Following the first three sessions of a group, the therapist is required to record his impressions of each child, limiting himself to objective observations. The intent of these reports is to assess each patient's initial adaptation to the group.

The report should focus on physical description and dress; social contacts, attitudes toward other patients and the therapist; the extent and quality of verbalization; the use of materials; role as neuters, instigators, neutralizers, etc. From the first impressions reports the supervisor, who is responsible for both the patients' progress and the functions of the therapist, should be able to assess the correctness of choice of patients for a particular group, the psychological balance of the group, and the therapist's functioning. First impressions also serve as frames of reference for changes in patients as therapy progresses.

Progress Reports

Two reports, one after three and the other after six months, on the progress of individual children, describing detailed observations on their behavior, attitudes, responses, and especially feeling-tones, are essential for the evaluation of the effects of therapy. Information on the adjustments in the home, school, and community, obtained from other sources by a caseworker, in conjunction with the therapist's progress reports comprise the substantive data for the integration conferences. Progress reports are most meaningful when they describe each child in the group and draw comparisons with preceding reports and first impressions, quoting briefly a few significant episodes and transitional phases of behavior and attitudes. An outline for a progress report follows:

1. *Attendance in the Group.* When did he first come to the group? Has he attended regularly or spasmodically since the last progress report? Does he come late or on time? Is he consistent in his habits of attendance? How many sessions has he missed since the last progress report, as compared with the total number of sessions attended?

2. *Physical Description.* Does the child appear tall for his age, overweight, underweight? What is his general facial expression? Does he have any malformations which might cause him to withdraw from other children? Give any other pertinent information.

3. *Personal Appearance.* Is he well-mannered? Have there been

changes in his personal appearance since joining the group or since the last progress report?

4. *Use of Language.* Record any language peculiarities such as stuttering, stammering, lisping, drawl, halt in speech, baby talk; whether he is sparse or effusive, calm or excitable while speaking. Record vulgarisms, curses and stereotypes. Give actual quotations.

5. *Attitudes.*

Cooperation. Does he help others in working with materials? Does he help in cleaning up the room? Does he offer to assist in washing dishes, setting the table, preparing the refreshments? Does he abide by group decisions? Has there been any improvement in these respects? Give examples.

Economy in materials. Is he economical in his use of materials? Does he request expensive tools and games? Does he exercise care in working with tools? Any improvement here?

New members. What is the patient's reaction toward new members in the group? Does he offer to show them what the group does during sessions and help them acclimate themselves to the new environment? Does he resent the new arrival?

Group therapist. Is he dependent to a great extent upon the group therapist? Does he seek his attention unduly? Does he resent sharing him with the others? Has he become more or less self-reliant and reliable?

Fellow members. Has he established friendships within the group? Does he try to "buy his way" into the group? Has there been any progress here?

Food. Describe in detail manner of eating; preferences in food; peculiarities; behavior in the group and restaurants at mealtimes; gluttony, anxiety, or indifference.

6. *Money.* Does the patient try to get money from the therapist on false pretenses? Does he exploit, wheedle, take advantage of therapist? Does he try to steal rides? Does he talk about or refer to money frequently? Is he avaricious, parsimonious, economical, or too conscious of money? Give examples.

7. *Adjustment at School.* Does the patient talk about school? Does he tie up his work at school with the work in the group? Has any change been noted in his attitudes toward school since he has been in the group?

8. *Activities.* Does the patient work steadily, sporadically, occasionally, or not at all? Is he calm, excited, or tense? Does he finish jobs, or is he a floater? Does he prefer special materials? Does he work with others or entirely by himself? Describe the general nature of his work, such as shape, color. Does he plan work, or is he impulsive? Give details.

9. *Integration of Personality.* Has the child grown? Has he become more mature during the period covered by this progress report? Is he part of the group, or does he withdraw and have little to do with the other members?

10. *Group Therapist's Comments and Interpretations.*

INTERGRATION CONFERENCES

"Integration conferences" in which the group therapist, his supervisor, individual therapist, if any, and his supervisor, parents' workers, if any,[1] psychologist and psychiatrist (when indicated) participate for evaluating the effects of treatment are held twice each school year. The first is between the two progress reports and the second at the end of the year, at which time plans are made for continuing, discharging, or transferring the patient to a different group or individual treatment. Developments in some cases may require "emergency" evaluative integration conferences, psychiatric consultations, and psychologic tests outside and beyond these schedules.

A word of caution is needed about parents who are involved in varying degrees in *exclusive, cooperative,* or *divided* cases. Therapists, be they social workers, psychologists, or psychiatrists, must be aware of the special relationship of the group therapist to his child patients, and they should be circumspect in their dealings with parents so as not to vitiate this special relationship.

OUTLINE FOR INTEGRATION CONFERENCES

First Integration Conference

The first step at this conference is to evaluate the patient's

---

[1] If parents are not in regular treatment, individual or group, information on the child's adjustment at home, in school, and the community needs to be obtained from a parent by special appointment with a social worker or a trained paraprofessional.

264

progress and, in cooperative cases (individual and group treatment), for the group therapist to gain insight into the general problem. This does not necessarily include psychiatric material or psychiatric diagnosis; rather the home relationships and adjustment in school and out of school are important at this point.

Also, information about the factors in the patient's life that gave rise to his problems helps the group therapist understand the dynamics of the patient's behavior and treat it more intelligently. From this material he can also determine which members of the group are either helpful or detrimental.

The second step in the discussion should be a brief summary of the patient's relation to the caseworker and the plan of the casework treatment, if any. The group therapist describes the child's behavior and other observations that are important concerning his personality and reactions. His relations with specific children and the total group are outlined. The group therapist also describes his plan of treatment.

The third step is a brief discussion of this material.

Fourth, a plan for treatment is jointly formulated.

Subsequent Integration Conferences

The caseworker outlines any changes in the home or school situation that may have occurred since the preceding integration conference that may affect the child's behavior positively or negatively.

Steps two and three are the same as in the outline of the first integration conference.

Fourth step. An evaluation is made by the caseworker and group therapist of the child's progress in and outside of the group, in his casework relationship, and his total adjustment.

Fifth step. An estimate is made of the values of the group in the treatment process.

Sixth step. Recommendations for future plans for treatment or for discharge of the patient from the group are made.

CLOSING SUMMARY

When group treatment is terminated, a decision which is reached at an integration or a special conference called for this purpose, a closing summary report should be filed in which the patient is fully described in terms of the original presenting problem, the treatment goals as originally stated, and the outcomes. An outline for such a report follows.

Outline for a Closing Summary

Date	Group
Name of client	Total number of group sessions
Birth date	Number of sessions attended
Age at start of treatment	Number of individual interviews
Age at termination	

Nature of the Presenting Problem

Summarize briefly the problem when referred, giving a description of the patient's personality and character, the nature of his adjustment in the home, school, and community, idiosyncratic behavior, and diagnostic findings. Give the reasons briefly why the patient was referred for group treatment and the treatment goals.

Evaluation

Describe the progress of the patient during treatment, correlating it with his present behavior, the presenting problem, and the original goals of treatment.

FOLLOW-UP REPORTS

In cases of exclusively AGT treatment, a follow-up of the child's progress a year or so after discharge should be done by a social worker, preferably attached to the group therapy department. An outline for this study follows.

Outline for a Follow-up Study (Exclusive AGT)

Date of visit	Name of client
Follow-up caseworker	Group

1. A general picture of the adjustment of the child at home, with special reference to the original problem for which he was referred.

2. His activities in his community: whether he has friends, plays with children of his own age in a normal way, belongs to organized or other groups in his neighborhood, whether he attends a neighborhood center or is a member of groups of other agencies such as Boy or Girl Scouts.

3. Adjustment at school, with special reference to the problem as stated in the original referral.

4. An interview with the former patient so that the caseworker can form some judgement as to the client's personality as a whole.

5. An evaluation and recommendation as to further needs of treatment for the patient.

SUPERVISION

Regular weekly supervision conferences are held with group therapists to review and discuss the protocols of each session. Emphasis in supervision is on the following: (1) the pattern and meaning of each patient's conduct in the session as related to his nuclear problem, with possible suggestions evolving from discussion of corrective steps to be taken by the therapist, if any, to inhibit or promote a child's behavior and activities as therapeutically indicated; (2) discussion of the therapist's responses to patients' reactions and to the group as a whole (but no effort must be made to identify the therapist's psychological reactions and attitudes). The supervision should be carried on purely a pragmatic, behavioral level, not involving the therapist's own feelings. In some instances and in advanced stages of his experience, when he is secure in his performance, it would be helpful to make the therapist aware of the unconscious elements in his responses. However, the supervisor cannot assume a therapist's role toward his supervisees. Decisions should also emerge from a supervisory conference on correcting, modifying, enhancing, or diminishing elements of the setting, equipment, and materials for each specific group. Plans for modifications of activities such as trips and excursions to movies or the circus grow out of supervision conferences. It is advisable that some of the conference time be reserved for discussion of general subjects in psychology, pathology, sociology, and philosophy to widen the intellectual and emotional perspectives of both the therapist and supervisor. Informal discussions with groups of therapists as often as possible have in our practice proved immensely fruitful, particularly when the sessions were led by the same person supervising all the therapists involved. Refreshments served at such times have always been welcomed.

INTERDEPARTMENTAL LIAISON

In child guidance agencies offering comprehensive clinical and related services, it is imperative that efficient communication and liaison be maintained among members of different departments in the interests of the patients and their families and, in addition, to foster a sense of unitary, purposeful endeavor among the various disciplines.

GROUP THERAPY DEPARTMENT RECORDS

For effective adminstration and supervision in a group therapy department, it is important that information be readily available through well-organized records on patients who are being considered for treatment, on all active groups, on groups in formation, on administrative plans, for statistical data, and for other relevant matters.

The basic records for each therapy group consist of two bound folders (loose-leaf type to facilitate addition and removal of pages). The first folder contains all pertinent records of children in the group, and the second is a repository of protocols of every session of each group. The material in both folders should be arranged in logical, sequential order, with page-numbered cross references to facilitate examination and study by the director of the group therapy department, a supervisor, the therapist, a researcher, or any other member of the staff. In addition to these folders, standard clerical forms are useful for administration, supervision, and research.

XIV

An Illustrative Case

Date of referral: 12/3/44   Caseworker: Miss K.

Name of patient: Bernard T.   Father: Born, 1901

Address: Mother: Born, 1907

Birth date: 12/14/34   Siblings: Barbara, born, 12/38

IQ: 101

Grade in school: 4A

Problem and Personality

Bernard was referred by his mother after she heard a talk by a social worker at a meeting of the Parent-Teacher Association, of which she is a very active member. According to her, Bernard was very stubborn in school, in addition to many other difficulties, and his behavior was "very erratic; sometimes he is a devil, sometimes an angel." She insisted that the clinic make no contact with the school because of her status in the P.T.A. The boy was extremely stubborn at home also. The mother described him as being at times very affectionate, cooperative, and "sweet with his little sister," dressing her and, on occasion, taking her along to play in the street. At other times, he was extremely negativistic toward his mother, refusing to get up on time in the mornings, dawdling at meals, refusing to eat what she served, and resisting going to bed on time. He usually became overactive in the evenings, dancing around, shouting, and interfering with his little sister, carrying on incessantly until he is finally given a sound beating. He had recently developed a habit of not answering when spoken to and refusing to talk. Bernard had no friends. Though he was a member of a neighborhood center for a long time, he participated little and recently stopped going there altogether. He attends a parochial school regularly, however, and likes it.

Physical Description

Bernard is stocky, somewhat overweight, with a round, flat, bland, childish face. His eyelids are lowered most of the time, and often his head is averted. He moves and speaks exceedingly slowly, his voice is low, and he speaks with a peculiar singsong. His person is always very clean and neat. When in a friendly mood he at times talks animatedly. He is very handy with tools.

Family Background and Economic Status

The father is a plumber's helper earning a very modest salary. The mother is an apt housewife, managing the family's limited finances well. Both parents are foreigners and had their limited schooling before arriving in the United States. They overemphasize education, demanding very high standards from their children, and are deeply disappointed in Bernard because he prefers to read joke books to any others. The mother has just begun to read and write English with a view of obtaining citizenship. Both parents are active in clubs whose members came from their homeland. Both parents are simple though very alert people.

School Adjustment

Not much is known about this, because the mother did not permit a school visit. Bernard used to be an excellent pupil until recently when he had difficulties with a particular teacher. Because of unruly behavior toward this teacher, Bernard was recently transferred to a different class.

Adjustment to Other Children

Bernard gets along with other children but only on a superficial level. He conveys the feeling that he does not care for them, which is probably not true. Upon meeting a very aggressive child in the social worker's office, he was able to assert himself without becoming wild. He loves to work with tools, doing woodwork, carving, cutting out figures, etc.

Adjustment to Adults and Attitudes Toward Authority

Bernard is extremely stubborn and defiant, but conforms if limitations are not too great. He seems to become uncomfortable and withdraws if treated with friendliness. At the age of seven he was placed in a shelter for six weeks while his mother underwent an operation. There he became extremely negativistic and tried to run away.

Adjustment to Camp

Bernard attended summer camp the previous year. He was a good camper.

FIRST IMPRESSION REPORT[1]

Date: 1/5/45

Bernard's movements are very slow and lethargic, and he speaks with a singsong. When thwarted in any way, he tends to whine and make facial grimaces. He is well dressed, rather clean and neat in appearance.

Bernard attended all group sessions covered by this report, and was always on time. During his first session (the sixth of the group), Bernard immediately proceeded to make a wooden bench. He seemed insecure and afraid to contact the other boys. He smiled in greeting the therapist, whom he had known from camp. Bernard's appearance at his first meeting caused Herbert to become restless. After kidding around with the other boys, Herbert took to teasing Bernard, instigating two other boys to join him. At one point, Herbert took Bernard's cap and was pursued by the latter, who became angry and started to push Herbert. Herbert pushed him back. Incited by Bert, Herbert asked Bernard whether he wanted to "fight it out" with him. Bernard responded whiningly, "Leave me alone." When Harold took a piece of wood which belonged to Bernard, the latter almost forced Harold to

---

[1]By group therapist, after fourth session.

give in to him, but Bert intervened. The boys continued to tease Bernard until he picked up his jacket and ran out of the room.

Herbert and Harold grew guilty over what they had done and followed Bernard trying to get him to return to the room. Bernard adamantly refused to return, and the two boys stayed with him outside the room, missing the refreshments. This was surprising about Herbert, who was always extremely anxious about food. Harold returned to the room, taking a piece of cake to give to Bernard. The three boys made up with Bernard, and all returned to the room. The therapist noticed that on the way home, Bernard accompanied Harold to the trolley car, the boys being in a jolly and playful mood. During the subsequent sessions, Bernard continued to work undisturbed on his bench.

Bernard quickly attached himself to the therapist. He came over to the therapist a number of times during each session asking for approval of his work. He seems anxious for reassurance and recognition from the therapist. In his work, Bernard is moderately dependent upon the therapist, and when the therapist is unable to respond immediately to Bernard's request for help, he registers disappointment by facial grimace. After asking the worker's permission, Bernard once took a model airplane and some wood home. During the subsequent session, apparently secure of the therapist's acceptance of him, the boy made attempts at talking to the other boys, although still spending most of his time working alone in a corner.

Bernard noticed a linoleum block cutout on which Bert was working, and proceeded to do the same. He is proficient in working with tools, and Charles, the strongest boy in the group, copied the wooden bench Bernard was making. This served to give Bernard a boost. Bernard never helped in cleaning up the room or in preparing refreshments, except once when he dried the cups at Bert's suggestion that it was his turn "to clean up today." His table manners are good; he eats very slowly.

Bernard brought a friend with him to his third session. This boy seemed younger than he and gave the impression of being dominated by Bernard. He had little initiative, working continuously with Bernard on his project. Bernard seemed very pleased when, in the presence of his friend, the therapist gave him the nails he had requested at a previous session. Bernard was the first to arrive for his next session. He now seemed more secure, participating in the group discussion as to how to divide the food. He also "kidded" around a bit with some of the others. At the end of the session, following Donald's example, Bernard returned, after leaving the room, to wish the therapist a Merry Christmas.

Bernard is one of the weakest boys in the group, with a great deal of insecurity in relation to other children. He requires support from the therapist, which should make it possible for him to become more assertive. The group may also help him give up some of his infantile behavior and modify his somewhat effeminate mannerisms.

INTEGRATION CONFERENCE

Date: 3/1/45

Present: Caseworker (who continued to see Bernard and his mother); group therapist; director of group therapy department.

Bernard was referred to the agency because he was negativistic to his mother, stubborn, at times affectionate and rarely cooperative. According to Mrs. T., Bernard's erratic behavior began when his younger sister was born.

The caseworker considers the mother to be seductive, and Bernard is responding to this seduction. Mrs. T. comes for treatment often and on one occasion told the caseworker that she is frustrated by her husband. She also complained that even Bernard has not satisfied her the way she would like him to. Her complaint was that instead of going to bed at night he undresses, wears only his pajama top, and jumps up and down on his bed. At night he pretends to go to the bathroom, but instead wakes his sister up, climbs into her bed, and tickles her. Bernard has been sleeping in the living room, which is separated from the parental bedroom by an archway. Bernard would usually attempt to go into his mother's bed, but when she rejected him he went to his sister's bed instead. Lately Mrs. T. informed the caseworker that their roomer had moved out of the house and Bernard now has his own bedroom. His sister sleeps in the living room. The mother also stated she has more privacy now with her husband and feels much closer to him.

The caseworker stated Bernard acted negativistically toward her therapy. She felt that there is a general slowness about Bernard's whole personality and described him as "heavy, having a sleepy way, and speaking very slowly." Sometimes Bernard may not speak for a half hour, and then suddenly he will speak easily and fluently.

Since he began treatment in the agency, Bernard attends the neighborhood center. When he originally went there, he "made himself so unlovable" no one could stand him. The therapist was informed about two weeks ago that there had been a considerable change in his behavior. He had become cooperative and works on projects there which he completes.

Mr. T. informed the caseworker that Bernard began to use obscene language after he started attending the therapy group and claimed he learned to speak that way in the group.[2] She has dissuaded Bernard from attending the therapy group sessions and also informed the caseworker that Bernard does not care to continue to see her. She suggested that the caseworker write to him asking him to come. However, Bernard has not done so. Mrs. T. spoke about sending Bernard to camp the following summer, and the caseworker informed her the "club department" would take care of it, if *Bernard* wanted to attend camp.

The caseworker felt there was no evident improvement in Bernard, but that the mother has shown definite improvement. The worker had given information about birth control methods to Mrs. T., something she had not known. She also impressed Mrs. T. that she has to do something for her own health. She was now being treated medically.

The group therapist reported Bernard attended nine out of thirteen sessions. He described Bernard as a chubby, childlike boy. Bernard's relationship to the therapist was that of a dependent, immature boy who whined and made facial grimaces if he did not get what he wanted. His movements were slow, and the boys in the group immediately sensed his weakness and attempted to provoke him. Bernard sought the therapist's protection in this regard and once, when the boys became too aggressive, ran out of the room.

Recently Bernard has begun to assert himself more with the boys, and helps to prepare refreshments. However, if he is attacked by a stronger boy, he still whines. He is becoming more independent in his work and is visibly less dependent on the

---

[2] This is incorrect, as the boys of this group rarely used obscene language.

therapist. He brought a friend to one session. Bernard had his friend constantly under his command.

Bernard is handy with tools and made a small bench. He is now working on a lamp. Bernard has good table manners and eats slowly.

The group went on an excursion recently. It was severely cold, the coldest day of the winter, and Bernard was the only boy to attend. In the museum he approached a number of strange boys and spoke to them freely. Worker feels that Bernard is now more assertive and better able to withstand aggression. He is still teased by the other boys when he whines, but this has decreased. While he was lethargic at the beginning, he now shows enthusiasm with regard to group activities.

Recommendations

1. Continue in activity group therapy.
2. Because of his resistance to individual treatment, the case is being transferred to exclusive group therapy.

FOLLOW-UP INTERVIEW

By caseworker attached to the group department.
Date: 5/15/45

Mrs. T. gives the impression of being a rather assertive and driving person, with high standards for her children. She seems to have a lot of warmth for Bernard and has probably infantilized him. However, she is unable to cope with the boy when he is defiant. She spoke of the younger girl as being "wonderful." If she shows any misconduct, Mrs. T. felt that this was due to her imitating Bernard.

Bernard has no friends except the thin youngster whom he brought to the group sessions. This boy is in the habit of stealing, and he once took twenty-five cents from the T. home. Against his mother's advice, Bernard openly accused the boy of having taken the money. Mrs. T. said that Bernard is this way with everyone, insisting on telling the truth, and she felt this may be responsible for his difficulty in keeping friends.

Bernard feels very close to his father and likes to spend time with him. They do Bernard's school homework together and various plumbing jobs. On the other hand, it is of interest to note

275

that Mrs. T. still ties Bernard's shoelaces, an example of her infantilization of the boy, since she admitted he knew how to do it himself. However, she does not refuse him when he asks her to do it. She merely teases him that he will never be able to get married if he does not know how to tie his own shoelaces.

Bernard is now doing excellent work in school, and the teachers have called him "Einstein." However, he got into some difficulty because of his behavior toward his present teacher. Bernard likes his group a great deal and speaks about it at home. He is particularly interested in woodwork. Mrs. T. said Bernard likes the "leader" a lot and still cannot forget the fact that on one occasion when none of the other boys came for a trip, he went alone with Bernard to the museum. Mrs. T. complained about "bad" words which Bernard had picked up in the "club." On one occasion he had told his mother, "Fuck yourself," saying that he had picked this up from the other boys in the group. When the question of camp was raised, Mrs. T. said that she was going to the country this summer, since she needed to convalesce following her operation. She would take Bernard with her, and he would be able to enjoy himself with his father.

PROGRESS REPORT

Date: 6/25/45

Attendance

Bernard attended twelve of the nineteen sessions covered by this report. He missed three sessions consecutively because his mother refused to permit him to attend after he came home and said that he had learned some "dirty words" in the group. He began to attend again, however. Bernard is among the boys who usually arrive early at the sessions.

Attitudes

Cooperation. There were only a few occasions when Bernard helped the therapist clean up the room. He seemed to enjoy preparing refreshments occasionally, especially when he and another boy went out to buy the food. Bernard was not active in group discussions at first but recently became more assertive and participates fully.

Materials. Bernard was at first insecure and worked on objects without finishing them. Recently he has shown marked proficiency and perseverance. Bernard is excessively concerned with having his work perfect and, when making a lamp, called upon the therapist rather frequently to help him. More recently, the boy has begun to work on a table, and has shown excellent skill in this. Bernard is still in need of reassurance by the therapist, asking him to measure off pieces of wood for him, to examine the filing, etc. In general, Bernard's current attitude is characterized by a newly gained purposefulness and proficiency.

New Group Members. Bernard showed no particular reaction to the addition of new members. In general, he was rather friendly and accepting of them.

Probably in order to gain security in the group, Bernard brought a friend, a thin, sickly looking youngster, with him for five sessions (not in succession). This boy was at first markedly submissive to Bernard, who used to order him around and make him do things for him.

Fellow Members. In the past, Bernard was fearful of making contact with other boys. This has changed markedly, and he is now moving freely about the room, making contact with all the others. He continues to be somewhat insecure, however, whining and making facial grimaces when thwarted by someone. On occasion he has been found to be quite assertive with other boys, insisting that he would go out and get the refreshments only if he felt like doing it. When convinced that what they ask of him is unfair, Bernard becomes stubborn and will not submit even when threatened. The boys have become aware of the change in Bernard and, while in the past they constantly used to provoke him and take advantage of his weakness, this has now greatly lessened. Bernard is still not able to fight back physically, and when attacked will complain and sulk or threaten to go home but never carries it out. Bernard has participated in "horseplay" with the other boys. He has also repeatedly approached them during the sessions, stating he would like them to go home using the same subway as he.

Group Therapist. At first Bernard related to the therapist on a dependent, infantile level. He no longer whines or makes facial grimaces as frequently as he used to. He is rather attached to the therapist, admires whatever he is doing, likes to walk near him on the street, and also sits next to him at the refreshment table, which at times gets him into conflict with other boys who compete for that location.

Evaluation

Starting out as an infantile, weak, and fearful youngster, Bernard has shown marked improvement since the first impression report.

GROUP THERAPY TREATMENT CONFERENCE

On the basis of preceding information.
Date: 6/29/45
Present: Group therapist; director of group therapy department.

Mrs. T. was seen by a caseworker on May 15, 1945 (see follow-up interview). She reported that Bernard had shown a great deal of improvement during the past half year. She still ties the boy's shoelaces, not because he does not know how to do it himself but because he insists that she do it for him. She does not want to refuse him, but she teases him about it. The director raised the question whether his mother wants Bernard to remain the way he is — an infantile and dependent child. Bernard's general lethargy and slowness of movement and his tendency in the past to half shut his eyes and avert his head when talking to people have to be watched. It was decided that the boy's progress at the neighborhood center should be investigated to determine whether there has really been any change since the last report was received from them.

Recommendations

1. Follow up Bernard's progress at the center.
2. Arrange a psychiatric consultation for February.
3. Since this has been an exclusive group treatment case, contact is to be maintained with the mother about once a month.

MEMORANDUM RE BERNARD T.

From group therapist.
Date: 10/31/45

Bernard has achieved further group status. He seems to be reaching out for more friendly relations with the boys in the group, and this seems to have come about as a result of his favorable experiences in such activities as boxing and woodwork. He has also reacted quite favorably to encouragement and approval from the group therapist.

FOLLOW-UP INTERVIEW

Interview with the mother.
Date: 11/13/45

Bernard has shown marked improvement at home in most areas during the past year. He is now cooperative most of the time. However, he continues to dawdle in the morning before going to school. He is so slow that the mother finds it necessary to help him get dressed. A few weeks ago, there was some improvement in this respect as well, since Bernard began working as an errand boy for a butcher in the neighborhood. This man has become very fond of Bernard, and the boy likes to work for him.

The boy's dawdling and her need to get him dressed in the morning were discussed with Mrs. T. She said that she felt "nervous" when she saw that it was getting so late. Last year he refused to attend the parochial school, and she could not change his attitude. Now he not only attends the school but also does excellent work there. She spoke of this progress. Bernard is doing better than average work in public school as well, but nevertheless she is disappointed, since her daughter has already expressed the idea that she wants to be a doctor, while Bernard seems to have developed no special interest yet.

SUMMARY FOR PSYCHIATRIC CONFERENCE

From: Caseworker attached to the group therapy department.
To: Dr. N.   Re: Bernard T.
Date: 3/4/46   Born: 12/14/34

This conference was requested following a decision at the last group therapy treatment conference of 6/29/45. Psychiatric clarification is needed in evaluating the diagnosis in this case and the effect of group treatment upon Bernard. Dr. E. originally diagnosed him as a case of "primary behavior disorder" of the oedipal type in February 1944. A Rorschach test, administered in May 1944, indicated "infantilism, negativism and a tendency toward emotional overexcitability" in this patient. In general, it was felt

279

that the boy had a neurotic personality structure with obsessional and hysterical components. The caseworker who was seeing him in individual treatment at that time arranged for Bernard to be seen by the psychiatrist in March 1944, but Bernard refused to talk or give any information to the psychiatrist. About one year after initial referral to the agency, the boy was placed in activity group therapy in addition to casework treatment.

As she continued work with the boy and his mother, the caseworker felt we were dealing with an oedipal situation. She felt Mrs. T. was seducing Bernard and her attitudes toward him were characterized by unconscious incestuous wishes.[3] The boy was reacting to this by trying to provoke punishment through his stubbornness and defiant behavior. It was also thought that the boy's play with his little sister was on a sexual level. His jumping and getting excited at night (which Bernard also acted out twice in the casework situation) seemed an unconscious acting out of coitus.

Following an integration conference held in March 1945, the case was transferred to exclusive activity group therapy because of Bernard's refusal to see the caseworker and the mother's complete withdrawal from individual treatment. A subsequent report from the neighborhood center where Bernard was still attending (as of October 1945) speaks of marked improvement in the boy. Unlike in the past, he has achieved group status and was now reaching out for friendships with other boys. He got recognition for accomplishments in woodwork and boxing. Bernard also was described as responding favorably to encouragement from adults.

His relationship with the group therapist continues to be a close one, but he is much less dependent than when he first came to the group. In the past the group therapist would have to do most of Bernard's work, while now it is sufficient to start some of the boy's projects and he finishes them on his own. Recently another trend was also observable, namely, a tendency of the boy to try to dominate the therapist and supplant him in the group.

---

[3] The mother once told Bernard that if "he ever did something bad" (apparently referring to masturbation or sex play), his penis would not grow.

PSYCHIATRIC CONFERENCE

Date: 3/6/46

Present: Dr. N., psychiatrist; director of the group therapy department; and caseworker attached to the group therapy department.

In regard to the original caseworker's assumption that Bernard's jumping up and down in bed, which was so disturbing to the mother, stood symbolically for coitus, the psychiatrist felt that this needed further confirmation. The same movements could be explained in terms of masturbatory activity.

It was felt that the problem was that of a passive, submissive, effeminate youngster with difficulties in communicating to outsiders when he was referred to the agency.

In view of the lack of Bernard's fantasy material, the psychiatrist felt that it would be difficult to determine the exact dynamics operating here. It was felt further that most of the difficulties Bernard presented seem to be of a neurotic nature, and that all of them appeared after the age of five. It is of interest, however, that no reactivation of these occurred at this time, when he is beginning to enter puberty.

Dr. N. felt that the birth of Bernard's sister, as well as his temporary placement away from home at about that time, may have been strong traumata which caused the boy to regress to an infantile level. At that time, he already had gone through the oedipal stage, and thus his regression was more a defense against growing up than a fixation on a primary infantile level. This may be the reason why Bernard improved as a result of activity group therapy, since he was able to work out his sibling relationship with the other boys and give up his defense against growing up.

There is also a possibility that his improvement is related to a homosexual submission to the group therapist. This would be indicative of strong pathology in the youngster (a position with which we strongly disagreed). This turn of events is improbable, however, since Bernard has not been revealing anxiety in the group. It was felt, however, that Bernard may be dealing with his anxiety by assuming a passive and "freezing up" kind of personality adjustment. In view of this, it was felt that his development should be watched closely for any further pathology.

Recommendations

Arrange for a complete physical checkup including a glandular examination.

FOLLOW-UP INTERVIEW

With Bernard's mother by the caseworker.

Date: 4/1/46

Mrs. T. reported there has been no change in Bernard's behavior since the last interview. He was still slow in getting places and was dawdling in the morning before school. She tries to "talk and talk," but this has no effect. Mrs. T. complained about her husband being too strict with the children. He seems to be a rigid person who constantly drives Bernard toward intellectual achievements, asking him to read books, etc. He has a quick temper and often hits Bernard as well as the younger girl. Mrs. T. wanted to know whether it wouldn't be possible to arrange an interview with her husband and discuss his handling of the children with him.

According to the mother, Bernard is now spending most of his free time out of the house, in contrast to his earlier tendency to stay at home. He plays with boys on the street and one weekend went on a hike to New Jersey with four friends. The father, who has extremely high educational standards for his children, insists that Bernard go to the parochial school. It was agreed that the caseworker would make a home visit to talk to Mr. T. about Bernard.

HOME FOLLOW-UP INTERVIEW

With client's father.

One is struck by the strong resemblances between Mr. T. and Bernard. He gives the impression of an immature, nonaggressive person capable of occasional strong and violent temper. He complained mostly about the boy's lack of enthusiasm and slowness, particularly in the morning before he goes to school. He admitted, however, that Bernard has improved since his original referral to the agency. He said that he used to hit, nag Bernard, and exert pressure on him, but now leaves him alone, realizing that he would achieve more this way. Mrs. T., who had been coming in and out of the room while the therapist was speaking with the father, interrupted here, saying that her husband still exerted too much pressure on Bernard, hitting him at times. Her attitude toward the boy seemed to be a definitely warmer one than that of her husband. Mr. T. defended himself, saying he always tells his wife to leave Bernard alone in the morning and not to nag. If he comes late to school, he would have to take the consequences. Mrs. T. said she had started this procedure this week and she hoped it would work.

In general, Mr. T.'s attitude toward the agency was a submissive one. He seemed very thankful for our interest and openly expressed his feeling of respect to us because "we know psychology." Both parents spoke about how much the group experience meant to Bernard. He would never miss a meeting, and he spoke of the therapist as "the one real friend he has."

The question was raised of a medical examination and an examination of glandular balance, as recommended by the psychiatrist during the last psychiatric conference.

PROGRESS REPORT

Date: 6/4/46

Out of a total of thirty group sessions held this year, Bernard attended twenty-two. Four absences early in the group season were due to a conflict with his parochial school, which was later straightened out. Since the group moved to a new room, and since Bernard lived nearby, he has always been the first to arrive.

Bernard shows more interest in food than was indicated in the first progress report. It seems that when he first came to the group he was too frightened and insecure to express his real interest in food. At present he asks at every session about the kind of refreshments the therapist has brought. He not only always finishes his portion but usually joins the other boys in asking for seconds. In contrast to his behavior the previous year, when he would sometimes join Leonard in preparing the refreshments, Bernard now works with tools and materials right up to refreshment time.

As Bernard became more accepted by the group, his cooperativeness increased. Toward the end of a session, when the therapist would occasionally clean up the room before Bernard was finished with his project, he would ask the therapist not to sweep where he was working. When finished with his project, he would clean up himself. On one occasion when the therapist accidentally spilled some paint, Bernard, on his own initiative, helped clean up. He eagerly helped other boys with their work and also offered to fix tools for them. Bernard participates freely in group discussions and often has been influential in affecting group decisions.

Bernard's proficiency in the use of tools and materials has impressively increased since the last progress report to the point where he now is the best craftsman in the group. His earlier infantile dependency upon the therapist, where he sought advice for every step in his work, has changed to a more independent attitude. He now calls on the therapist only when it is really necessary. Bernard has been receiving a great deal of recognition from the other boys because of the attractive and complicated projects he creates.

Bernard stopped bringing his friend to sessions this year. This is probably because he now has gained sufficient security in the group and no longer needs the support of a friend. One of the most significant changes in Bernard's adjustment occurred in the area of his relationships with the other boys. From being a frightened, weak, and infantile youngster, who would complain, sulk, and threaten to run away when teased, he now has become freer and more assertive. He stands up with determination when provoked and on one occasion had a physical fight with Leonard. In the group, Bernard is closest to Herbert (who serves as a "supportive ego"). The two boys live near each other and apparently spend some time together. Herbert has been observed to imitate Bernard's work, and as mentioned previously, Bernard's attitude toward the therapist is freer and less dependent. On occasion he displayed a desire to displace the therapist (father): he would make such remarks as "You see, I'm here before you" and repeatedly asked to unlock doors and cabinets. Other times there were indications of wanting to be the "only child." When alone with the therapist, he would talk against the other boys, saying, "Don't give them paper, they always take it anyway." He would also tease the other boys about the good time that he once had when alone on a trip with the therapist. In general, it is the group therapist's impression that Bernard is now able to give up much of his infantile mannerisms. As he gained security and acceptance, he became more assertive and less fearful.

1946 Summer Camp Report

Bernard is a pleasant youngster who was well liked by both the counselor and his bunkmates. He got along well with the boys and made new friends. When he got sick and was in the infirmary, the boys felt sorry and missed him. He improved a lot, was in all activities and most cooperative. He was not excessively aggressive.

There was nothing very outstanding to report on Bernard. He presented no difficulties at camp.

Follow-up Interview

Date: 10/25/46

According to the mother, Bernard continues to be cooperative most of the time aside from the tendency still to dawdle in the morning, which she now recognizes to be directed only against her. Fighting with the younger sister has completely subsided, and Bernard gets along very well with outsiders. All people make it a point to tell the mother how well he behaves and how intelligent he is. The excellent adjustment at school continues; Bernard is doing above average work. He also does very well in his parochial.school. In response to a question, she said that Bernard does not stay at home as much as he used to and goes out to play. However, he has no friends, and the mother explains this in terms of the fact that there are mostly aggressive youngsters in the new neighborhood.

Progress Report

This is essentially a new activity group with a different therapist. Date: 1/23/47

Out of a total of twelve sessions to date Bernard has attended eight. Most of these absences were again due to conflict with parochial school and other activities which his mother forced him to attend. In the group, Bernard shows less interest in food than indicated in last year's progress report and has never asked about refreshments.

In general, there have been modifications in Bernard's behavior and attitudes toward the group from those described in the previous progress reports. This is undoubtedly due to the fact that the present group and the therapist are new. Herbert is the only other member of the former group in it. Although Bernard has worked on projects and participated in group activities, he sometimes walks around the room in a dreamy state and talks to the group members with aloofness, never greeting anyone on entering the room. However, on leaving, he always asks someone to accompany him. He is not as cooperative in showing other boys how to handle materials as he was, nor does he participate much in group discussions, but he has talked to others about camp experiences. On a few occasions, he joined in dueling, and during one session, he and Harvey playfully tossed plasticine pellets at each other. On one occasion he expressed overt aggressiveness against Harvey, whom he chased around the room and pushed when he caught him. It is this therapist's impression that Bernard has not yet accepted his new group mates.

He works well with materials and made some very nice linoleum cuts, a leather shopping bag, and a clay mask. He is a perfectionist in his work, but tends to minimize his abilities. It has been difficult for him to accept the change in "leaders," and he still feels the loss of his former therapist. He has kept away from the new therapist, except occasionally to ask for materials. Once he threw a piece of clay as the latter played checkers with another boy. The pellet dropped near the therapist, and Bernard apologized, saying somewhat tensely, "Excuse me."

It is the therapist's feeling that Bernard has shown some degree of regressive behavior because of the changed group. However, he continues to maintain positive gains in terms of no longer being fearful and acting more assertively. There have been no attempts by him to ingratiate himself with the therapist or the other boys. His extreme dependence of two years ago is absent, and the effeminate mannerisms have not been observed. He may solidify and extend his gains by further group attendance.[4]

FOLLOW-UP INTERVIEW

Date: 2/27/47

Mrs. T. stated that Bernard has been quite upset during the last few weeks, since he has been transferred to a junior high

---

[4] Whenever possible we transfer a child to a second group to wean him from the first, both as an exposure to an extended adjustment experience and for observing his adaptive capacities to a new situation. When no other suitable group is available, we add new members or "shuffle" the membership of two groups of the same age.

school which is attended by a majority of black children. Bernard has been repeatedly beaten up by aggressive boys, and some went so far as to stick him with a nail. Mrs. T. had been to see the district superintendent, but the interview was not satisfactory, since the superintendent stated that there was nothing she could do about it. In talking about Bernard's adjustment at home, Mrs. T. felt that he was now more mature and more outgoing. The only complaint she had was that he still tended to be slow in the mornings. She said that Bernard now had close friends and goes out to play every afternoon.

In regard to Bernard's failure to attend the group sessions, he complained that the boys in the "club" were "too rough." However, he told her that he would go occasionally. It was agreed with the mother that the group therapy caseworker would arrange to see Bernard and talk to him about his "club attendance" if he should not come to the next session of the group.

MEMORANDUM RE BERNARD T.

Date: 3/5/47

Bernard was assigned to a school far away from his home, which involved two transportation changes. The mother telephoned the superintendent, stating that Bernard refused to go that far to school, and the superintendent promised to try to place him in a school nearer his home.

FOLLOW-UP INTERVIEW

With the group therapy department caseworker.
Date: 3/13/47

Bernard told the caseworker about his recent difficulties at school with black boys who picked on him. He does not dare to fight back because they have knives and are also members of gangs. They seem to pick on him more than on others because they know he will not fight back. With regard to home, Bernard said that "things were satisfactory." He expressed some slight resentment of the mother's "babying" him and gave as an example the fact that his mother does not let him go to bed later, insisting that he do so every evening at nine o'clock. He admitted that his mother has to wake him up in the morning but he was emphatic in stating this was not always the case.

He did not feel he was as slow in getting ready in the morning as he used to be; he was getting along quite well with his sister. They fool around on weekends having pillow fights, which Bernard enjoys. Despite the difficulties he has been having in school, Bernard attends regularly. He likes junior high school and the departmental system and is doing well. He did not have much trouble with children in his own class and related an incident where he was able to fight a boy, and as a result, this boy no longer bothered him. Bernard stated that he has a number of friends with whom he goes bike riding or on picnics.

In talking about the "club," Bernard at first complained it is not the same as it used to be since there are not enough tools, there is no jigsaw, and the trips are less frequent, but he admitted his failure to attend was related to the fact that there were "rough kids" in the new group. He talked about his feelings regarding other children at length when he stated there was only one boy in the group who was stronger than himself. He then said that, once the boys learned he is strong and willing to fight, they would not bother him. It was agreed that Bernard would try to attend the group as often as possible, although he could not do it every week because he now also had music lessons every Friday (when the group met), in which he was very much interested.

Group Therapy Department Treatment Conference

Date: 4/9/47

Present: Group therapist; director of group therapy; department caseworker.

Caseworker reported on the school difficulties. It was felt that Bernard's failure to attend his group sessions was related to a large extent to these upsetting experiences at school.

The group therapist reported some regression in Bernard's behavior since he took over the group. This was related to the change of therapists and Bernard's early strong transference to his previous group therapist.

Recommendations

1. Continue in activity group therapy.
2. Encourage Bernard to attend the sessions more frequently.

Interview with mother.

Date: 4/15/47

Mrs. T. stated in response to a question that the school difficulties have been settled. She went into great detail to explain how upset she had been over this issue. She called some of the school and district administrators "Nazis" because of the difficulties they had caused her. Since the incident where Bernard was beaten up by boys in school, he has manifested some concern with physical complaints and became extremely concerned about possible injuries.

The question of an endocrinological examination was again raised, and she promised to take him to the Endocrine Clinic because of his overweight. (This she has never done during the entire course of therapy).

Bernard was getting along well with his sister. There was no longer the symptom of jumping up and down in bed with her, getting excited in the evening, etc.

By therapist.

Date: 5/21/47

Until the last session, which took place on May 16, Bernard continued to maintain a distance between himself and the therapist. At this session he asked the latter to play ping-pong with him. Being an excellent player, he enjoyed the game very much. He wanted the therapist to strike the ball harder, and at no time did he try to win. He does not seem to have a competitive spirit, but enjoys the game for its own sake. He tried to prolong the game and attempted to talk other boys out of playing with the therapist, so he could continue. In general Bernard is now a more mature youngster. He now seems acclimatized in the new group and with the new therapist. He offered to help the therapist in setting up the refreshment table. It is the therapist's general impression that he has shown considerable growth in the past four months. No effeminate mannerisms or interests have been noted.

Because of Bernard's improvement and diminishing attendance in his group, it was decided at an integration conference on June 27, 1947 to transfer him to another group to ascertain whether his improvements were mere accommodations to situations or are permanent personality changes operative under new and different circumstances. Bernard has had a fairly difficult emotional accommodation in his new group members, his new group worker, and a really threatening school situation. While he has not emerged from it with flying colors, he has made an acceptable adjustment in view of his basic temperamental constitution, which he either inherited from his father or adopted by identification.

We shall, therefore, summarize the subsequent reports and conferences for this patient:

Progress reports on him before closing the case were received on 2/3/48, 6/4/48.

Follow-ups were made on 3/30/48, 6/7/48, 6/22/48, 4/4/49.

Conferences had been held on 6/15/48; memos received on 7/15/48 and 1/5/49.

PROGRESS REPORT

By 12/3/48, Bernard had attended fifteen out of sixteen sessions. One absence was due to an overnight hike on a school holiday. There has been a marked change in Bernard in all areas: work, relationship with the boys and therapist, whom he greets warmly and invites to play games, as well as sports, and in his self-image. He considers himself a champion in ping-pong. He has much more confidence in himself and no longer complains or whines; is more outgoing, and a feeling of warmth emanates from him. All infantile mannerisms disappeared.

In the 6/22/48 follow-up report with Mrs. T., she stated that Bernard had improved in most areas: extremely well at school; dawdling, negativism, etc., disappeared. He now stands up for himself and cooperates on household chores and helps his father as secretary of a lodge. He no longer jumps up and down on the bed, and the sibling rivalry with the sister has disappeared. He has no interest in sex and in girls and often claims that he will never get married (repression). The father thinks that Bernard is O.K., that he will grow out of the minor difficulties he now has, but she, who had strenuously opposed treatment, insists he needs therapy.

In the same follow-up, the caseworker saw Bernard and found the boy had grown. He had lost weight, though he still gives the impression of chubbiness and a certain quality of passivity. There was no anxiety, and he related well. He is an honor student and would like to be an accountant, being good in mathematics. When he volunteered that he knew boys picked on others who cannot defend themselves, the caseworker suggested seeing an individual therapist, but he could not see how anyone could help him with such a problem by mere talking. What he needed, he said, was boxing lessons (in which he had made considerable progress in the groups). Bernard here brought out some feeling of being afraid of hurting others and also of being hurt.

As to individual treatment, Bernard finally agreed he would like to try it out in the fall. It did not make any difference to him whether he had a man or a woman caseworker. He remembered how he used to see Mrs. K. in the beginning and how he withdrew from treatment, but now he was more "grown" and thought he could accept individual treatment on a different basis. In response to the worker's question as to whether he was interested in girls, Bernard stated that he was not. Then the question of the "club" was raised.

Bernard became anxious, and when it was indicated to him that there might not be a "club" for boys next season, he picked this up to say that in his "club" now there were boys older than he. Couldn't he be in a club, although he would be somewhat older than other children? The caseworker stated that he would try to find out and if there was a suitable "club" next season, he, of course, would hear from the office.

It was felt that since the group meant so much to Bernard it would be desirable that he be permitted to continue in group treatment for one more year. This might also be desirable in view of the fact that Bernard might be receiving individual treatment in the fall and the group might serve as a setting for reality testing in regard to his fears about fighting back when attacked. As a timid person, being the oldest and largest boy, he would acquire inner strength in relationships which he might carry over to other relationships.

In the progress report of 6/4/48, it was stated that Bernard attended thirteen out of nineteen sessions. The reason for the absences is not known, but they are understandable in view of the boy's age and outside interests. He was the most active member of the group when a new boy was added; he helped orient him to the new situation, taught him ping-pong, and encouraged him to take part in the group's activities. He was preoccupied with ping-pong and became the best player. The changes in bearing, outgoingness, impressive self-confidence continued, and his relation with the therapist continued to be warm and friendly.

A treatment conference was held again on 6/15/48, at which were present the second group therapist, the group therapy department caseworker, and the director of group therapy. The mother could not be seen during the preceding period because of illness, being "in and out of the hospital." It was felt that while Bernard had made great strides in improving his behavior and reactions to people, his nuclear problem of diffidence and the remnants of feminine identification (due to a dominating mother and a preferred sister in the past) ought to be worked through in individual treatment. The caseworker was to see the boy with this in mind again and evaluate his readiness to become a member of a neighborhood group.

On 2/15/48, a memorandum was sent to the intake worker for assignment of this boy to individual treatment. In a discussion of this case on 1/5/49 with the intake worker, the group therapy caseworker learned Bernard would require a very experienced male caseworker, and since one is not available at this time, it was decided to continue Bernard in exclusive AGT.

MEMORANDUM RE BERNARD T.

A follow-up interview was held on 4/4/49 by the new caseworker of the group therapy department. Mrs. T. was distressed by the change of caseworkers and wondered if the new man knew "Bernie." She repeated with a proud mien that Bernie had "really changed a good deal over the years." He still helps his father with the books from the lodge, and he is able to do very complicated bookkeeping. He has a lot of friends, does good schoolwork, and helps her when she asks him. He doesn't "go with girls," and she thinks that he is at an age when he should be interested in girls.

In the main, Mrs. T.'s anxiety about her son seems to have been removed. She considered him "still immature" in many respects.

From the record, it can be postulated that Bernard has been helped to mature to a great extent, but it is quite possible that we shall never be able to alter his temperamental character structure, try as we may.

TREATMENT CONFERENCE

Date: 5/26/49
Present: Group therapist; new caseworker of the group therapy department; and director of group therapy.

The director agreed that this boy was very much improved. However, he suggested another Rorschach. The reason for this is that this boy came to us emotionally very sick. He was obsessional and hysterical. The purpose of the Rorschach would be to evaluate progress and to determine what degree of residue there was.

CLOSING STATEMENT 8/22/49

Bernard, who is now almost fifteen years old, was referred in 1944 by his mother, who complained that he was not working up to capacity in school; his behavior was erratic; "sometimes he was a devil, sometimes an angel." At home and at school he was extremely stubborn, though at times he could also be affectionate and cooperative. Other times he became extremely negativistic, especially toward his mother. He would not get up in the morning, would dawdle at meals, refused to eat what she put in front of him, and would not go to bed on time. He was overactive in the evenings, danced around and shouted, did not let his little sister go to sleep, and carried on until he was given a sound beating.

Following one year of individual treatment, which failed because of continuing resistance, Bernard was referred for exclusive activity group therapy. In the early sessions of the group Bernard was found to be a slow, lethargic boy, infantile and very dependent. There was a good deal of whining and fear of physical contact with other children. In time Bernard gained increasing ego strength and developed more mature behavior patterns. His whining stopped; he grew independent of the therapist and began to relate to other children. At the same time the mother, who had refused guidance or therapy for herself, reported a great deal of improvement in the home. There were fewer temper tantrums, and he shared more of the household activities. At school his work improved greatly; he made the honor roll and was in the top third of his class.

At an integration conference, it was found that Bernard had made great strides through activity group therapy. A Rorschach was suggested to check improvement and to see whether there was any neurotic residue. Bernard was seen subsequently during the 1949 season by the group therapy department caseworker, and Bernard's improvement was confirmed. Since Bernard was reluctant to take the Rorschach examination and the psychology department had a tight schedule, it was felt that this could be waived.

In view of Bernard's impressive improvement at home, at school, and in the neighborhood, we are closing this case in group therapy and in the agency.

PART II

ACTIVITY-INTERVIEW
GROUP PSYCHOTHERAPY

XV

Activity-Interview
Group Psychotherapy

Basic Assumptions of A-IGP

As we proceeded with our work in AGT, it became clear that some latency children referred to groups were too seriously disturbed to be accessible by an ego type of treatment, either because of overintense fears and anxieties or because their uncontrolled hyperactivity and aggressions would prevent the therapeutic climate essential for AGT. Most of these children were found unresponsive to individual therapy but required, in the opinions of their therapists and consulting psychiatrists, "socialization experiences." We attempted a compromise procedure that involved both elements—psychotherapy other than on the ego level, and group participation. To meet both these needs, the procedure had to deal simultaneously with psychonoxious personality structure and manifest behavior. It was obvious that corrective experiences of AGT alone would not suffice to dissolve the strongly cathected feelings and urges that had been built up in these children.

The procedure, which we later labeled *activity-interview group psychotherapy* (A-IGP), was aimed at correcting intrapsychic difficulties through the traditional methods of play therapy for children, which these patients rejected in a dyadic situation, by exposing them to the impact and catalytic effect of a peer group. But because of the age of the children, the materials supplied to the groups were of a more therapeutically advanced nature, and the interviews were carried on a more conceptual content level, with some insight. While neurotic traits can be sloughed off in

AGT by primary behavior disorder patients, the neurotic constellations of these young patients were more intense and more deeply structured. Their anxieties, guilts, conflicts, and confusions had generated in them internal tensions which were manifested in deviant acts and symptomatic reactions.

Selection and Grouping

However, by and large, the chief diagnostic criterion for inclusion in A-IGP was still "behavior disorder," but complicated by strong oedipal components, unusual fears, anxieties, and symptoms such as sleeplessness, enuresis, encopresis, and sexual preoccupations disharmonious in the children's developmental phase. Still, where the symptomatology was massive, individual therapy exclusively or in addition to group sessions is required. Many of the children we included in the groups have been exposed to sexual overstimulation through sharing parental beds or bedrooms, the influences of seductive parents, rigid toilet training, sex play, serious harshness and/or inconsistent treatment, prolonged violent conflicts, and even witnessing physical struggles between parents, and similar deeply affecting and anxiety-generating family phenomena.

In selecting patients for A-IGP, it is important to avoid including children with difficulties that may prove detrimental to the group's therapeutic effectiveness, such as uncontrollable aggression, autism, psychosis, brain damage; children with severe sibling rivalry, affect hunger, psychopathic trends, and devoid of impulse control

A-IGP, dealing as it does with internalized conflicts and fears, as well as with behavior, conforms to the basic elements or dynamics of analytic psychotherapy. These are transference, catharsis, insight, reality testing, and sublimation. To employ these effectively in A-IGP with latency children, these dynamics must be modified and scaled down to suit their ages.

VARIABLES IN BASIC DYNAMICS

Transference

Transference reactions on the part of young children are of rudimentary nature. The therapist is not specifically a transference object in AGT, i.e., he does not become the recipient of libidinal feelings entertained toward parents. Because of the therapist's impersonal demeanor and his accepting attitudes, he appears to the child's mind as the personification of what parents *should* be. Ordinarily, the child's emotions are neither intense nor are they activated to a degree that invokes the specter of the evil father or the "witch mother" in the person of the therapist. However, as we shall see presently, in A-IGP the therapist, by his role characteristic in all analytically oriented psychotherapy, *does* evoke to some degree active or suppressed negative feelings.

Catharsis

If there is any cathartic activity in AGT, it takes the form of motoric acting out which transmutes affect into action against the inanimate environment or fellow group members, and only very rarely toward the therapist. The therapist, as already described, is the *ideal* human. It is in this idealized quality that his strengths and his therapeutic powers lie. Catharsis in A-IGP, on the other hand, is the discharge of more deeply affecting emotions through both the activities provided and the interview or discussion segments of the group sessions. In A-IGP the materials are intended to assume more deeply affecting significance as they are employed symbolically to represent elements in the inner life of the child and other persons and events that disturb his psychic homeostasis. Because these events and persons are lodged in the young patient's disturbed unconscious and the meaning of his conduct remains unrecognized by him, the therapist's function is to help bring these meanings to consciousness.

INSIGHT

Obviously the depth of insight and its scope are limited in children. They do not bring to the therapeutic situation the extensive and intensive mass of knowledge, perceptions, relations, and understandings that adults possess. Prepubertal children have not yet acquired understanding of the human psyche in depth which even a subaverage adult may possess, as limited as the latter may be. The therapist in A-IGP, therefore, needs to be guided by his young patients' developmental limitations in his efforts to evoke what in adult psychotherapy is designated as insight. In fact, one is limited in this regard also in the treatment of adolescents, in whom the perceptual scope is considerably greater than in prepubertal children.

In all analytic therapies, as well as in AGT, we must rely upon the spontaneous formulation of *derivative insight,* by which term we mean the insight to which a patient arrives without verbalization of a therapist or of a group discussion. Derivative insight arises as a result of reflection or, more often, from explosive inner recognition of the relations of seemingly disparate facts, ideas, or experiences.[1]

Reality Testing: Allotropy versus Egotropy

Reality testing is part and parcel of all psychotherapies, as well as to varying degrees of the less intensive helping modalities such as counseling and guidance with adults and adolescents. However, reality testing is an essential part of analytic group therapies. The most important and pressing reality for the child is, of course, the workaday world in which he lives and to which he is required to adapt.

Adaptability and obedience to reasonable controls are essential in childhood as bases not only for social adjustment later in life, but also for ego strengthening and personality integration. However, adaptation and obedience are potent contributions to character formation only when they are transitory, are not overstrict, and are limited to the early stages of the child's development. The wise parent and pedagogue recognize when freedom of choice and self-determination become progressively more appropriate operational modalities for the evolving individual. In psychotherapy the child needs to be exposed to realities *consistent with his developmental and idiosyncratic suitability:* physically, intellectually, emotionally, and socially. Unlike individual psychotherapy of disturbed and socially maladjusted children, in which their experience is limited to an individual relationship that meets only partially the welter of their needs, group psychotherapy supplies all of them. Thus the group becomes for the child an arena of growth-producing reality testing as well as a modality for total personality integration.

[1] See also Levels of Interpretation, below.

The group's chief importance is its service to young patients as a transition from narcissism and egocentricity to allotropy. A group by its very nature is alloplastic. The inescapable pressures for adaptation to, as well as the stimulations from, a group modify and diminish egotropism. Some professionals, however, employ groups exclusively in a blanket fashion as a "socializing experience"; they seem to be unaware of the many other values groups hold for the maladjusted and that the roots of sociotropism are in earlier interpersonal relations. As mentioned elsewhere, some patients require individual treatment before joining a group.

SUBLIMATION

In the ascending climb from infancy to maturity, much of the original instinctive "baggage" with which the human animal comes into the world needs to be either suppressed or sublimated. Only a comparatively small segment of his original instinctive nature can be carried by a human being into the social complex of his adult life. The vast mass of instincts require a "refining" and acculturation through the impacts of the micro- and macro-cultures into which the individual is born so as to bring him into harmony with the inescapable world around him.

Much of this sublimative and repressive process is automatic as a result of the implacable pressures from his environment upon his biopsychologic adaptive mechanisms. Part is familially and socially planned through discipline and schooling. One of the unavoidable sources of conflict between children and their elders is the antagonism between the child's raw instinctual urges and adult norms. The elders are given to explosive impatience with their offspring and pupils, an impatience that grows out of the lack of understanding of the time process involved in the movement from childhood to maturity; i.e., their impatience with the *childishness of children.*

Therapists, whether in individual or in group treatment of children, need to be aware that they serve as models after whom their patients "fashion" themselves. With children (and adolescents) particularly, this is a critical situation; it is an integral part of the therapeutic (and educational) process. Activities and verbal and nonverbal interactions in groups are geared toward affecting repressions and sublimations. When these are further supported in the life beyond the group, encouraging results can be expected. This is why family members, other than the patients, frequently need to be involved in the latters' treatment and guidance, and it is the central rationale of the so-called "family therapy," more appropriately designated "family guidance" or "family mental health."

Groups also meet the fifth requirement of psychotherapy: the acquisition of sublimations. However, it must be kept in mind that the structured nature of therapy groups, operating in a conditioned and somewhat ideal environment, offer a limited field for achieving sublimated life patterns. This is the function of the world outside: the school, the neighborhood, and the cultural and world climates. The most that psychotherapy and good education (not schooling) can do is to generate in the individual the *disposition* to suppress (or repress, as the case may be) and sublimate native egocentricity, aggression, rage, and other, socially baleful, if human, trends and characteristics. In fact, all psychotherapy is the process of rendering the resistive individual accessible to the educative influences of his community.

Obviously, in children of the age included in A-IGP, the quantum of sublimations is limited. They still operate more by the controls imposed by various elders and by displacement. Children in trouble have been dominated too strictly and too rigidly and may have resentfully conformed, but at the same time they have internalized resentments and baleful constraints from which they have to be freed if they are to become healthy. Others who have rebelled against repressive authority grow "maladjusted" as they displace their reactive hostility on innocent others and on society. Psychotherapy aims through corrective emotional experiences to eliminate or at least reduce some of these and sublimate others into acceptable forms of expression.

ALTERED ROLE OF THERAPIST

It is clear from what has already been said that the therapist's neutral role in AGT precludes emotionally significant communication with his patients. This rule does not apply to activity-interview groups. The therapist in A-IGP may at times initiate directional questioning and exploration of significant feelings with individuals and the group as a whole which, when brought to awareness, reduce or eliminate their cathectic hold on patients.

Analytic therapists who are accustomed to evoking or supplying interpretations with adult patients should avoid attempting the same interpretive level with children. Here the interpretations need to be conceptually much simpler, brief, more direct, and devoid of complex elaborations. Statements need to be concise, pointed, and most often derived from the patient's own verbal responses.

What is important in work with latency children is not so much setting them off on a train of thought, but rather bringing clarity as to the *source and implicit intent of acts*.[2] Thus, while insight in analytic therapy is one of the objectives, its level is much more rudimentary. While in A-IGP the therapist centers upon the usual therapeutic dynamics, he should not underestimate the more subtle, nonverbal gains such as the release of anxiety through motoric channels and children's satisfactions that freedom of action, self-determination, and unconditional acceptance yield. The *sloughing off* (rather than "working through") of symptoms as an indirect result of the living situation and freedom in the group is incomparably more common in children in both AGT and A-IGP than in the therapies of older persons.

The interviews and discussions in A-IGP that deal with feelings and experiences are threatening to children, though to a lesser degree than in patients of more advanced age. Because the therapist is a central figure in the group deliberations, he automatically becomes a libidinal object for displaced feelings of love and hate. This situation is what motivates children to continue attendance in these groups. In AGT it is the ego gratifications that bring children to the groups, while in A-IGP it is the positive feelings toward the therapist and the group. This significant difference has a strong bearing upon the process and the therapist's functions.

Activity therapy groups, to hold their members—unless they are impelled or brought by parents or surrogates—must be pleasurable. The climate is therefore an essential consideration.

---

[2] This technique is detailed in Part III of this volume.

This is not as critical a factor with analytic-interview groups. Though the climate may be chaotic at times, the children will still return because of their emotional ties to the therapist. In actual practice, we found that A-IGP groups hardly ever become as disorderly as do activity groups, partly because of the nature of the patients selected, but more because the therapist has the means for restoring order by calling for a discussion on the spot to trace the causes, and sometimes even the meaning, of an outburst. These ensuing discussions are of considerable therapeutic value, since they bring into the open feelings of anger, hate, and resentments, i.e., interpatient and patient-therapist transferences, that can be used with effectiveness.

LIBIDO-ACTIVATING MATERIALS AND THEIR EFFECTS

We have characterized the materials furnished for the manual activities in AGT as *libido-binding*; i.e., they favor preventing the child patients from excessive animation (or floating libido) that would lead to chaos and disorganization. In A-IGP, on the other hand, the materials supplied are *libido-activating*. Because of the neurotic element of the patients in these groups, the supplies are designed to evoke disturbing feelings involved in their neurotic constellations so that they can be worked through or sloughed off. Thus, an activity-interview group contains tools and materials that facilitate aggression such as hammering and sawing, as in AGT, but these should be fewer and of a much more limited variety and conspicuousness.

In addition to water, water colors, crayons, paper, and plasticine, which represent symbolically anal and urethral preoccupations, play materials and toys (taboo in AGT) that replicate difficulties in interpersonal relations in families are among the more important supplies. These include dolls of males, females, and children of both sexes, urinating dolls, large dollhouses with all the rooms in a typical home—kitchen, bedroom, bathroom and toilet, dining and living rooms—with movable furnishings for each of these. This equipment leads to reenactment of traumatic situations and memories which, with their concomitant feelings, can be employed in the therapeutic grist with each child separately or with the group.

An example of this is a girl in one of the groups who furnished the bedroom and placed a woman and a child doll in bed, covered them up, and placed the male adult doll on the floor outside in the hallway. Another instance is a boy who attempted to stuff a girl doll into the toy toilet bowl, obviously trying to get rid of his rivalrous baby sister. In setting up the dining room of a dollhouse, children often omit some member of the family at the table. These acts and omissions are employed by the therapist as starting points for individual and group discussions, bringing into the open sources of feelings and helping the children recognize, within the range of their understanding, the meanings of these arrangements in the light of their problems.

Similarly, drawings and paintings of fights and battles and scenes of violence and cruelty against persons and animals bring into awareness angry feelings the children may have been afraid to express verbally, as a result of which they have suffered the inner disturbances that such suppressions generate. However, in these groups, as is also the case in AGT, the opportunities for cathartic discharge offered by the play and construction materials in themselves serve to relieve inner pressures in children through the process of transmutation of feelings into neuromuscular, motoric channels. Play with bottles, rubber tubing, baby bottles and nipples, and messing with water, color paints, and plasticine, bear anal-urethral significances and relieve children who have been subjected to restriction, punishment, and shame in these areas.[3]

Emotional tensions can also be reduced by the discharge of aggressive or angry feelings by seemingly purposeless banging with a hammer or violent sawing of a piece of wood, as well as by aim-directed carpentry work, the fashioning of guns or swords and other artifacts of aggression. All these overt and covert manifestations, including so-called "creative activities," have significance in terms of conscious or unconscious preoccupations in all children, but especially in those who require psychotherapy. We designate this quality of materials, which stimulates the emergence to the surface of latent feelings, as libido-activating.

---

[3] These activities coupled with improved self-image form the dynamic of sloughing off.

LEVELS OF INTERPRETATION

However, the therapist must guard against making use of *every* significant act by a child. His explorations and interpretations need to be limited to those acts in which the meaning is transparent and can be readily understood and accepted by a child. The principle of *readiness* should be strictly observed here even more than with older patients. A child could easily be led to understand the meaning of his placing the father doll on the floor outside the bedroom or stuffing a baby doll into the toilet bowl or having it fall out a window or omitting to include some member of a family in setting the dining table. A child can also be led to recognize his violent banging as a discharge of anger. The therapist, however, would be hard put to get him to see urethral and anal significance in playing with fluids and plasticine. The therapeutic benefits from such play would have to result from the organismic transmutations, sloughing-off release, and perhaps, from what we have called derivative insight above.

THE SPECIAL NATURE OF CHILD "RESISTANCES"

To the therapist who has been trained for work with adult patients only and has become accustomed to their resistance against self-revelatory verbal catharses, the ease with which children take to group interviews, once their insecurities and diffidence have worn off, is at first, indeed, a refreshing experience. Unless resistances flow from basic character structure (such as one finds in schizoid personalities), children in the earlier years of latency and even more in the preoedipal stage, enter into the discussions with ease. Lacking the rigid built-up discriminations of what is proper or improper, what is permissible or taboo, and in the absence of the strong feelings of shame that plague adults, children lay themselves bare unhesitatingly, displaying little of what is known as "resistance" in the ego-defensive, psychoanalytic sense.

However, some children who have been intensely mistreated by adults may respond defensively. Such "defensiveness" is not of the same genre as are ego defenses in adults, however. It stems rather from pervasive fear of being hurt or punished. In individual psychotherapy, a child may be diffident and in a tenuous sense "resistive," but his resistance is against the person of the therapist as a representative of the adult world that caused him pain, or as part of the biological survival mechanism of fear or caution which is displayed also even by domestic animals toward strangers. However, as soon as initial apprehensions are worn off, the child easily relates to the therapist and communicates freely both in action and, within his limits, verbally.

Groups greatly facilitate these processes, since the group represents protection against the "strange" adult and offers convenient escapes from the inescapable confrontations that a dyad situation imposes. In addition, the pronouncements of one or a few of the less diffident members serve as catalysts for the others to join in the interviews. The child therapist is thus spared the problems that hound the therapist of adolescent and adult patients. The Machiavellian caution and strategies used by therapists with adults, and especially with adolescents, are superfluous with children. The therapist can be as open and direct as are his patients, provided he does not make the mistake of exceeding the scope of their interests and comprehensions or in any way threaten them.

ACTING OUT, REENACTMENT, AND ABREACTION

Beneficial results in A-IGP are achieved in some patients by the processes of acting out, reenactment, and abreaction as described in relation to AGT. Children are governed by the same psychic laws in both types of groups. However, because of the neurotic element in the former, actions and activities assume different, more extended meanings, which are discriminately utilized by the therapist. For example, a child banging aimlessly in AGT may be permitted to "let off steam" until he automatically calms down and turns to another activity less disturbing to the group. Or, he may be diverted from his purposeless noise making by the therapist, who may ask the boy for the hammer which he "needs to work with."

In A-IGP, on the other hand, the therapist may remark to the offending child in passing, "I guess you must be pretty angry today, Charles." He would not, however, say, "Maybe you are angry at me (which may be actually the case); that's why you bang so hard." His unoffending first statement would not arouse defensiveness or guilt, which the alternate statement would.

307

However, it would still serve to bring to the awareness of the young patient the hidden intent of his act against the therapist and the group. "Where the id is, there the ego must be."

INDIVIDUAL INTERVIEWS

In interview analytic groups with adolescents and adults, the therapist may focus attention on an individual patient. This practice is therapeutically indicated also in A-IGP. Individual interviews may in addition be required when the therapist recognizes a need for working through feelings that a child reveals by some act or statement during the session. However, the individual interview in A-IGP is initiated by the therapist only when not engaged in group discussion. The therapist may take a seat next to the child or, better still, ask the child to retire from the locus of his activity to a corner away from the others. Then he can explore with him the feelings that evoked the particular act or statement in accordance with analytic procedures as modified for child therapy.

These sporadic interviews with individuals are not only effective as a means for working through a problem, but even more important, they also bring the child emotionally closer to the therapist. All children yearn for such closeness and kindness, patients requiring psychotherapy more than the usual. As gracious and indulgent as an adult may be toward the group, each child is left not fully satisfied unless he has some contact with the adult. The therapist in A-IGP, therefore, makes it a point to make such contact with as many children as he can manage. He may address himself to some untoward incident or the unusual tension the child has displayed, or he may just inquire, "How are things going?" In every such instance the child's response will set off a dialogue between the two which the well-trained and skillful child therapist can utilize therapeutically and for strengthening his relation with his patients.

GROUP INTERVIEWS

The group interviews, which may be called, for the children, the "talking parts" of the "meeting," as differentiated from the "working part," are started off by the therapist asking the children to gather around a small table designed to accommodate five or six boys and girls and the therapist. As can be expected, some will dilly-dally for various reasons before they join the group. Among the reasons for the delay may be challenging the therapist, diffidence, or a genuine interest in finishing a handiwork project or game. The children are allowed to take their time in joining the group.

The therapist seats himself first, and after all but one or two of the laggards are in their chairs at the first session, he declares that, "I think probably all of you know that you have come to the *group* [not club, in this case] because you had some problems in getting along, some at home, some at school, and some in both, and that some of you are not too happy about it. We want to talk about these things and see if we can make things better for ourselves. Who would like to start?"

If after a few minutes no response is forthcoming, the therapist may turn to one of the participants who appears to be the least likely to be threatened by it and ask him, "Jimmy, why do you think you were sent to this group?" The likelihood is that he would blurt out "I don't get along in school!" or "I always fight with my little sister [or some other sibling]" or "I fight with my mother."

The therapist then asks the child to elaborate on his statement as to how these conflicts originate, always being careful not to convey a feeling or idea that any person is at fault. If the child hesitates, the therapist helps him by asking, "When was the last time you had any difficulty with your mother [or sibling, or teacher or classmate, or whomever the child had specified]?" After receiving a definite answer, the therapist then asks, "How did it start?" The response to this query sets the "interview" on its course.

The therapist then has the choice, dictated by the nature of the responses and the reactions from the other children, whether he will explore the incident with a view of bringing into focus (without so specifying) the patient's part in setting off or encouraging the incident, or involve the other children to react on the spot, in the course of which each may reveal his own difficulties and thus set in action the group therapeutic process.

It may be advisable to spend a few sessions in thus "going

around," i.e., asking each member of the group in turn to state the reason for his coming to the group or the nature of his problem as each sees it. On the other hand, it may be (in the judgment of the therapist) better to throw the discussion open to the others to react to the original statement by the first child at the first session.

After these preliminaries, which may take several sessions, the youngsters' feelings of strangeness with each other will wear off, and the therapist may deem it advisable to focus discussions again on individual group members. One way in which this can be done is to describe a specific act or a series of acts by a child during the activity sector of the session which, in the judgment of the therapist, had significance in relation to his problems. The procedure consists of the therapist's asking, "I wonder if any of you have noticed how Paul was sawing the wood and banging away at the nails when he was making his box, and how his face looked?" Or it may have been his breaking up a box he had previously constructed, or tearing up a picture he had drawn, or how he repeatedly annoyed another child trying to provoke him into a fight. The reaction of the group and of Paul, himself, cannot but prove fruitful in making him aware of some underlying feelings, which he may or may not bring himself to verbalize at this point.

Again, the therapist, according to his judgment, may leave the topic inconclusively, or he may pursue it by asking the group, or the patient himself, why he felt impelled to work with such impetuosity or destroy his handiwork or persist in annoying a fellow group member. A plethora of explanations, often accusative, meets such questions from the others about a fellow member (as a sibling substitute), for the children's self-esteem rises by being so placed in a judgmental hierarchy over him. When the list is exhausted, the therapist may ask Paul which of the explanations offered he considers to be correct.

Sometimes a choice is forthcoming, but quite often the subject of the inquiry hesitates and meekly replies, "I don't know." Here again the therapist is placed in the position of selecting an appropriate line of action. According to his judgment as to the degree of embarrassment and the sensitivity of the target under inquiry, he may take one of four lines of action: (1) he may say to Paul, "Think about it and see if you can make a decision"; (2) he may select on the basis of his knowledge of Paul's personality the most likely reason offered for Paul's behavior; (3) he may offer a series of determinants, academically, without directly imputing any of them to Paul; or (4) he may ask Paul to try to recapture the feelings he had while he was performing the acts. What was he thinking and feeling at the time?

It is important that the therapist step gingerly in situations involving feelings: he must under no circumstances push the youthful patient beyond his emotional readiness to withstand the pressure or his intellectual capacities to understand the explanations given or arrived at. Latency children are much less vulnerable than are pubertal children, adolescents, and adults, and can accept directness from the therapist (they are given to it themselves) with less disturbance than older patients. Nonetheless care should be scrupulously exercised not to overstep their ego strengths and thus make errors affecting the transference feelings of the children toward the therapist.

The latitude of permissible encroachment upon the privacy of patients, of course, widens with time, as it does in all analytically oriented therapies. As the warmth of relationships, intimacy, and confidence grows, the therapist may take more liberties of entering more deeply the threat areas of his patients. The "exercises" outlined in the preceding paragraphs prepare the children for the ever-widening scope that their treatment ultimately takes. They also implant the rudimentary awareness of cause and effect in human emotions and conduct which forms the basis for psychological literacy later in life.

In time the therapist can abandon his role of initiator and facilitator in opening the group interviews. In later sessions, the patients often rival each other to relate emotionally significant incidents and dreams for discussion. In fact, after the first session, it is appropriate for the therapist to ask, once the children have gathered around the table, "Is there anything anyone would like to talk about?" This signifies to them that they may become self-starters.

The focus of the interviews has a double thrust. One is that communicating frustrations and disturbing preoccupations relieves inner pressures and tensions. It automatically establishes homeostasis where stress has been, bringing on a feeling of well-being. Another is the resulting insight or understanding of the disturbing problems, thereby reducing cathexis and bringing them closer to control. In achieving this, both the group and the therapist are involved.

As already indicated, the malleability of the child's psyche in the absence of fully constellated and rigidized defenses renders him more susceptible to modifications. At the same time, the child's egocentricity and narcissism impel him to regress to original feelings and conduct which are worn down (deconditioned) by repetition as a particular experience recurs through the comforting group acceptance and belonging (reconditioning).

GENERAL NOTES

Activity-interview groups may consist of same-sex or mixed membership. Groups for boys should have male therapists; groups for girls, female therapists; sexually mixed groups may have either male or female therapists. The length of session may vary from 60 to 90 minutes to two hours (the "talking part" not more than 30 to 45 minutes), and the group may meet once or twice a week. Taking notes is permissible in A-IGP. When asked, the therapist tells the children frankly that he is writing so that he may remember what each member is doing and saying.

EQUIPMENT FOR A-IGP AND ITS USES

We have listed in their context equipment and materials for an AGT room, where activity-interview groups may also meet. When they do, they should have separate cupboards containing only the essential few, simpler tools and toys that readily serve for discharge of aggressive feelings. They should not tie children down to prolonged pursuits such as producing complex utilitarian objects, and thus become libido-binding.

The items required are a few small hammers, one or two small crosscut fine saws, wood, mostly strips that would suggest swords and sabers; plasticine; water colors; paper and crayons, and dolls, dollhouses and furniture, building blocks, and masks of various types of persons and animal faces with which children can play out fantasies.

Thus, to assume the guise of a lion can serve for the aggressive boy to project an image of ferocity, strength, and aggression, while a frightened or diffident child may find in it a means of realizing what he would like to be. A-IGP equipment should also include toy pistols to play out similar fantasies of destroying persons who in real life cause them stress and/or provoke revealing homicidal wishes. A dollhouse may be used to reflect rejection and destruction wishes and fantasies. Toy pistols are additional and less disguised means for attaining such ends. The supplies should also include quiet games in which two or more children can participate, and some puzzles.

Therapists need to be alert to the use of plasticine when it is fashioned into images of persons and then squashed. This is unmistakable evidence of elimination wishes, which in some more sophisticated children may assume the extremes of death wishes. Drawings and paintings can convey similar covert or overt feelings and urges. Patients often make drawings and paintings of babies, children, or adults and then obliterate them, usually with black paint, or destroy the paper on which they had been drawn. All these manifest difficulties with members of families and serve as catharses by symbolically discharging noxious feelings toward them as well as serving as jumping-off points for individual and group interviews.

XVI

Summary Report of a Sexually Mixed Activity-Interview Group

The following is a report of one year's experience and results attained in a group of seven children, four girls and three boys, in latency years. The children had been in individual treatment with the psychiatric caseworker who organized the group. Some of the boys and girls had known each other through occasional contacts in the waiting room. The treatment was carried out in the neighborhood where the children lived and outside the official locale of the sponsoring child guidance agency.

The therapist, Mrs. Betty Gabriel, was the first to organize and conduct a group on lines that were later designated as activity-interview group therapy by the Director of the Group Therapy Department of the Jewish Board of Guardians.[1]

Descriptions of the children in the group follow.

Linda, aged nine, a bright, alert child, was referred to the agency in August 1932, because of "nervous hysteria." She was frightened by any unusual sound. At an early age she began to suffer from vomiting spells, and this became a problem when she entered school. She did not allow her mother out of her sight and refused to play with children.

Investigation disclosed that during the mother's pregnancy with

---

[1] We are indebted to Mrs. Gabriel for the inclusion of her report which first appeared in the *American Journal of Orthopsychiatry*, 9(1):146-169, 1939.

Linda the father lost his job and they were forced to live with his mother. After the birth of the infant conflict arose between the two women over its care, and the mother finally had to assume a dictatorial attitude toward her mother-in-law. The mother ascribed the child's nervousness to the worry which she herself had endured during pregnancy. The mother blamed herself for the vomiting episodes, confessing that she neglected to consult the clinic for advice in working out a feeding formula because she was ashamed to admit that she had a baby who required so much medical attention.

The crisis in this child's development was due to a shock. Linda had been struck in the back by a truck, but she was not injured. Several other seemingly minor accidents then followed which served as traumatic experiences, as evidenced by her apprehensive attitude, fears, insecurity, and fantasies.

The parents were intelligent but emotionally unstable, middle-class, fairly young. Under favorable conditions their living standards would have been good, but intermittent financial reverses and enlargement of the family by the birth of twin boys, after the agency entered the situation, forced the family of six to move into one room, renting out the remaining three rooms in the apartment in order to make ends meet. Both parents were interested in their children. The mother was inclined to gossip before them.

Linda's fantasy revealed an intense sibling rivalry, a running away from unpleasant situations, a feeling of rejection and insecurity.

Emma, aged eleven, Linda's sister and brought to the group by her, was attractive, bright but very slow, felt aloof from the group, as she considered she had no problems, but came to attend her sister, who "had something wrong with her." The parents did not consider her a problem. As treatment with Linda progressed, the mother recognized that Emma was jealous of the attention the younger child was getting and under the caseworker's guidance attempted to help her.

Emma, because of a feeling of inferiority on the intellectual side, continued being jealous, as evidenced by frightening Linda and quarreling with her. She began associating with boys and girls older than herself and repeated to Linda information on sexual matters, for which the latter was not ready. As treatment

316

progressed, she made unusual progress in school owing to her competitive drive (Linda had skipped and had been rated one of the brightest children in her class). Once Emma outdistanced Linda and was termed the "perfect" child in school, her behavior was modified. She was helpful at home, and quarreling between the sisters diminished.

Annette, aged ten, IQ 96, was referred in February 1933 by the school. She was then in the first grade, presented the following problems: she annoyed children by pushing and pinching (and was disliked as a result). She failed in first grade. The teacher considered her "wayward." She was a tattletale and unreliable. She was an unattractive child.

The basic problem was one of deep rejection on the part of the mother, who considered her a "peculiar child even before she was born." The child was sickly in early infancy, and the mother left no stone unturned to try to cure her. A nurse attended her until she was fifteen months old; then the paternal aunt became housekeeper for the family, which consisted of the father's three children by a former wife, in addition to Annette and a younger sister. All Annette's activities annoyed the mother and, as she said, "brought out my worst possible traits," such as cursing, vile language, and utterance of death wishes for the child. She rejected Annette even to the extent of neglecting to dress her properly, even though she could have afforded this.

During Annette's early childhood the family was very wealthy, the father engaging in bootlegging activities. At the time of referral they were penniless and the mother was harassed by this poverty and the difficulties with Annette.

The mother claims to have loved her husband even before his first marriage. She courted his friendship to the extent of becoming a frequent visitor at his home and ingratiating herself with his wife and children. After his wife's death she married him and accepted his children as though they were her own. Her husband never questioned her affection for his children, though there was conflict between her and his daughter for his affection. When Annette was born, the mother was unable to accept her emotionally, viewing her as a further rival for the father's affections. The mother's rejection of the child was consistent, resulting in guilt and anxiety feelings. In marked contrast to her rejection of Annette was her extreme attachment for the younger child. The father was fond of Annette and enjoyed her quick repartee and clever remarks. It is doubtful whether the child got sufficient satisfaction out of this relationship so that she was able to work out the oedipus situation. The relationship between Annette and her half brothers and sister was one of indifference, and she was ambivalent in her relationship to her own sister.

After therapy, the mother showed a greater interest in Annette, supervising all her activities; at times her attitude even bordered on a show of affection. The financial condition greatly improved, again through illegal business activities.

Jean, aged ten, was referred in July 1934 through Linda's mother, presenting the problem of "bed-wetter." Jean was an only child. The family lived with the maternal grandparents, who were in comfortable circumstances. The child's mother, an unusually beautiful young woman, lost her right arm at two years of age, but was brought up to function in as near a normal manner as is possible with such a handicap. The mother's attitude toward her child was always objective. She felt it unwise to give Jean too much love and affection and was unable to recognize that she carried this to extremes. She was unable to see that the child was attractive and bright.

The mother tried to help Jean overcome the enuresis by punishing, by withholding all approbation, and by reasoning with the child. When suggestions were made by the psychiatrist these were not followed, indicating that the mother needed the child's problem to continue because she could use this as a substitute for the real issue, which was the fact that her husband never supported her, did not confide in her, probably didn't love her, neglected her, and engaged in some dishonest practices. The mother made a point of the fact that she accepted her lot in life with very little emotional affect and, in a measure, could identify the child with herself in this same respect. Jean showed little concern over the bed-wetting and when with children assumed a submissive role, just as her mother did in the family relationship and with her husband.

Jean reacted to the home situation by gaining attention through her bed-wetting. She showed hostility to her grandfather, with whom she spent much time, and occasionally exhibited an outburst of temper when with her mother. In treatment she gave evidence of anxiety feelings which were concerned with the loss of her mother's arm and with masturbation. However, the treatment revealed that this child showed no overt behavior problems besides the enuresis.

We could not meet with the father because of his resistance. We feel that Jean did not receive very positive satisfaction from him, though he did devote Sundays to his wife and child. He was easily irritated with Jean.

Mike, ten years old, IQ 108, was referred by the school in January 1936. The boy had few friends, was hypersensitive, and cried when called on to recite in the classroom. The mother stated that he presented no problem in the home, mentioning briefly that he stuttered a little. Mike had a sister of fourteen who was considered an exceptionally well-adjusted girl. The mother, neurotic and sickly, had an infantile tie to her own mother, who was described as a "matriarch," and there was a close family bond. The mother spent the major part of her time with her own family. She resented the child's being referred to us but did not object to our interest "because the school was so very considerate." The father, a butcher, maintained a fairly comfortable home. He resented his wife's attachment for her family and understood that she should be more available to the child. He seemed, however, to be a negative factor in the situation.

Mike began to stutter to a marked degree. His schoolmates thought he was insane because he cried "for no reason." The teacher's antagonism was caused by Mike's belligerent, hostile manner, evidenced by muttering and cursing under his breath. Treatment revealed a great deal of sibling rivalry and hostility to the mother, who he felt did not love him. He was constantly compared unfavorably with his sister.

Hilton, aged ten, IQ 87, was referred by the school. He was reported to be disorderly, disobedient, and a stealing problem. He was the fifth child in a family of six children. Shortly after his birth his mother became insane and was committed. The child was placed in a shelter and later in a series of private boarding homes. However, his behavior was so uncontrollable that he would rarely be kept for more than a week or two. He did adjust in one home but had to leave after a year because of the illness of the foster mother. Foster mothers always complained about his excessive eating, his stealing, disorderly conduct, disobedience, and destructiveness. On one occasion he attempted to set a house on fire.

The mother was returned to her home about five years ago. She became pregnant immediately, and it was considered unwise to bring Hilton back into the home. Treatment revealed that for three years Hilton did not know he had parents, since they never visited him. When he was finally returned to his home in 1935, he became extremely destructive, hyperactive, fidgety, impertinent, and disobedient, stealing from the home and from tradespeople. He was often discovered standing before a mirror making facial grimaces. Of the entire family group the only one exhibiting any positive feeling for Hilton was the older brother, but he was tubercular and unable to do very much.

The mother was a manic type, had a winning personality, and ruled the family, the children being strongly attached to her. The family was devoted to the youngest boy, who presented no problem, and comparisons unfavorable to Hilton were constantly made. The father was a completely negative personality, very sickly.

Carl, one of three children, was referred by the school. He was fifteen years of age. He was a stealing problem, was disliked by his father, and had difficulties with his mother and one of his sisters. At school he was disobedient, disorderly, and failing in his work.

Carl was not a member of the group. He was mentioned briefly in order to show how well these children were able to accept a boy fifteen years of age. Carl had been under (individual) treatment and came to visit the therapist, remaining because he was interested in the activities of the group. He therefore attended a number of sessions, during which he was merely an onlooker. The children did not seem to resent him, reacting in such a positive manner that it was felt he had some influence, though it was more by inference than by actual deed. They called on him for assistance on several occasions, particularly when they organized the "club" and officers were chosen. They realized they did not know how to conduct a meeting and requested Carl to do this for them. Carl did it very modestly and earnestly and then turned the chair over to the elected president.

In December, Linda and Jean played together and although Emma was present she took an entirely negative role and merely chatted with anyone on a superficial basis. She felt that she was bringing her sister because "she presented a particular problem." Annette joined later in December, and Mike and Hilton joined the group in February. At first the play was more individualistic, each child interesting himself in whatever drew his attention, but gradually they began playing together. It was then that the various problems, relationships, and attitudes were treated.

In the beginning Jean did not seem inclined to talk when the other children approached her. However, the therapist felt that she enjoyed the opportunity of playing in a conditioned environment because the therapist was able at times to relieve her by turning the attention of the children to other things. Jean played quietly. Later, as she began to feel more secure, she frequently went into an adjoining room which was cut off by a movable wall. On these occasions the child looked uncomfortable when she returned, and the matter was discussed with her in private interviews. She generally acquiesced to suggestions made by the other children, resenting, however, Linda's constant domination of their activities and play. After several weeks she asserted herself and then blurted out to the therapist that she was "sick and tired" of having Linda always telling her what to play. This conversation brought forth information about their activity together in the neighborhood.[2] Jean recognized that Linda was jealous of her and that she sulked because Jean had friends. When Jean was asked what she did about it, she said that she refused to play with Linda. As the interviews with these children progressed, Jean spontaneously said that she and Linda "were getting along much better."

When Hilton joined the group, he burst into the room in his accustomed manner, talking loudly and dominating the scene.

[2] Children who have known each other before coming to a therapy group bring with them their problems of attitudes and relationships that created difficulties. These antecedents modify the free flow of initial reactions.

The therapist introduced the children. Jean was very shy, looked askance at him, and during the rest of the time drew away from him whenever he came near. She was building a house and refused Hilton's help, telling him that she wanted to build her own house and play in her own way. At this point it seemed evident that the child's shyness reacted to some extent on Hilton's exuberant spirits, because he unconsciously lowered his voice whenever he spoke to her. In the following interview it was observed that Hilton still remembered Jean's reaction to him, and he responded in a quiet and almost respectul manner. Jean's response was to lead Hilton on in a coy manner, becoming a bit aggressive. For instance, when he built a house, she threw it over; when he pretended to punish her, she charged at him.

During this group session the children played at a table—some were drawing and others were building. Jean drew a picture of a man and brought it over to the therapist. Jean pointed to the belly button and giggled. Beside the picture she had written, "A man going to the bathroom in a nice clean pot on a summer day." On another occasion she drew a girl holding her skirt and urinating. Beside this picture she wrote, "The children are saying 'shame' and one is wetting her pants." The children were all laughing good-naturedly as Jean came over to the therapist, and she laughed, too. In a low voice the therapist said, "Are you ashamed when you wet?" She nodded. The therapist asked whether it bothered her, and she said she was trying to stop. She tried to stop masturbating too; she did it every night. She was afraid of being punished, and her mother knew, and she didn't want to do it any more. It was interesting to note at this point that Jean confided that whenever she played with Linda, Linda acted like a baby. "She always wants to play house." When the therapist asked her what she would like to play, she wished she had a sister. Linda, overhearing her, said, "Maybe your mother could adopt a little girl." Jean replied, "Do you think I'd want that kind of a sister?" The therapist asked her what she meant. She said she would want her mother to have a baby, and giggled.

Jean continued to hold her own with the group, and the therapist never permitted them to take advantage of her. About two months after the group started, Jean brought her little friend Alice. Linda's jealousy took on an aspect of fury. She complained to the therapist that the children refused to play with her. When this was investigated, it was found that Linda made the complaint because the children refused to do her bidding. Finally, Jean and Alice went into the adjoining room while the therapist talked with Linda. Linda could not concentrate but kept calling out loudly, using names such as "dirty rat." Jean and Alice disregarded Linda. The therapist talked this through with Linda, and later, when the children came together, they played as though nothing had occurred.

The conversation revealed that Linda was projecting on Alice her own behavior pattern. Linda and Alice had retired to the other room while the therapist talked with Jean. Linda called out every few minutes, "Jean is talking about me." Jean looked at the therapist in surprise but said nothing. This conversation revealed that Jean had a good deal of insight in her play with children and in her own home situation. As she discussed the relationship between her mother and the grandparents, she ended by saying, "My grandmother always wants her own way and my mother always gives in to her. If I were my mother I wouldn't do it. My mother knows more than I do, but I won't give in to her all the time."

When Hilton came in and asked to play with Jean, she said, "I don't have to play with you." Hilton responded with nonchalance, "Okay, I never force." When Jean, in speaking to the children, referred to a caseworker as "she," Linda immediately corrected her, but Jean made no response. Jean continued to build with the blocks. When Hilton told her she was making an error, she said, "Oh, yes, I can see that I am making the same mistake you made, but I don't want help." To the therapist she said, "I don't like to play with children who are bossy," while Hilton moved away self-consciously. She then modeled a figure out of clay on which she hung a small penis. She covered it with her hands and brought it over to the therapist so no one could see it, laughing self-consciously and seeming amused.

During the end of March, Jean did not talk much about bedwetting, but she was suffering from anxiety. This anxiety was brought to a conscious level through seeing a large water bug in her room when she went to bed, and she feared it would crawl in with her. As she related this, she was modeling clay, and made a baby doll with a large penis which she sat on a toilet. "The little boy has to go to the toilet often because he does not like to wet his bed at night." The children who heard her all laughed good-naturedly. Quietly the therapist asked her, "Does it help if you go to the toilet in the daytime?" Very seriously then Jean indicated her anxiety about her bed-wetting. She goes to the toilet often in the daytime. Though she tried hard not to wet the bed, some mornings the bed is wet and she "feels terrible." She whispered in the therapist's ear at the following interview that she's through bed-wetting and had not wet since the last time she had seen the therapist.

At about this time her mother got a job. The child's problem was fairly well cleared up and she was playing with all the children. She had had a few "accidents" and voiced her disgust with herself, but she whispered into the therapist's ear that she had entirely stopped "tickling" (masturbating). She was no longer afraid of the water bugs, because her grandfather showed her how he killed one. She told the therapist that she enjoyed playing with Hilton now because Hilton was not as rough as he used to be. It seemed to the therapist that she got a good deal of relief in that she could talk out her problem of enuresis in an atmosphere that was friendly and uncritical. If she got satisfaction from "tickling," other children did too. As she became more secure, this was carried over in her play activity and she was no longer submissive.

Annette courted the commendation of the other children by telling them of her good marks in school. She entered into play with them, and some of her comments in the group indicated that she was rather keen. She played with the plasticine and blocks, showed a great deal of patience, and helped the other children make things. The children, however, resented her being so "bossy" and commented to the therapist that they didn't like her. Annette seemed conscious of this and came to the therapist for security and affection, which the therapist gave her by putting her arm around her.

As Hilton felt more at ease with the children, he began to display more daring behavior, playing with the door, swinging it open, banging it shut, obviously testing the therapist. When no comments were made, he picked up toys, threw them around, and annoyed the children. He asked whether the therapist would write and tell his mother, and the therapist wondered if this was worrying him. Hilton said he didn't "force anyone." When he was asked whether *he* was forced, he commented in the presence of the other children that there were two boys in the neighborhood who forced him to take things and if he didn't they whipped him. He seemed to feel that he had said enough, because he began to sing loudly one of the current popular songs, while patiently replacing the blocks in the box. Hilton said that the reason he put the blocks away was that he got disgusted, for after his house was built, the father (doll) threw it over. He picked up the large rubber doll and beat it again and again, pounding it on the table, tearing the legs apart, and shouting, "You busted up my house."

The therapist asked whether that was how he happened to live with another family, but he looked unconcerned and continued to spank the father harder than before. The children laughed at him, and when they heard the therapist ask whether that was how he happened to live away from home, Emma came over to the therapist and asked her to tell her more about it. The therapist told her that Hilton would tell if he wished to, but he did not hear the question because he was busily engaged.

Linda and Jean had been playing quietly. It was significant that the therapist was now able to take Linda apart from the group. She talked as she modeled about the "pupu" (vagina) and said that the little girl whom she modeled learned to play with her "pupu" because she lay on her stomach. She holds her "pupu" so no man will get it. Her mother told her that she would need an operation if she let a man get at it. When the therapist asked her about it, she replied that she thought the bad man put poison there, and that worried her. She didn't worry when she played with it because she had been playing with it since she was two and a half. She got the habit just as her little brother did, from lying on toys. She said that Emma played with hers, too. Linda then modeled a little boy on whom she put a large penis. When the therapist asked her about it, she said she was giving him the kind of penis her father had; she had watched him take his bath.

When the therapist asked her to close the door, she told her,

"That's another thing I'm afraid of." She feared the door would lock and related a dream which indicated that she had death wishes and accompanying guilt toward her twin brothers. She disclosed intense rivalry between her and Emma and projected on the latter her own quarrelsome disposition. She hated to give in to Emma, who always got her own way. Linda complained again about Annette, but when the therapist said that she didn't have to have her in the group Linda said she wanted her, indicating that she got some pleasure from being with her.

In the following session the therapist observed that Emma was unhappy because Linda was catching up to her; she was skipping in school. The therapist allayed her anxiety by utilizing the time with the group and not talking privately with Linda. The girls displayed a good deal of ambivalence, quarreling one moment and becoming reconciled the next. They told of the fun they had coming to the "meeting," how they went through one turnstile together and saved one (subway) fare. This was discussed rather fully by the group who, although they knew it was wrong, thought it a lot of fun. Linda reverted to the time when she had played with Alice, who was "selfish" and the kind of girl "who let you down for other friends," calling upon Emma to corroborate this. Annette and the girls discussed this in terms of everyday relationships among the children, concluding that this caused a good deal of heartache to the neglected child. Linda, in telling about a party to which she had not been invited, brought out the fact that she had been criticized for not looking clean. Very seriously she assured the group that her dress had been washed and ironed, and both she and her sister defended their mother, although not one word to the contrary had been said.

Emma then said that Linda called her "a dirty rotten thing," and Linda hit her. Linda then said, "Why doesn't she tell you that she cursed me?" She added, "She said that she hoped I'd drop dead." At this point Linda had to go to the toilet and asked Emma to go with her, which Emma refused. Linda said, "Don't you want me to show you the toilet?" Emma said, "No." Linda then said that she didn't really have to go. Annette looked at the therapist as though to get her permission to accompany Linda, and the therapist asked the latter whether she was afraid. She said she was, that she thought there might be a "bad man" there.

The therapist told Linda that there were no bad men there, and Emma began to tell a story Linda had told the therapist about a man who accosted them in the hall and attracted their attention to his penis.

Linda had not been playing with Jean the past week because Jean "wanted her own way," and Linda thought "all people wanted their own way." The therapist said, "You don't like that, do you, because you'd rather have people do things your way." Linda saw the point and smiled. Linda sighed deeply, telling a dream which indicated anxiety about a man being under her bed. Linda commented for the first time that she always seemed to be worrying about something, mentioning her worry about that "worm business" (taken up in individual interviews). She got over that fear by sleeping close to Emma. Here Emma and Annette laughed and Emma said, "I don't like that so very much." They began to talk about their masturbatory activities, and Annette laughed and said she didn't do that. The therapist discussed this in terms of its being a habit that very little children sometimes get into but outgrow as they grow up and find other interests and engage in activities. However, Emma very calmly said, "But I enjoy doing it," and Linda looked at her sister, both girls starting to laugh heartily.

The following week Linda was very restless and laughed hysterically and talked about bad dreams, indicating anxiety, but saying that she liked being near Emma. Another dream which upset her was that she was holding her brother while walking toward a door. A big, fat man was coming in the door with a big knife and she was so scared she dropped the baby. The man killed nearly everyone in the whole city. The therapist did not go into this for interpretation but began to play house with Linda, while Emma sat by playing with clay. Linda wanted to be the little daughter, wanted the therapist to do everything for her, and spoke in babyish accents. Did she want to be a baby again so her mother would give her all the attention? Linda admitted that she wished she were the only one in the family but corrected herself to say that she could accept her brothers but not Emma.

Linda continued to talk baby talk, and when Annette laughed at her Linda grew angry and played at fencing. She was excited, and before Annette had a chance to defend herself, Linda accused her of being too rough. Annette, in a very polite manner, said she was sorry, that she didn't know Linda so well and didn't know how to play with her. Annette turned to the therapist and, when Linda interrupted, said, "You always want all the attention." Linda denied this vehemently, but then admitted that she does "mind other people's business." The therapist asked, "Whose business?" and she replied, "Emma's." She then complained about the boys in school punching her in the stomach and said she told her teacher. Annette said that she wouldn't let them do that to her. In a complaining voice Linda said, "The teacher doesn't watch the little ones." The therapist pointed out to Linda that she is unhappy unless she can claim all the attention. Linda seemed sad, and when the therapist commented that she was angry with her she denied this and then said, "Well, I am unhappy," sighing deeply. She said, "I didn't have a happy day at school," and the therapist added, "Nor here." The children all played with clay, and as Annette and Emma showed more originality than Linda, the latter would look to the therapist for praise by boasting of her school achievements.

Annette did not look well at this session. She had been troubled about her family not recognizing her effort to do well at school. She had overheard her mother beg her father to place her in an institution. Her father had not responded, and Annette said happily, "I know my father was on my side." She was glad she had a good father; if it hadn't been for him her mother would have sent her away long ago. Then, as though defending her mother, she told that several in the family were beginning to realize that Caroline, the sister, started the fights. Linda took up this point—she, too, faces this difficulty. The therapist felt that Annette seemed to feel superior to the other children and she held her own very nicely against Linda. Annette complained of feeling ill, and the therapist sent her home. (It was later learned that she had had an attack of appendicitis and that she had been worried about an operation. Yet it seemed as though the child would have liked to get this attention.)

From the beginning of Hilton's advent into the group he made himself the caretaker of the toys. At this time he was stealing from tradespeople and from the home. In the group he exerted great care to make sure that nothing disappeared and always gathered the things and packed the box with utmost care. One day he asked whether anyone had used the toys since he put them away. The therapist said they had, and he was disappointed. When told the therapist knew that he didn't like that, he thought about it and then said, "Oh, well, that's all right," apparently recognizing that the toys were there for all the children. He was excited, and as he opened the box, withdrew the father doll and began to spank it, he commented. "I remember how you broke up my home." The therapist thought his behavior was exhibition-istic even though it did release hostility. Questioned as to whether he thought his father wanted him out of the house, he refused to respond but looked for the paintbrush and commented, "If I can't find it I'll kill myself."

At this point Jean and Linda entered, and Hilton accepted them as old friends. He told them about the house he had built last week and how the father had broken it up and how he hit the father. The girls made no comment, and he invited them to paint, but Linda refused, saying she would play house. Jean said, "I don't have to play with you if I don't want to." Hilton said, "I don't force you." He painted, sang, and in talking referred to the therapist as "she." Linda corrected him and he said, "You bet!" Linda and Jean began to build a house (of wooden blocks) and Hilton told them that if they built it larger than he did "maybe papa will go into it today without busting it up." The girls refused his help, and he said, "I've got a good idea, now. I will make a birthday cake for my father and trim it with candles." Thereupon the children began making plasticine cake and can-dles. Jean asked whether she might paint the candles, and Hilton said, "Do whatever you wish, I know Mrs. Gabriel will not object —she's a kind lady."

Jean teased Hilton about breaking up his house, and Hilton asked her not to. It seemed that Hilton had released a good deal of hostility and he was feeling differently about his father's breaking up the home, because he commented in an aside, "He's a good old papa." Furthermore, it must be remembered that he had made the birthday cake. He became excited and jumped around the room yelling. "Who's been fiddling with the bricks?" He began building and, when the building did not go up well, threw up his arms in disgust. When no attention was given his show-off behavior, he calmed down and finished his building. He asked the therapist whether he might paint the house. The therapist hesitated for barely a second and he said, "I better not; the other children may not like the colors I do." Just previous to his building he had asked Linda to make a choice between a large and small paintbrush. When Linda expressed no preference, Hilton seemed surprised, as he fully expected her to choose the large one, as he would have done. His later comment to the therapist about painting was undoubtedly influenced by Linda.

Hilton enjoyed running wildly into the hall, and the therapist told him that this was one of the things not permitted here. The other children agreed with the worker and continued their play while Hilton defiantly left. He returned in a few minutes and asked for another appointment.

During the following month Hilton was extremely wild and uncontrollable. He generally burst into the room noisily, ran about, and dashed madly through the halls. The children looked at the therapist for comments, but she made none for a while, continuing to occupy herself with them and their toys. Finally, it seemed advisable to limit Hilton's boisterousness, and the therapist called him over, saying that we all came here to talk and play, and that running through the halls was one thing we couldn't allow. Hilton sat down near the therapist, his pupils large and almost covering the iris. He was restless, and when the children invited him to build some blocks he joined them. While working, he commented, "I guess father wanted everyone in the house. He must have thought that I wanted to leave the two children and mother out of the house and that's why he busted up the house." The therapist asked which of the children, and Hilton glanced at her and began tearing at the father doll, biting into it and finally opening the window to throw it out. The therapist said he'd have to bring it up again if he did because the things were here to play with. He grew quiet for a moment.

Mike entered the group now for the first time. The therapist introduced him, and the boys commented that they had seen each other in the neighborhood. Hilton began banging on the door, and Mike told him to close it, saying, "The other children looking in might be jealous." The therapist asked what he meant, and he began to laugh. The boys began to talk about fighting, and Hilton commented, "I can't fight well." When the therapist asked him why, he said, "When I was a kid I was in the hospital because I cut my lip." The other children all laughed at this and told of similar experiences which didn't interfere with their ability to fight. The therapist asked Hilton whether other things also interfered with his ability to fight, but he didn't answer and turned to Mike and asked, "Does your mother force you to come here?" Mike said, "No, I come because I want to." Hilton said, "I come because I'm forced." The therapist said, "Does that make you feel like not coming?" He said, "Yes." The therapist then said that she could understand that he would not like to be forced. He said that he got pretty annoyed at home. By whom? His sister. She "gets into my ears; every place I go I can hear her." (His sister definitely rejects him.)

Mike talked about school. He commented that he enjoys school when his teacher is interested in him. "I was pretty bad last term, so my teacher didn't like me. This term I turned over a new leaf." Investigation revealed that he was angry at his teacher but he got angry at home, too. There he would play with a cousin who "cheats." This Mike disliked. In response to a question, he said he would leave when his cousin cheated. General conversation resulted, in which the children decided they disliked cheats and dishonest people. Mike was asked by one of the children whether his mother became angry when he left. He said she frequently hit him and enumerated some of the difficulties that arise. To show his hostility he would whistle.

The therapist discussed with Mike the jealousy on the part of the other children. Mike thought the children looking into the room would be jealous because of the good relationship within the group. The therapist asked whether he often felt jealous. Yes, he did feel that way when his sister got more things than he. A general discussion followed on this topic while the children modeled in plasticine.

Linda and Emma generally joined the group late because of the necessity for traveling. On their arrival they were always greeted noisily and drawn into the play as soon as they entered the room, sometimes not even being permitted to remove their coats. Linda generally had a disparaging remark to make about her sister. This time Emma called her "a rotten stinker." The children howled, and Linda immediately defended her sister. She said they never used such language but learned it at the neighborhood school they attended. Their mother urged them to discontinue, she said.

The play activity which followed enabled Linda to verbalize that she did not play well with children. "I don't know what it is, but I can't agree with my playmates." The children tried to tell her what was wrong. Linda said, "I always want to do different from what they do, and if they don't follow me I go home." Here, the therapist explained that this is a carry-over of infantile play; as children grow older they learn to change places. Linda said, "You mean I have to give in and do what others do? And later others do what I want?" The therapist said, "Yes." Linda realized from this discussion she was frequently left out of activities because she did not cooperate better. The children indicated they were affected by this conversation. The therapist noticed a greater readiness on their part to give up things. Hilton, particularly, cooperated much better. A very interesting discussion followed which revealed what the children had gained from it. They also discussed freely their sibling rivalries.

Because of Hilton's extreme behavior he was given more individual interviews than the others. He finally came to the conclusion, "When I talk, little by little it makes me happier and good." Hilton informed the therapist that his mother and sister observed this, too.

During the following interviews with the children they discussed movies, Hilton saying he stayed all day long and as a result became ill. The children were astonished that his mother permitted his long absence from home. The ensuing discussion revealed that all mothers "boss" too much, and the children brought up the point that their mothers did not keep promises; they bossed and were unfair. At this point the therapist gave some interpretations of sibling rivalry which might influence them to feel that their parents were unfair.

Hilton and Linda reverted to baby talk as they frequently competed for the therapist's full attention, Hilton becoming aggressive when he felt he was being neglected. At one point, however, he requested, in a grown-up manner, the therapist's permission to remain after the others left in order to pack the toys safely. He showed concern about possible losses of toys. It is interesting that at this time a stopwatch disappeared when the psychologist gave him his psychological examination and Hilton was suspected but never admitted the theft.

The girls accused Hilton of pulling their panties down when they played on the other side of the movable wall. The therapist treated this by discussing with the children their ideas about the differences between boys and girls. They all knew these differences, and the therapist commented that there seemed no further need then for curiosity. Hilton looked embarrassed; the others continued to play without further comment.

Linda came in, describing a recent illness, and Linda and Emma displayed new garments. Everyone admired them. Linda made the point that toys, too, were purchased especially for her. She indicated her guilt by admitting that she used to nag Emma. "I wanted everything she'd play with." Hilton animatedly told of his feelings regarding his brother, emphasizing the same point. Mike became angry and made facial grimaces as he told of experiencing the same jealousies. He also told of "grouching at the table" for which he got hit. The children recognized Mike's experiences as having occurred in their own lives. Mike wished he could break himself of the habit of displaying angry feelings, mostly "my teacher, my father, my mother, my sister." The therapist commented that he was angry at a lot of people.

Linda mentioned that she worried over the poor relationship between herself and Emma. "It isn't nice to dislike your sister." She added that she liked her brothers "because they're cute." (In individual interviews Linda had been revealing fantasies and had repeated dreams, most of which expressed anxiety and curiosity about birth, what happened to the fetus, and also the role the father played in the birth phenomenon.) During the discussion period Linda carried this over and told a dream. She had been kidnapped and taken to a dark dungeon, where the man said he was going to kill her. She screamed. As she related this, she commented, wonderingly, that all her dreams were formerly bad but now she had nice dreams, too. She dreamed she was getting married; when she awakened she was eager to find out whether she was really married. The therapist said it was a nice dream and asked whether she thought a lot about marriage and having babies. She admitted this. There was some discussion about differences between boys and girls. She was asked whether she worried because she was not built like a boy. Her response was "No," she knows boys are different, they have a penis. Her mother had even told her that she would need an operation if she plays with her "pupu." The therapist asked whether she believed this. She said, "Mothers don't lie."

Emma discussed masturbation frankly. Jean, in a carefree manner, laughed. She isn't afraid of operations. At this point Emma and Linda got into an argument, each protesting that she did not wish to impose too much on the other. Linda always procrastinated when she was told to do something and always wanted to be waited on. General conversation then led to a discussion about habits of eating and other daily home activities. A significant point was that their aggressive and hostile behavior resulted from the fact that they were "forced" to eat food they didn't want.

Progress had been made by all the children. Hilton was showing more control, but when noisy his behavior was extreme. For instance, on several occasions when, on arriving, the therapist was still interviewing some other person, he would scream out, the veins of his neck distended, "Must you always have someone here when you expect me?" During play Hilton frequently burst into song. He always tried to get extra time, and when this was not granted, aggressive behavior resulted. The children looked to the therapist for comments and when she made none, would themselves reprimand him. Linda showed some self-consciousness at this point in relating her dreams, speaking in a confidential tone of voice. Now she was a princess and had many people at her command. Then, coming back to reality, she informed the therapist that she played nicely with the children on the block, helped her mother, and had fewer quarrels with Emma.

Mike at this time was again having difficulty in school and was considered a "mess" by his teacher. The poor behavior was carried over to the group, and he displayed a grudge against everyone. When he was spoken to, a smoldering expression of antagonism appeared in his eyes. When Hilton joined the discussion, Mike became exhibitionistic. He described a fight, gesturing and acting out his part in it. His movements were rather effeminate. Hilton intuitively seemed to sense this as he questioned

Mike for details. Mike ignored pointed questions and described another fight, painting himself as the aggressor and something of a hero.

In response to the therapist's question, he said that he frequently gets into fights although he was not aggressive up to five years of age, but at that time he accidentally tripped over his mother's foot and had a bad fall. A "concussion of the brain" resulted. Hilton listened intently. The girls, too, showed an interest, all exhibiting great patience and tolerance with this stuttering companion. Mike showed affect in describing the fall and stated he hated both parents and his sister too, adding, though he didn't always hate them. However, he liked to borrow money from his mother and not return it. (This may be interpreted as recognition on Mike's part that he was not getting the love and satisfaction he should get from his mother. He hated her because she didn't love him. Money represented love to him; if he could not have her love he would take her money and keep it.)

Hilton tried to match Mike's stories. He, too, had been incapacitated for a while as a result of a slight accident. The boys went into a tumbling match. Mike confided in Hilton that "now he tells his teacher to go to hell." Hilton was surprised. The boys were still in a clinch when suddenly Hilton arose and gave Mike a vicious kick in the jaw. Mike received a severe lip wound and suffered a hemorrhage. Interestingly, though, he said to Hilton, "It's my fault" (though it was not). The therapist felt that his acceptance of the blame ties up with the story he had told earlier in which he saw himself as the hero. Both boys received a severe jolt; Mike because he was wounded, Hilton because he was frightened. Hilton dramatically asked the therapist, "What shall I do—kill myself?" The therapist said, "Call a doctor." Emergency treatment was imperative.

The girls had left earlier and failed to see this incident.

The following day Hilton was visited at school. He expressed relief and admiration for the therapist because she had not informed his parents. We discussed the "accident." Hilton expressed guilt and, almost as a peace offering, sent along stamps for Mike. In the following interviews Hilton's mood was quite chastened.

Mike was appreciative of the therapist's follow-up visit to him and made light of his injuries. When the boys met next in the group, they stood for a moment looking at each other, undecided as to how to proceed. The therapist said, "Well, boys, are we going to shake hands?" Spontaneously they shook hands and in a few moments were on the best of terms. When the girls arrived, they all played a game of matching cards. Mike stole one from Hilton. Annette was the first to see it. She glanced at the therapist but made no comment. She continued to play with Linda and Emma but did not concentrate. Hilton realized that the card was missing and showed suspicion of Mike's having it, although he did not accuse him of it. Hilton then offered to play for the missing card, and this time all the children pounced on Mike. He looked nonplussed and continued to deny having the card. Hilton assured him that the card had been in the deck. The two boys ran out into the hall, and when they returned Hilton had the card.

The boys then played with Annette. Again a card disappeared. Hilton accused Mike, and Annette commented it was wrong to accuse Mike when three were playing and it could very well have been she who had the card. The therapist discussed this, commenting that it was easy to be blamed for something when one was not guilty. The therapist commended Annette. The card was found under a couch.

The school report on Hilton at this point was very favorable, the only complaint being that "he seeks attention." There were still complaints about Mike, but his teacher was not yet sympathetic to him. Mike's mother placed the blame for the boy's poor behavior on constipation.

Linda expressed antagonism because she was not interviewed first by the therapist (in the private interview conducted in the far corner of the room). In discussing this with her, she revealed that she was unloved. She was resentful because at home the babies got all the mother's love. This was explained to her as the normal way these things work out. Parents love their children, and it is natural for them to give helpless babies their attention. The older children are able to do many things for themselves, but this does not indicate that their parents don't love them. Linda seemed happy as she returned to the group.

At this point Carl appeared as a visitor for the first time and told that he had been to the circus. Hilton and Mike had not been permitted to go. They displayed antagonism and anger. Hilton stamped around, hopped on chairs, shook the folding door, etc. Mike stuttered and in a sarcastic manner exhibited hatred against his mother, whom he described as "so anxious about him that she couldn't let her baby boy go." Carl amused himself by building a house (of blocks), which Hilton promptly destroyed. He looked around to see what further damage he could do, snorting with anger. The therapist placed a limitation on this activity, stating that we have a responsibility in the use of this room. Hilton was still defiant, but the activity was minimized.

In succeeding sessions Hilton and Mike played with plasticine while the girls painted. Hilton dreamed that an octopus had closed its tentacles around him. He illustrated, and there was a good deal of affect. He stated that he talked to himself every night. He wanted to be a doctor so he could "save many people." He talked about blood tests he had seen at the clinic, and he dreamed that a nurse stuck a needle too far into his arm and it became fat. Following this he played with the plasticine. He built imaginary blood vessels which he pretended to be studying. Mike made canoes out of clay. The girls withdrew into the other room, where they played quietly. The boys fashioned the plasticine into long round strips. Mike said with a smirk, "Oh, see what he is making." Hilton looked puzzled. The therapist asked Mike to "give us a clue." This was given. Hilton took the clue. He placed the penis symbol as though it were in action and began to march up and down the room. Mike hastily fashioned small balls of clay and began marching up and down and dropping them from the area of his anus as though defecating while walking. They marched soberly up and down for about ten minutes, completely disregarding the presence of Carl and the therapist. Finally Hilton remarked, he knew a girl who played with "her penis and her hiney." Mike knew a boy who liked to expose his penis, especially whenever a woman passed him. Both boys laughed.

Mike grabbed Hilton's symbol, which caused him to cry out, "Give me back my penis. I must have it!" He picked up a piece of clay, modeled it into a long strip to give him a better opportunity to protect it. The therapist asked Mike whether he defecated daily. He boastfully replied that he rarely did it. Hilton said, "I do it every day." The therapist explained elimination to the children, using the furnace as an analogy of what goes on in the human body. (This interesting play revealed a singular freedom from self-consciousness, which was possible because of the therapist's completely noncommital but friendly attitude.) Several weeks later Mike's mother informed the therapist that constipation had been overcome.

Shortly after this Hilton said that he was beginning to feel more grown-up because he had been able to have several quiet talks with the therapist. The therapist asked whether he preferred his individual visits to the play group, and he said, "It makes me feel like a grown-up." Immediately, however, he asked the therapist to accompany him to the Y.M.H.A., where he would join a club. The therapist did this. Hilton conducted himself very well and discussed clubs intelligently with the club director. However, he never followed this up, continuing to attend the therapy group regularly.

At the next session all the children were present. They came in quietly and in a grown-up fashion. Hilton was courteous to the girls and exhibited little restlessness during the interview. The last few sessions of the season with the children revealed an interest in painting. Hilton applied himself diligently and worked neatly. As they worked, they talked about everyday occurrences and about plans for the summer. There was still an exhibition of jealousy on Hilton's part, particularly because the therapist was cultivating Emma. In private discussion with Emma, interrelationships and behavior deviations common to all people were taken up with her. The therapist explained that it was helpful to discuss some of our attitudes and feelings in order to have a better understanding of why we sometimes do the things we do. Hilton's jealousy was indicated by his attention-getting behavior. He finally jumped on the windowsill, crawled underneath the safety rail, and perched in a perilous position. The children gasped. The therapist tried for a while to be indifferent, but when she felt that the situation had gone far enough, she pulled him back. Later the therapist discussed with him his evident desire to make her worry about him. He angrily muttered something and left. This incident both upset and angered the other children. The therapist told them that this was Hilton's way of showing aggression toward her.

Mike had been present, taking no part in the activities. This was typical of Mike. It was felt that he was probably not ready for group activity. He had built up a pattern of inability to give anything of himself in retaliation for not being loved. His behavior was generally asocial. When Mike first came, he stuttered only at rare intervals. As the individual treatment progressed, the therapist observed more stuttering, which he explained as a device he used to attract his mother's attention. When he was small he constantly had to say "Mom-mom-mom" to get her attention. It was interesting that he tied this up with the experience when he tripped over his mother's foot and was injured. He was extremely hostile, projecting his annoyance with his family onto the school and society. Treatment did not release this boy of his deep-seated problem but apparently increased his guilt so that he used extreme stuttering to conceal his true feelings. The children tolerated his stuttering, but when they found he could sing without stuttering frequently said to him, "Sing it."

It had been apparent for some time that Linda had been trying to tell the therapist that she was worrying about birth. When this was taken up with her, Emma was playing by herself while the therapist talked privately with Linda. The rest of the group joined in, while Linda was telling of a dream which clearly indicated that this was the opportune time to discuss birth. The essence of the dream was as follows:

The little girl went to the zoo. She fed an elephant, and he squeezed her and gobbled up her hand and squashed her to pieces. The mother cried. Linda said, "At first I thought it was me. Did I wake up!" On questioning her, there were evidences of guilt feelings. The child expressed a fear of being locked in a room from which there would be no escape, and that she would therefore never be able to eat. This sort of thing worried her all the time.

Linda changed the subject. Both she and her sister feared that they were being followed by a man on their way here. What did she fear? "He would do bad things to me." We discussed this, and it led to a discussion of babies. With an assured manner she said, sure, she knows that babies are in the stomach. Emma drew near and the other children, too, and they all began drawing pictures. Hilton refused to join the group, and Emma excitedly told him what they were discussing. He nonchalantly waved her away, "Aw, who wants to know?" A visiting child drew straight lines but in correct formation of the female and male genitals. Linda placed twins high in the mother's chest, realized the position was wrong, and drew a more correct placement. Emma drew a completely dressed young woman.

The children knew that the "seed" is placed in the mother by the father. Linda wondered how the seed got there. Mike was disgusted. Linda thought the baby had to be taken through the mother's throat but laughed while the others joined her. When the therapist asked what she really thought, she said, "I guess they have to cut the stomach open," explaining that her mother told her this. A little boy visitor who was present (the son of a physician) explained in grown-up manner, "Sometimes a caesarian operation is necessary." In response to eager questions from the children, the therapist explained in such terms that they would have no fear. The children were told that after nine months of development in the mother, when the baby is ready for birth, it "knocks" at the mother's abdomen. This is a sign that it is ready to come out. Nature then takes care of it by opening the parts. They seemed to worry about the caesarian, and the therapist explained that it is a rare occurrence, and often beneficial to mother and child.

Linda looked pensively out the window. Then with a deep sigh of satisfaction and obviously relieved, she impulsively threw her arms around the therapist and kissed her several times. Hilton had steadfastly refused to join. Emma implored the therapist to make him come over. The therapist said it was obvious he was not ready to discuss this, just as they had not been ready up till now. They had known the therapist for a long time and not shown this interest before.

Emma then quickly wrote from one to ten in a vertical column. She requested repetition of terms used and enumerated, "No. 1—vagina; No. 2—penis," and so on. After she had finished writing, the therapist asked her what she intended to do with this list of terms. She said, "Show my mother. She stalled me long enough." Both she and Linda had known all about menstruation, and Emma proceeded to tell a number of smutty jokes, indicating that she had undoubtedly indulged in a great deal of sex discussion with her friends. She said she had seen her father hold a "scum bag" to the window and examine it. She awakened Linda. Both girls asked why he examined it. Questioning revealed that they knew its use. The therapist explained that the father puts the seed in there because if placed in the mother there is a likelihood of pregnancy. Emma said, "Now I'll go get intercoursed." The explanation was given about responsibilities accompanying this.

During all this Hilton played very quietly, and we may surmise that he listened. A visit was made to the children's homes in order to apprise the mothers of the type of discussion we occasionally carried on. In the case of Emma and Linda the parents immediately segregated the girls from the parents' sleeping quarters.

Following this Linda, Emma, and Hilton discussed sleeping quarters. Linda sadly related that she disliked the new arrangement. She said, "I would like to be inside my mother again," indicating that she could not bear the separation. In response to questions she said, "So I could live longer." She elaborated, indicating that she had been thinking about her relationship to her mother. She would like to be reborn at her present age, but with a closer bond to her mother. Her sister asked if she meant that she wants to die. She said no, but that she used to be afraid of dying when she went to sleep. Emma explained that they "got nervous" after their tonsils were removed.

Linda and Emma accused one another of having started this fear of death, and it was apparent that Emma was guilty. Hilton, who listened attentively, made light of the whole thing. He sleeps in the same room with his parents "because there's no room." He facetiously commented, "Who knows! I may die tonight."

Annette and Mike played little part in this discussion. Each of them shared a room with one sibling.

In following sessions Emma was still questioning about intercourse, and she remarked, "Why do they intercourse in such a nasty place?" Linda answered, "You can't kiss and have a baby," and in disgust replied directly to Emma's question, "Just because

341

they want a baby." Annette took a minor role in these discussions, probably because of a guilt feeling. She informed the therapist in individual interviews that she had some sex play. (Mike's sexual activities are not known.)

Emma said that their mother informed them of a law prohibiting intercourse in children and questioned it. The therapist explained that there is a law to protect minors. When Linda was asked if she had been thinking about these things, she admitted that she worried about whether it was harmful to have intercourse while the baby was in the mother's "stomach." This was discussed in terms of anatomy. Emma tried to get Hilton interested. She said, "I came from my mother's stomach. Where did you come from, Hilton?" He replied, "I don't know." Emma said, "Don't you ever ask?" "No! and I never will!"

Emma inquired about the physiology of breasts, and this was explained. She said, "I want to stay young a long time because I want to live long." As a result a discussion of ages arose. The children made comparisons between the therapist and their parents.

Linda thoughtfully said, "I'm still thinking about how the pipe fed the two babies (twins) that were in my mother's stomach." The therapist drew a picture and explained it to her. She said she had been having daydreams like "when you're worried." The therapist said she could understand that these things were on her mind. She said, "Now that I know I won't need to think about it any more."

During following sessions, Hilton displayed a good deal of aggression. It was apparent that he was angry because the therapist was paying too much attention to the others. This was indeed a reality situation for him. Again he made an attempt to throw himself out the window. At the next session the therapist directly explained to him that she realized he doubted her sincerity and interest in him. After this the group hardly ever had real trouble with this child. He was occasionally restless and noisy, but never again was he annoying as in the past.

Mike had been ill but resumed coming to sessions and Carl, too, was coming regularly. The days were hot, and the group had cooling refreshments. Mike could not relate himself to the group but refused to give it up. It is interesting to note that Mike complained to his mother about the "vile" things the therapist permitted the children to discuss, and this complaint was carried by the mother to the school. This situation, of course, was dealt with. He continued to show hostility, talked about masturbation and "boys who think about dirty things." At one time while painting he stated that he was "painting out the boys who talked dirty." At another time he released a great deal of his aggression against his mother. "She gives me a God damned pain in the neck because she takes my money away from me." (Mike was the only one who used such language in the group.)

During the three sessions that followed the children got along on a friendly, free, and pleasant basis. They played quietly, and there was very little show-off behavior. An observer might easily have believed this to be a group of well-adjusted children. From this time on, they played with paints and decided to organize a "club." In discussing organization, they called upon Carl for advice and help. Some of the old conflictual behavior reasserted itself. However, the children settled differences themselves without any help from the therapist and finally elected a president. The children were very fair and selected Hilton because the suggestion came from him. When he attempted to serve in his official capacity, he realized his lack of experience and called upon Carl to show him how. Linda and Annette were very unhappy; they wanted to be president. They accepted Hilton's nomination with poor grace. When the "club" decided to keep minutes, Annette volunteered. At the next session the children went through the motions of parliamentary procedure. They then decided that a name was necessary. These suggestions followed: "The Happy Children; The Good Luck Children; The Thursday Afternoon Children; The Merry Children."

Hilton and Mike decided that a club needs money, and the entire session was devoted to plans for fund raising.

In celebration of Carl's graduation, a party was held. The children made their purchases and took care of the proceedings themselves, performing their tasks very nicely.

To close the season's activities, the group decided to have a farewell picnic. They excluded Mike but showed fine sensitivity in sparing his feelings. The day was well spent and with only one annoyance. This occurred when Hilton left the group. The children themselves dealt with him. They entered into a discussion initiated by a remark Annette had made to the effect that when she is away from her mother she does not do things her mother would not wish her to, and yet when with her mother she can be "so bad." The children all admitted that they do things that their mothers disapproved of. They all wrote stories about the day's outing.

The children then disbanded for the summer. All wrote from camp, Hilton writing daily. He signed his letter, "With many kisses."

Two cases will give a concrete example of an evaluation of the group experience as it affected individual children, their development in the group, and how it carried over outside the group:

LINDA

Problem

"Nervous since birth," fears, anxieties, sibling rivalry, running away from unpleasant situations into illness. Feels unloved and insecure. Gets satisfaction from claiming mother's attention through her fears.

Background

Mother apparently rejects this child, who was born while family was under severe financial stress and had to move in with father's mother. Struggle between grandmother and mother ensued over care of the child as mother felt grandmother was spoiling her. This mother seems unable to exert authority and recognized that she is inclined to take the line of least resistance. She seems to prefer Emma because of no overt problems presented by her. Linda seems to get positive satisfaction from *father*. Since the birth of twin brothers, feels rejected by father, too. Father leaves bringing up of children to the mother.

Early Behavior in Group

Petulant when does not get own way. Always wants to be first. Plays she is a baby and goes through all the motions. Fears the dark. Refuses to go to the washroom. Became hysterical when accidentally locked in a room with Jean. Quarrelsome with sister. Imitative. Jealous and feels that children talk about her.

344

Progress

Suspicious at first. Soon established a friendly relationship. Group interaction stimulated more grown-up response. No longer plays baby. (Mother helped here by playing Linda is a baby once again.) In the group Linda learned to make the adjustment which helped her to accept a minor place, especially when the group was being organized. She accepted that the therapist could like all the children equally well and therefore she did not need to stay at her side continually. Her changed attitude carried over to the outside. She made and kept friends. A free discussion of sex fantasy and the reality relieved her curiosity regarding birth and helped her overcome most of her fears, such as dark rooms and locked doors. Gradually she became more aggressive in the group and at home. She has less need to claim attention on levels formerly utilized. Some recurrences might be interpreted as trying the therapist out to see whether she can still love her and maintain an interest in her under any conditions she sets up.

HILTON

Problem

Disorderly child, disobedient, stealing problem, eats beyond all bounds, destructive, hyperactive, impertinent, facial grimaces, can't get along with children, sibling rivalry.

Background

Mother has a dominant personality, rules the home as an autocrat. *Father*, a weak, ineffectual person. Mother is hyperactive, was at one time committed to a mental hospital. On her return two years later immediately became pregnant, and it was therefore inadvisable to return Hilton to his home. He had been living in foster homes. For a period of three years he was never visited by his family and during this time was shifted from one home to another because he was too difficult to cope with. On his return to his own home two years ago his behavior became extreme, as already described.

Early Behavior in Group

Extremely noisy and hyperactive. He used the therapy room as though it were a playground. He struck at the children and the therapist. Once kicked Mike severely in the jaw. Was frightened and asked, "What shall I do? Kill myself?" Though Hilton's

345

behavior was so asocial, he reached out for group play and generally introduced activity which included the others. He seemed the only one who wanted group play from the first. He was alert and generally ready with suggestions. He never used bad language but frequently engaged the children in rough play. He insulted the therapist when she did not give him all her attention. Hilton freed himself of a feeling that his father broke up his home by beating, tearing, and biting the father doll. Through the play activity he disclosed feelings of rejection when he told that he had not been visited for three years by his parents or siblings.

Progress

Frequent reminders by the children gradually had an effect on the boy. He definitely showed that he was eager to be liked, though he did little at first to gain this end. As Hilton felt the friendly interest of the girls and boys and of the therapist, his behavior became considerably modified both in the group and at school. Then there set in a period when he became ingratiating. From the first he carefully guarded the play material and enjoyed the responsibility and feeling of superiority which grew out of this. As Hilton became more sure of himself, he was able to play more quietly and with greater concentration, although he did at times lapse into his former behavior. Where at first Hilton was greedy when refreshments were served, he later shared treats with the children, and his entire behavior became more restrained. An outstanding improvement was Hilton's restraint in eating. Where formerly he was wont to eat the meal prepared for the entire family at home, if he could get at it (and he often did this), his food habits are now more normal.

COMMENTS AND INTERPRETATIONS

While the children busied themselves with their play and activities, the therapist generally sat in one corner of the room. From the very beginning she openly took notes, as she did also in individual interviews before and after starting the group. When asked, the therapist told the children frankly that the notes would be used by her to remember what went on in the group. In her comments on the group, Mrs. Gabriel states, "The outstanding gains to the children in group treatment are that feelings and inhibitions were released and the children realized they were no different from other children. They were able to reactivate the family setup and to relive their sibling rivalries in the group situation, satisfying and constructive, compensatory behavior resulting." It would seem, however, from the extraordinary content of the children's verbal productions, the psychodynamic reconstructive gains went beyond external and pragmatic and adaptive experiences. Another point to be kept in mind is that the therapist continued to see the children individually and improve their milieu by working with their families and schools.

This report unmistakably reveals the possibilities group treatment holds for emotionally disturbed and socially maladjusted children. The unusual cathartic quality in the group achieved by Mrs. Gabriel cannot be matched by anyone less adept and intuitively attuned to patients than she is. Her apt interventions and her superb capacity for identification with her young patients played a critical role in attaining the perfectability and success in her work with this group of children (and many others later on).

The student of this volume should be aware of the uniqueness of the membership of this group of four girls and three boys, and the seriousness of their intrapsychic problems. To begin with, all children had been in individual play therapy with the same therapist for prolonged periods. Thus the pattern for the interviews was to an extent set in advance, as was their content. The children's communications and their awareness of their problems had already been patterned. Because all but one or two had known each other before the inauguration of the group through contacts in the waiting room, they were freer with each other from the very outset than they would have been otherwise.

Another significant factor that stamped the character of the group was that the therapist was fundamentally individual-therapy-oriented. Group therapy was alien to her mind and skills at the time and without being aware of it she continued individual treatment *in the group* rather than *by the group*. The latter process emerged not because the therapist set the stage for it, but because of the inherent tendency of animals — human and others — to interaction in compresence.

Mrs. Gabriel well recognized the interpersonal and intragroup dynamics as they made their appearance and used them creditably in the therapeutic grist. However, her original orientation, if not intent, was not groupistic. Were it so she would not have included Mike, whose problem she well knew because he had been a patient of hers; she did become aware of this error, but somewhat too late.

Our impression of Mike was that he suffered a brain injury, probably a slight one, but this diffuse hostility, distractability, and the occasional irrationality of reactions pointed in that direction. He was not group material at this stage and probably would never be. A neurological examination, including an EEG, is indicated for children manifesting symptoms such as Mike's. The inclusion of Hilton can also be questioned, because of his irascibility, jealousy, and motility.

It requires no great psychologic perspicacity to recognize that the source of Hilton's problem was affect hunger. This was clear not only from his rivalrous conduct in the group, in relation to the therapist and his sibling substitutes, but also from his anamnesis. The key to his therapy is a deep, sustained, monopolistic individual relation. The pathetic regularity of daily communication with the therapist while at camp is ample evidence of this overpowering need for an affectional tie. He could not countenance, and suffered greatly at, sharing the only truly maternal person he had known. The dual role of the therapist was destructive for this boy.

Hilton should have continued in his individual relation with the therapist and should have been placed in an activity therapy group. He would have been difficult there, too, but not to the same degree, for Hilton would have had the emotional anchorage in his individual therapist, and his inner correctional process would have made greater strides. However, one cannot be too sanguine as to the outcome of a case of such deep affect hunger as Hilton's. To attempt to satiate an affect hunger is like trying to fill a bottomless container.

It must also be noted that Hilton was at the same time devoted to the group and seemed to prefer group to individual activities and communications. This preference may contain an index to the direction that therapy for one with his family history should take. His mother was obviously schizophrenic; hence his own weak ego resources were limited. Since the basic elements of the ego are somatic — biochemical and especially endocrinologic — their dysfunctions can be genetically passed from generation to generation (Slavson, 1959). When this is the case, uncovering therapy is threatening to the patient, and Hilton may have sought escape from it in group activity which, unlike verbalization, threatened his ego minimally. These hypotheses require validation such as psychologic testing, including a Rorschach, and careful observation of the boy's reactions to specific stimuli.

Another unique feature of this group was the inclusion of two sisters. This is generally prohibited because of the complications such combinations present to a group. Even friends are ordinarily barred. The presence of Linda and Emma, however, did not create the difficulties one would expect. The situation was probably mitigated by the two girls' antecedent sharing of the therapist and their knowledge of each other's problems. Their symbiotic relation was to a degree diluted through the introduction into their lives of other children to whom they redirected their sexual and nonsexual libido. The "discussions" in which other children also participated, rather than indulging in dialogue with each other, tended to decrease their exclusive need of each other. The fact that they shared their "secret"—their sex play—with the group and therapist served to decathect and gradually correct their relation.

The profound unconscious content of the children's communications in the group: their fears of destruction, preoccupations with death, sexual fantasies, anxieties, and guilts, and the corrective outcomes of the cathartic reenactments and verbalizations amply support Freud's monumental formulations and the efficacy of his analytic techniques in cases of psychoneuroses. His detractors, with their shortcuts in the treatment of psychoneuroses, should take heed of what these prepubertal children revealed (Slavson, 1972).

FLEXIBILITY IN A-IGP

While AGT is an uncompromisingly rigid technique in which the least divergence from the procedures described negates its effectiveness and may lead to dire outcomes, A-IGP permits a considerable range of flexibility. The media, materials, activities, explanations, and interpretations are such that the therapist is constrained to respond verbally and in action in accordance with the varying requirements of a situation. This includes not only the structure of the situation itself, but also the condition of each patient at the time of its occurrence. For these reasons, verbal interchanges and the criteria for membership are less stringent than in AGT, where all patients, with very few exceptions, are dealt with largely in a blanket fashion. In A-IGP the role of the therapist and his reactions, motoric and verbal, vary according to the needs of the patients as individuals and the appropriateness of the situation.

The group on which the preceding report is based, for example, had to be restricted in its movements because it met in an active neighborhood center. The therapist did not hesitate to impose restrictions but explained to the group the reasons for them. Emma's response was that the therapist was "a good and a just" person. All the others accepted the limitations without demurral and conformed to them. Should a similar situation arise in AGT, the restriction would have to be imposed by letter to the therapist from an official of the building, which the therapist would have to pass on to the group in a manner already described.

A-IGP is flexible also in the matter of initiating treatment and in the therapist's therapeutic style. We have presented two procedures of organizing and conducting an activity-interview group. In the first the therapist and his patients make their acquaintance at the beginning of the group. The children are invited as they are for an activity group. The first introductions are similar, until the point where the children are asked to gather around the table for a "talk." The next steps have been outlined earlier in this chapter.

The other method is to form a group from the clientele of one therapist, as in Mrs. Gabriel's case, which may at first be used to supplement individual interviews, or vice versa, and either continue the double approach, or discontinue individual interviews with some or all of the patients, according to therapeutic indications. The style as in individual and group treatment can, in fact should, proceed from the therapist's own training, convictions, and methodology. Every theoretic formulation on which agreement may exist is inevitably applied to some degree differently according to the knowledge, judgment, temperament, and insights of the particular therapist.

POSTSCRIPT

It is most unusual that the follow-up information covering an extensive period of time after termination of treatment is available on child patients such as those reported on in this study. The authors learned in a recent communication from Mrs. Gabriel of the state of her former patients, *four decades* after treatment. It has not been unusual for Mrs. Gabriel to maintain contact with numerous of her erstwhile patients years after formal termination of treatment. To quote directly from a letter to the authors dated August 19, 1972:

"Of the group of six which I described, the two sisters are in touch with me annually. Both are happily married. The older one (Emma) has a son who is in college—an "A" student. Her husband holds an important position in the U.S. government. Linda is married to a college professor in New England. She has an adolescent son and a daughter. She herself will receive her bachelor's degree within the year.

"Hilton had a satisfactory army career. He later married a nice girl from his neighborhood. They have one child. He is in the publishing business.

"Two of the group were killed in the army."

PART III

PLAY GROUP THERAPY

XVII

Play in Growth
and in Therapy

Play group therapy (PGT) is an analytic form of group treatment employed with preschool children approximately four to six years of age. Using *libido-evoking* materials, the patients reveal through play their life problems, usually related to parents and siblings, and the attendant fears, tensions, confusions, anxieties, anger, and other emotions. PGT is similar in some respects to A-IGP in that in both forms of therapy the patients' behavior and play themes are explored for underlying meanings and feelings and "interpreted" by the therapist in a manner comprehensible by children of this age. The essential differences lie in the ages of the patients and their levels of physical and emotional development. The age factor and maturational levels require modifications in both the procedural methods of the therapist and the nature, range, and depth of interpretation as well as in the therapeutic setting.

THE NATURE OF PLAY

Before describing the principles and methodology of PGT, it would be helpful to examine the antecedents of normal play in biological and psychological development and the values of play in child psychotherapy. The origins of children's play, its importance in the life of children, its universality and idiosyncratic manifestations throw light on the significance of play forms of emotionally disturbed children.

355

Origins of Play

Motor activity of children is a part of normal biological function. It has been established that when infants and children are deprived of opportunities for adequate use of the neuromuscular apparatus, physical, intellectual, and emotional growth is impaired. The investigations by Spitz (1945, 1946) of the vitiating effects on infants of prolonged *hospitalism*, for example, offer dramatic evidence of the disastrous consequences of sensory and motor deprivation. As the infant and later the child is free to employ his sensorimotor apparatus, increasingly complex activities arise as he passes through the stages of kyrokinesis, macrokinesis, and microkinesis. Activity gradually becomes more purposive and more directly responsive to specific inner and outer stimuli. As the qualities of will and intent are added, and with the advent of cognition, the young child can be considered capable of play.

Play Patterns: From Simple to Complex

The earliest play forms are predominantly imitative behavior responses, followed later by independent mimicry actions. The young child reaches a significant stage when he grows able to include symbolic representation as part of play. Piaget and Inhelder (1969) describe the child's use of symbolic play not so much for adapting to reality but rather to assimilate reality to himself. The outer world is very difficult to comprehend for the young child and is entirely beyond his control. He develops a sense of comprehension, mastery, and security not by coping with the overwhelming outer world, but rather by incorporating component parts of it, rendering them assimilable and usable by him.

His growing intelligence makes the child increasingly facile in symbolic play. According to Piaget's findings, symbolism in play reaches its apogees between the ages of two and three and again at five and six.[1] With the acquisition of what represents for the young child extraordinary and advanced skills, more rapid locomotion (running, jumping), language, ideation, and conation, play becomes an even more expressive and experiential form of behavior.

[1] Note also the fact that play group therapy was found particularly appropriate with children up to six years of age.

Interest in the form and substance of material objects comprises the "curriculum" of play. One gets the impression of the toddler's need to indulge the senses as he views, touches, tastes, smells, listens to, drops, and retrieves almost everything within reach. (In psychotherapy of children four to six years of age, such behavior often reappears in a regressive context.) This kind of play, which has much to do with learning and familiarization, becomes modified as the child consciously begins to experiment.

Play patterns and content progress from simple exploration of form and substance of objects to more complicated themes enacted in role play related to significant objects—parents and siblings. Still later there is need to find out about the nature of objects and persons beyond the confines of the home and family.

Representational Play

In this form of play the child attempts to duplicate objects, animate and inanimate, in his familiar environment, which usually takes place through toys and by the child's assuming the identities of these objects and imitating their movements.

Mimicry in Play

Mimicry is not consciously conceived by the child as a need to *be* like the object, but rather as a way of *knowing* it better through assuming its qualities. This is depicted by a young child who plays at being his puppy dog by crawling, growling, and nipping; or the child who takes the nursing bottle from his mouth to feed his mother. Mimicry assumes a further dimension of pretense and role playing as the child approaches the second year of life. Now there is elaboration of the "plot" as the child, in play, consciously modifies the behavior of the persons he chooses to imitate. He uses their role—and his own—to enact real-life situations which affect him in important ways, but now he is able to discharge ambivalent feelings in play. The child can now mirror the real world, adapt it, and make accommodations to it.

Reproductional Play

Another advanced form of play activity is the child's portrayal of reality through reproduction: drawing and painting. Using pencil, chalk, crayon, finger and brush paints, he moves from random experimentation with scribbling, lines, and color to attempts at portraying reality in terms of his own imagery. The most primitive stick figures of persons, or irregular, ill-defined colored paint blotches, meaningless to an adult observer, are tantamount to literal representations of buildings and trees in the child's eye and mind. Pictorial representation provides significant feelings of mastery for the child. Drawings also disclose valuable content for psychotherapy. A child who draws three stick figures and informs the therapist that they are "Me-mommy-daddy," insisting under gentle inquiry that there is "no baby," when in fact an infant sibling does exist, provides therapeutic leverage for exploring feelings and wishes.

Play and Identity

A child's developmental need to foster his identification by acquiring the attributes, characteristics, and skills which, in very subtle and complicated ways, are being communicated to him as necessary for his sense of identity, is helped along through play. Such activities constitute "exercises" in maturation. An example of this is the child consciously assuming the roles of persons in his immediate family. There are permutations of such play, when the child, in fantasy, attributes to the imagery of the family roles he reenacts qualities that are in reality nonexistent.

As children grow more aware of others approximately the same age, playing together becomes a way in which social horizons expand. This fosters development away from egocentricity toward increasing allocentricity. The maturing influence of play in groups is a factor used to advantage in group therapy.

Play in the Service of Curiosity and Psychic Equilibrium

Play and motoric activities in general "are more natural communicative pathways. Subtle complexities of thought and feelings, which would be difficult to describe otherwise, become expressed more readily through a spontaneous language consisting of words, gestures, enactments of life situations with dolls and puppets, paintings and drawings and still other methods" (Schiffer, 1969, p. 95).

Play not only represents the means by which external events and objects can be explored, with new perceptions and meanings added to those already integrated, it is also the principal instrument for satisfying normal curiosity. In the main, play is basically *self-serving,* because the young child is more absorbed in using it to gratify his own impelling needs and is not concerned with what adults deduce from it.

The young child's inability to cope with tensions, frustrations, and emotions, and to satisfy normal, surging curiosity through thought and language impels him toward active discovery, manipulation, and other direct exploratory methods. Each child must be his own Columbus. Learning, integrating, and reasoning are the child's prerogatives. As time passes, he discovers that play can also help communication with his parents and others, and he will consciously use it to make himself understood. In psychotherapy the child is helped to discover an entirely new dimension to play as the therapist utilizes its content to reveal hidden meanings and to promote "understanding."

Increasingly, play helps to distinguish between reality and unreality. As some of his more primitive needs are frustrated or incompletely fulfilled, the child uses it to compensate for deprivation. In this way he copes with restricting and disciplining elements of the outer world, to which he must accommodate. Erikson (1940) has characterized young children's play as "autotherapeutic" in that through representational and fantasy play the child reconciles what is denied to him and which causes his feelings of frustration and defeat.

Susan Isaacs (1933) also addresses herself to the emotional equivalents in play: "It [play] ... brings him psychic equilibrium in the early years. . . . In his play activities the child externalizes and works out to some measure of harmony the different trends of his internal psychic life . . . he learns to relate his deepest and most primitive fantasies to the ordered world of real relations" (p. 425).

One of the authors (Slavson, 1948), in contrasting play with recreation, says, "To the young child, play is life in the deepest and most meaningful sense. Healthy emotions and a vigorous intellect require full release of the play impulse in early childhood. Not only are the emotions distorted by denial of play, but aggressiveness, which can be turned into curiosity, is stunted. . . . [Organized] recreation . . . does not imply *primary growth* as play does in the case of the child" (pp. 2-3).

Play Counters Passivity

Freud has described play as a "revolt against passivity," among other things. He comments that in all areas of their experiences young children have a tendency to convert impressions which were received passively into active form (play). The child "tries to do itself what has just been done to it." So great is the need on the part of children to gain security through mastery that it leads them to convert into active play passively received experiences which were disagreeable (Freud, 1931, p. 236).

In an earlier paper Freud (1907) compared the child at play to the imaginative writer, "in that he creates a world of his own or, rather, re-arranges the things of his world in a new way which pleases" (pp. 143-144). This kind of play is serious, and much emotional meaning is attached to it. Even so, the child is quite capable of distinguishing his play from reality. His use of the "objects and circumstances" from the outside world in his play is that which links it to reality and distinguishes it from daydreaming. In later adult life, when the pleasures of actual play are denied, humor and make believe (fantasy) become substitutive "play" outlets. "Actually we can never give anything up; we can only exchange one thing for another" (p. 145).

PLAY IN PSYCHOTHERAPY

Play as Ego "Defense"

Play is used at times by *all children* as an abreactive outlet. Feelings and behavior suppressed through fear of punishment, or impulsively acted out despite fears, may be transmuted at opportune times and circumstances into safer play forms. The emotionally disturbed child leans heavily on play to defend himself against anxiety, fears, and emotional conflicts which are more pervasive and less transient than the episodic stresses that all children periodically encounter. For the disturbed child, play may be considered in the context of an ego-defense mechanism, such as denial and displacement, for example. In therapy, play not only relieves the child of some of the emotional effects of hurtful experiences, its content themes also help the therapist to explore their latent meanings. In group treatment, the presence of other children playing in a similar fashion makes it easier for a child to learn how to alleviate or mitigate his emotions.

Because the young child's libido is still fluid and his defenses minimal, emotions surface easily in play. Nuclear problem elements of young children can be uncovered with much less technical therapeutic procedures than are required with older patients. Melanie Klein (1932) stated this observation succinctly: "The way back to the unconscious (in the child) is easier to find."

Levels of Fantasy

Fantasy is the "magic wand" of play that enables a child to cope with the gaps or obstructions in his life caused by outer restraints, inhibitions due to fears and anxiety, and realistic limitations attributable to his physical and intellectual immaturity. What the young child cannot solve, conquer, gratify, or in a general sense, deal with appropriately, he resolves with the omnipotence and omniscience of fantasy. Fantasy is an effective method for escaping excessive stress; it can create, change, and master circumstance. When used in reasonable degree, fantasy is a quality of normal play which in most children slowly changes to more closely approximate reality with lapses when stress is too demanding or occurs under conditions of fatigue.

The troubled child employs fantasy to an extraordinary degree in the context of his play to cope with adverse circumstances in his life. Exclusive fantasy, perseverative with repetition of the same themes,[2] is an indication of emotional difficulty. This furnishes the therapist with opportunities to trace the etiology of emotional difficulties, to assess points of fixation in development, and to explore the underlying themes with the child. Children's misconceptions such as false ideas about conception and birth which cause confusion and aggravate already existing problems are often revealed in perseverative symbolic and fantasy play. In

---

[2] In *Beyond the Pleasure Principle*. Freud (1920) speaks of this perseveration in children's play: "Children repeat unpleasurable experiences for the additional reason that they can master a powerful impression far more thoroughly by *being active* than they could by merely experiencing it passively" (p. 35, italics ours).

addition, forbidden pleasures find vicarious gratification at regressive fantasy levels.

Inhibition of Play

A continuing inhibition of play in a young child signals even
deeper emotional disturbance, since even a naturally shy child
usually overcomes his initial diffidence in the therapeutic setting
and uses play materials which are intrinsically significant. Marked
or total inhibition is a condition of immobilization of activity and
implies an extraordinary fear of expression and a defense against
contact even through play. Given this circumstance, severely
charged emotional content is an indication of autistic levels, and
the child's distress remains unalleviated since he is apparently
bereft of means to relieve it.

While much of the play content of a normal child reflects his
attempts to grasp the meanings of reality, the play of the emotionally troubled young child is a dramatized personal documentation of his difficulties, usually related to his parents. A normal
child is motivated to explore the meanings of the world about
him and how it *relates* to him, but the disturbed child in his play
depicts more his concern for what the world (family) is *doing* to
him.

Symbolic Play in Therapy

As noted, symbolic play is an advanced stage in the normal
evolution of infant and early childhood play, and it reflects the
child's growing powers of cognition. With disturbed children in
play therapy, representational symbolic play is common because
it is difficult for them to assuage distress through reflection,
intellectualization, and verbalization alone. They use play objects
whose symbolic identities are frankly manifest, i.e., family dolls
to reenact their problems.

With young children, the "history" of disturbance is current
and actively experienced in its immediate impact. While adolescent and adult patients struggle to recall—and also resist
recalling—the anamneses of their emotional difficulties, young
children, using appropriate symbolic play items, *actually depict*
the manifest nature of present and not too remote conflicts. Thus,
a child patient may attack and literally destroy the "symbolic"

baby doll, which represents his newborn sibling, identifying it as "naughty baby, bad baby." Inquiry by the therapist, gently probing for the true identity of the symbol, easily unmasks the thin disguise, and the patient, now without fear, reveals his strong jealousy of "Susan, Mommy's baby," and his wish to do away with her.

As fear of retaliation is reduced, identifications are more specific, e.g., the "little boy" in the drama yields to "*I* hit her!" and the "bad lady who went away" becomes "*Mommy* leaves me in the house." A lessening of symbolism and a more direct depicting of actuality in the life of the patient through play is an indication of (1) growing security in the transference relationship with the therapist; (2) absence of fear of expressing primitive and regressive feelings; (3) freedom to abreact and to gain cathartic relief.

In these ways children in play therapy are helped to explore the symbolic play representations associated with their fixations and regressions. With the assurance and support provided in the transference, symbolic play material now becomes translated into direct language, with which the child bravely states his real feelings and often intense anguish over the situations that beset him.

Associative Nature of Play Content

The content of play, symbolic or otherwise, follows the laws of association, the logical relationship of mental components. A true understanding of his patient's play cannot be reached by the therapist merely by considering its separate elements but rather must come through awareness of the relatedness of these elements to each other and their connections to what is already known about the child's early development, his familial circumstances and prior behavior. He must also be mindful of how readily the young patient can mutate an object symbolically, converting it to his need of the moment, e.g., a small block cylinder may variously represent "ka-ka," "wee-wee," a gun, or just a "block." The child facilely invests it with the interpretative dimension that his play scenario demands at the moment, and it must be identified promptly and accurately by the therapist if he is to comprehend its relationship to the cathexis associated with the play.

In play therapy, a therapist would impede or subvert the patient's associative thoughts or play sequence through premature or unnecessary interference with the flow of content. However, there are times when the therapist may, with circumspection, join the child's associative play sequence to encourage production of additional content and thus explore meanings. In PGT one effect of such participation by the therapist is that it draws other children into the play, and the associated content is elaborated and further enriched, particularly in matters that affect the children in common. The therapist will be successful in this only if his line of inquiry and his manner serve to *complement* the child's or the children's associations and not act as foreign intrusions, which would have an extraneous, limiting effect.

One of the authors had the following interesting experience with an eight-year-old boy, illustrating this technical "assist" to the associative play process.

Bernard spoke of a movie he had seen about Hitler and the uniforms "those men" wore, with that "thing" (swastika) on it. "Here, I'll show you. It looks like this," and he drew a fair resemblance of it on paper. "Then there was that other man (Mussolini), who they hung up on his feet and hit and kicked and then knocked him down and kicked him into nothing!" (The "educational" effects of the movies and TV!) Bernard continued drawing swastikas and asked the therapist if he knew how to draw a uniform. The therapist shook his head. Bernard then took the cap pistol (with caps) and proceeded to enact the roles of "robber and cop" and "good and bad guys" in turn. The therapist sat through all this, silently watching and responding monosyllabically to direct questions or nodding when Bernard occasionally looked to see if he had his complete attention.

A new element was added to this aggressive play when Bernard mentioned how powerful one character was. He added, "My mother said if you eat certain foods for breakfast you get big, powerful muscles like this!" (laughingly showing his biceps, gun in hand). Therapist: "Powerful is strong." Bernard: "Yeah, you can do anything." Therapist: "You don't have to be afraid." Bernard: "Not of nothing!" shooting the pistol caps furiously. Bernard then went into a complicated enactment of how "Hitler" *shot himself* at the end, falling to the floor as if dead. Several times this was repeated, with Bernard now identifying his role variously, but always as a "bad man."

At one point, he lay on the floor on his back, rigid, eyes closed, head near the chair of the seated therapist, who peered down. Bernard opened his eyes and lay quietly, looking up at him. Therapist: "The bad man got killed?" Bernard, strangely soft now: "Yeah." Therapist: "If he did bad things, maybe he felt bad after. Sometimes it's like that." (Tentative bridging from symbolism to identification.) Bernard nodded, still quiet and appearing almost moody. Therapist: "Sometimes children worry about what they do, or even what they don't do but think about up here," pointing to his own forehead. Bernard: "When you were little, did you sometimes worry about what you did, too?" Therapist: "Yes." Bernard: "I worry sometimes."

His last comment was quite true. Bernard had only recently become able to express, *only in play,* some of the massive hostility he had never been able to discharge otherwise. Aggression had been filtering through at home and in school, as reported by his parent. His strong ambivalence about aggression was reflected in abreactive play in therapy as he acted out his anger, really intended for his quarrelsome parents, and his guilt and other retributive reactions, such as a need to be punished for "bad" thoughts.

Following this meaningful exchange, Bernard sprang from the floor, asked the therapist to reload the cap pistol, and then proceeded to shoot the caps in reckless and gleeful abandon.

Rate of Change in Play Therapy

Changes in behavior patterns, personality, and character can be brought about relatively rapidly in children four to six years of age because of their malleability and minimally developed super-egos. With much less difficulty than in the case of older persons, they are able to free themselves of superego constrictions, and fears and anxieties are consequently tapped. This takes place even with emotional content which is regressive, on pregenital and genital levels. It is anticipated that an average patient four or five years of age, who is responding with reasonable success in play therapy, should show improvement within a year or less.

THE NATURE OF THERAPEUTIC PLAY

To recapitulate, the demands on the growing child inevitably frustrate or interfere with his primitive, narcissistic, self-serving impulses causing him pain and discomfort. As a result, the parents, who are the primary agents of these frustrations, assume the images of hostile, repressive agents that engender ambivalent feelings toward themselves, feelings that only too often grow into active stubbornness, resentment, and hostility. The concept of the "witch mother" is commonly accepted as being part of human social and psychic pathology.

When some parents, through callousness or ignorance of children's nature and needs, or as a result of their own emotional immaturities, continue to impose massive restraints, denials, and punishments, children's coping abilities are excessively strained and relief is sought through destructiveness, defensive fantasy, and compensatory play. Also, because the psyche of the child is lacking adequate defensive and compensatory mechanisms, he erupts with anger and spite to which parents usually react with even greater restrictions and punishments, thus increasing the intensity of his already hypercathected feelings.

Specific types of play alleviate a child's stress. A child who "destroys" a doll figure, for example, by causing it to fall from the height of a play building, may "play out" homicidal wishes toward a parent or a sibling. This genre of play can be viewed as *self-therapy*. Such conscious or unconscious enactment of intent is *therapeutic* because draining off feelings relieves inner tensions and has the effect of self-therapy.

The concomitants of such play may also generate fear, guilt, and anxiety since in the past acts of this nature led to criticism and punishment. In the treatment setting, however, the therapist is permissive and understanding; he respects the child and his activities and *accepts* them without comment, or he employs them to convey to the child the underlying meanings of his acts. The child is relieved thereby and is then able to advance his emotional maturity. Thus, the nuclear elements in therapeutic play are (1) uncritical and empathic acceptance by the therapist of the child and his productions and (2) an environment containing materials that either suggest or respond to the child's emotional needs.

In one group of five-year-olds, a girl set up the bedroom in the toy house placing the mother and child in bed and the figure of the father on the floor in the hallway outside the bedroom door. The child's enactment of her wish was obvious; and were this fantasy enacted in the home, some adults, most probably the mother, would either admonish the child for being so cruel to the father or, being amused, narrate the incident to the father or others in the presence of the child. Either of these reactions would generate guilt, fear, and embarrassment in the child. Whatever her reactions, the experience would certainly not be therapeutic. In such instances, the catharsis that impels the child's act does not serve as relief, but rather maximizes his difficulties.

Another example is supplied us by little Conchita, a five-year-old member of a day-care kindergarten in a neighborhood settlement house. She and five others—three girls and two boys—of approximately the same age were selected for a separate group that met once a week because they did not adjust adequately to the larger 35-member kindergarten class. Conchita refused to participate in any girls' activities; she played only with the boys and partook in all their boisterous projects. In fact, she was the leader in most of their acting out. Conchita refused to wear girls' attire, preferring boys' clothes. This problem stemmed from the fact that Conchita, being an only child, her father, for reasons of his own, treated her as though she were a boy. He played boys' games with her and taught her the various athletic skills that were in the province of masculine interests.

In the small group Conchita attached herself to one of the boys, and they made almost an exclusive twosome for several months. Their daily game was playing out a family: she being the mother, her playmate the father, and one of the toy dolls their "baby." They bathed the infant, fed it, lovingly "put it in the crib" (a small couch that happened to be in the room where the group met). As already stated, this weekly game was repeated for three or four months. One morning Conchita appeared at the kindergarten with a skirt over her pants. This became her regular attire. Once, one of the assistant teachers inadvisedly asked Conchita, "What would you like to be, Conchita, a boy or a girl?" Conchita's answer was, "A girl," but she quickly added, "Also a boy."

An amusing byplay of these events was the response of the "father" in this fantasy play. One day, as he was carrying the toy baby-feeding bottle which he had filled with "milk" (water), he absentmindedly began to suck at the nipple. He quickly checked himself mumbling, "I'm some father, drinking from my baby's bottle!"

Here the problem was faulty identification and this prolonged role-playing altered the girl's identification which could not have occurred in any but a therapeutic setting. Even if the same equipment were supplied at home, for example, the "mess" that the children created would not be countenanced. The permissiveness of the woman in charge of the group, who was a volunteer with no training in any field related to psychotherapy, made the girl's improvement possible. Her function was limited to replenishing materials, keeping notes of the children's activities, and setting up simple refreshments. In fact, she had taken up a position in a corner, at a distance from the activity area of the rather large room, and was partly obscured by furniture.

The above development, one of many of a similar character, tangibly illustrates the two nuclear elements of therapeutic play: suitable climate and equipment, and the role of the adult.

Resistance in Child Therapy

The psychoanalytic concept posits that resistance is opposition against attempts to expose the unconscious. Freud (1932) pointed out: "The whole theory of psycho-analysis is . . . in fact built up on the perception of the resistance offered to us by the patient when we attempt to make his unconscious conscious to him" (p. 68).

The therapist who treats young children through analytic methods, individually or in groups, using play materials, does not encounter resistance of a clinical type to a significant degree. What is sometimes construed as resistance is fear, or *nonneurotic* anxiety in children about how the therapist will treat them and respond to their behavior. The child is concerned with consequences, e.g., pain, anger, punishment, withdrawal of love, abandonment. Therefore, the therapist needs to be concerned with creating the climate of freedom. Assured of this, and encouraged by the therapist's interpreting the underlying meanings of some of his play, the child patient can rapidly demonstrate a lack of resistance as he proceeds to enact highly regressive, libidinal material.

It is understandable why young children oppose treatment at first. After all, why should they be expected to accept a stranger, the therapist, and permit him to share their feelings, when even their own parents are not privy to their conflicts and emotions? The skillful therapist is able to surmount this initial blocking. In PGT it is usually more easily dealt with than in individual treatment because the children are encouraged to relax and communicate through their catalytic effects upon each other.

Children are not self-aware patients; it is the parents who seek relief for distressing circumstances. Despite the discomfort or pain caused by emotional factors, the young child is not a willing participant at first. While it is important to have him understand, within his capacity to comprehend, something about therapy and why he is a patient, he is too young to decide for himself whether he should be one. It would be just as illogical as asking for his permission to use antibiotics for an infection. Important decisions affecting physical and mental health are never surrendered to children. Nor should young children be allowed to terminate when they encounter frustrations in treatment.

Groups are particularly efficacious in dealing with recalcitrance, suspicion, and fearfulness in beginning patients. The presence of other children is comforting to each who confronts the "stranger" and the new setting for the first time. At least other children are familiar, even if they are strangers.

Awareness in Play Therapy

A new dimension is added to the child's play the *very first time* he is helped to see an underlying, personal meaning in it. This discovery comes about when the therapist correctly conveys understanding of a nuclear element of the child's problem. This sharing of common knowledge is furthered even more when, at other times, patient and therapist continue to draw correct meanings, of which the child may not have been conscious. As the therapist demonstrates his understanding of the child's play in its manifest and latent levels, he makes of the child a willing and cooperative collaborator in the search for further (perhaps twilight) understanding and eventual emotional relief.

Increasing Verbalization

Play becomes utilized more consciously as a result of the new experiences, and language assumes increasing usefulness in the overall communication between the child and therapist. This is particularly important for young children whose problems have neurotic features. While it is true that a good deal of what play therapy offers to alleviate emotional distress comes from abreactive play, analytic interpretation is appropriate when activity of itself does not help dissolve anxiety and/or fear. When a child verbalizes readily and feels comfortable in so doing, he will sometimes show an interest in pursuing meanings by asking the therapist for explanations. It is not uncommon at such times for him to ask, "Tell me what it means when...," or "if."

A technical error would be committed in psychotherapy by overindulging the verbal and reflective capacities of children. Interpretation and verbalization are necessary only at appropriate moments in the evolvement of the therapeutic process. If, as a result of enabling a young patient to talk about meanings associated with his play and feelings, the therapist were to verbalize excessively, both the meaningful content and the associative context of the child's play would probably be diminished.

In PGT each child becomes increasingly receptive to explore the underlying meanings of his own play and that of other children. This is an outgrowth of *interstimulation*, a dynamic characteristic of groups.

VALUES OF PLAY FOR PATIENT AND FOR THERAPIST

In summary, in child psychotherapy the values of play are:

1. Release of tensions, anxiety, and fear through reenactment and abreaction, particularly as these are associated with traumata.

2. Finding acceptable outlets for primitive impulses.

3. Dissolving the hypercathexis associated with fixations, and finding sublimations for them.

4. Drawing off excessive aggression through play materials which can absorb the effects of displaced aggression.

5. Developing ego strength through feelings of mastery and accomplishment.

6. Gaining a measure of insight into the underlying causes of disturbances.

7. Fostering the growth of socialization.

For the therapist:

1. It furnishes him with a method of communication which the child can tolerate.

2. The content and methods of play enable him to assess the emotional and physical state and development of the child.

3. Play provides a measure of relative strengths and weaknesses.

4. Play is a means to determine the nuclear facts of a child's problems.

5. The patterns of a child's play can be used as a rough index of his intelligence.

6. Signs of sensory or motor abnormalities can be detected.

7. Differential diagnosis is facilitated.

XVIII

Basic Elements of
Play Group Therapy

Interstimulation

Much of what has been described about the nature of play, its meanings and values, is applicable in both individual and group treatment of young children. However, there are elements that recommend PGT as a preferred modality. One obvious advantage is that it enables the therapist to treat large numbers of children. In addition, through interstimulation children perceive, learn, and utilize different methods of play, thus widening opportunities for self-expression. Other children serve in place of psychological siblings and are of use in working through problems associated with real siblings. Moreover, PGT has value in making the young child more conscious of others. This, plus the growing realization on his part that narcissistic, pleasure-seeking urges must inevitably be accommodated to the needs of others, eventually forces the child into pathways of suppression and sublimation. In this way, social development is achieved.

Still another important advantage of PGT is that the setting provides a social entity in psychological miniature within which reality testing takes place. It is an empirical field with built-in safety features where the patient may assay new behavior modes. Much more than in individual therapy he is able to experience, immediately and directly, the results of different ways of responding to social demands. At the same time, his perception of alternative ways of behaving and reacting is greatly magnified because he finds himself in many common activities with others and is frequently confronted with identical situational problems.

While the young child is still highly individualistic, in reacting to emotions of others in the group, he develops a *resonant empathy*. This is not true empathy that comes with advanced maturity. Rather, in the young child resonant empathy is more conscious awareness of similarities. One child mirrors the emotions of another.

This occurred when Peter, a frightened four-year-old, was brought into the group playroom for the first time. He sat down, wide-eyed, and watched some of the other children busily occupied. Almost immediately tears welled up in his eyes and Peter, upset by the separation from his mother only moments before, began to cry silently. Mary, who had been involved in isolated play with a doll, noticed this, took a few steps toward Peter, knelt on the floor, doll in hand, and also began to weep silently. Mary, who was a timid child, had attended several sessions before this and seemed to have accommodated herself to the group though with obvious strain, but she had never wept before. She and Peter looked at each other for a few moments. The tears stopped; Mary began to fondle her doll, and Peter watched her.

Children as "Auxiliary Therapists"

Children at times unknowingly act as auxiliary therapists in an advanced play group as a result of having been exposed to analytic procedures and the informative and modifying effects of interpretation by the therapist. Children have an unusual capacity to assess correctly the reasons for another child's behavior, sometimes even pointing out underlying meanings. In so doing, they may not only aid the affected child to understand his behavior but, in addition, may enrich their own reflective capacity.

Jonathan, age five, pushed Sam hard so that the latter fell and began to cry. With that, Jonathan ran behind a chair and peered out first at the weeping Sam, then at the therapist. Before she could move toward Sam, the therapist overheard Susy, who had observed this fleeting episode, say to Jonathan, "She's [therapist] not going to hit you. She's not like mommys. You hurt your brother." (Jonathan did have a brother; so did Susy, and in both instances the brothers represented sibling problems. However, there was no indication that either child knew about the existence of the other's sibling.) Jonathan yelled, "He's not my brother, and I don't care if he is!"

The Group as a Behavior Modifier

The play group members exert moderating influences upon each other also in controlling aggressive behavior. In AGT this social force eventually evolves into what may be termed a group superego, but in PGT it is not so prominent an influence, for the reason that group awareness is less developed in younger children. Nevertheless, it does occur when social disapproval of a limited type begins to act as a behavior-modifying force. More commonly it is seen when one child and sometimes a team of two or more children exclude another from their play because he was "bad." This is not a total group response, but nevertheless it has impact because it deprives a child of sought-after gratifications and thus increases his awareness of others.

SELECTION OF PATIENTS

Indications and Counterindications for PGT

The emotional problems of four- to six-year-olds are structurally and dynamically different from postpubertal psychic conflicts. It is questionable whether true neuroses exist altogether in younger children, since these originate during the oedipal stage and come into bloom postpubertally, as a result of the unresolved oedipal conflicts. Neurotic traits and neurotic reactions can be treated effectively in PGT because these manifestations are etiologically not fully developed into full-blown neuroses, also because they have not yet been fully repressed and the anxieties connected with them are more easily accessible. PGT is also eminently suitable for only children, children who are exceptionally antagonistic toward adults and peers, and children with diffuse anxiety. In addition, children who manifest beginning disturbances in sexual identification are good candidates for PGT.

Before a child is accepted for PGT, the degree of libidinal distortion and sexual attachment the child has for his parents, especially the parent of the opposite sex, should be ascertained.

Children whose parents or older siblings have been seductive, sexually provocative, and overstimulating, who have slept in the same room with their parents or in the same bed, or who have witnessed the primal scene require more intensive individual therapy.

Other children for whom individual therapy is indicated are those who have been subjected to serious traumata—a sudden catastrophe, prolonged exposure to a series of traumatic occurrences, or a total traumatizing environment within the family. The anxiety bound up as a result of such intense psychonoxious experiences has to be released in the security of a positive transference, and treatment must be focused on dissolution of the bound-up anxiety. Children in such straits require the security of a relationship with a therapist who helps to remove the burden that weak and unformed egos have to carry. We have found, however, that children with even such intense problems can gain from participation in a group if individual treatment is unavailable. Some children with such serious disturbances may require conjoint or tapering-off group experience following individual therapy to solidify their gains.

PGT is valuable in treating sibling rivalry problems. However, where such rivalry is unusually intense, a period of individual treatment may first be necessary to dilute its intensity, following which treatment in PGT may be indicated. Children who have been physically and/or emotionally seriously maltreated may be unsuited for PGT, as they tend to reenact the family pattern against fellow group members. It may be possible to include one such child in a play group; more than one would overexcite and frighten the others. If there is no rapid amelioration of the aggressive acting out of such a child, he should be removed and treated individually and may be referred back to a play group later.

Group Composition

Group Balance Not Crucial

The grouping of children for PGT is much less crucial than in AGT or A-IGP. Balancing of problem types in PGT is not fundamental, nor is the mixing of sexes an important consideration, except that it would be unwise to have too few of one gender in relation to the other.

In PGT, as in all forms of analytical group therapy, where treatment of the individual occurs *in* the group, as differentiated from noninterpretive forms of group treatment where therapy is accomplished *by* the group, psychological balance is less important. Thus, the question of the number of aggressive and withdrawn children who may be placed together is also not a pressing one, because the intensity of aggression in young children is ordinarily not great, and furthermore, the therapist addresses himself to such behavior directly when it occurs, which is not the case in AGT, for example.

Heterogeneous Grouping

Some considerations with regard to grouping in PGT should be kept in mind. Including boys and girls in one group has merit because the content of therapy is enriched, particularly with respect to physical differences and body functions, about which children are curious. Confusion, misconceptions, ignorance, fears, and anxiety over such matters are usually present even in young patients, and the presence of boys and girls elicits important content more readily and adds an element of reality to the problem.

Grouping by Age

In early childhood, a year's difference in age makes for considerable disparity in emotional and physical development. Whenever possible, a play group should consist of children of the same age. There may be special circumstances that make it advantageous to group children more than one year apart in age. This might be the case with a younger child who is large for his age or who tends to act aggressively and would be withstood better by older children.

Size of Group

Five children is an optimal number for a play group, since more than five makes it difficult for the therapist to attend to the needs of young children, observe their feelings, activities, and interactions, and respond at points where he should be involved. In PGT the therapist is the chief agent of therapy and not only must be alert to the pattern and content of each child's play and that of several children as a subgroup, but needs to assess constantly the underlying meanings of play activities to determine whether to use them for extending inquiry or to overlook them.

Empirical Tests of Group Composition

Questions as to the suitability of a group's composition can be gauged during the first several sessions and indicated alterations made (Schiffer, 1969, pp. 26-32). This has proved to be an effective procedure with young children and does not subject them to feelings of rejection, because they do not establish relationships of any moment after a few sessions.

Effects of Changes in Group Composition

When the composition of a play group is altered by either removal or addition of a child, the therapist should anticipate some reaction on the part of the others, and be prepared to answer to their satisfaction questions that may arise. The loss of a child from a play group raises more questions than does an addition.

Emotionally disturbed children become uneasy with unexpected alterations in the treatment situation caused by either changes in the membership of a group or substantive changes in the setting. In the case of a loss of a group member they are easily reassured when the therapist gives an uncomplicated answer to their questions, e.g., "She moved away" or "He goes to another group." Such replies are sufficient to allay uncertainty or mild anxiety.

The addition of a patient to a group is likely to bring about heightened feelings of rivalry, varying in degree according to how prominently sibling rivalry was a factor in the original problems of the children. Here again the therapist, depending on the nature of the patients' reactions, may choose to explore their feelings.[1]

---

[1] It may be advisable to apprise the group of the impending addition of a new member.

WORKING WITH PARENTS

The parents of children in PGT usually require help, through individual or group counseling, social casework, or more intensive therapy. In agency practice there is an advantage in having parents meet in groups for counseling at the same time their children's groups are in session elsewhere in the building. Over-anxious mothers are more easily supported in a counseling group. Such groups help modify parents' attitudes and their child-rearing practices. It is, or course, imperative that parents' psychologic needs be determined by clinical considerations in each instance. Where psychoneurotic elements underlie a parent's relationships with a child, these need to be dealt with through individual treatment. In some instances participation in a counseling group, as well, may prove a valuable supplement to individual therapy (See Slavson, 1958).

In private practice it is more difficult for a therapist to make use of the procedural methods just outlined, which are commonly followed in child guidance agencies and hospital clinics. For the private practitioner to have parents seated in a waiting room while he is with a play group may be unavoidable, but this creates many problems. The children are not only tempted to rejoin their parents during sessions, but the parents are bound to discuss various subjects related to their children, themselves, husbands, the therapist, and others. It is conceivable that despite the social amenities, abrasive situations will arise. Conflictual incidents may appear, driving some parents into increased resistance and even leading to withdrawal of their children from treatment.

It is, therefore, almost unavoidable that a private practitioner of PGT must make use of other therapists to supplement and support the treatment program with the child. Therapists who employ individual and group therapy of latency-age children and younger find it feasible to work cooperatively. Another advantage in such cooperation is that it makes available larger numbers of patients, thus simplifying the problems of selection and composition of groups.

Interpretation (Explanation) in PGT

Levels of Comprehension

It is unnecessary to interpret behavior to children in the PGT age range in terms of the unconscious; their unconscious is still quite meager. The unconscious has its origins in the need to develop defense mechanisms, especially in the management of stresses during the oedipal conflict that appears later in childhood. With children four to six years of age, *explanation* of behavior is sufficient to achieve a level of therapeutically effective meaning.

While it is not necessary for a patient in PGT to become privy to all the deeper implications of his behavior, including those related to instinctual drives, it is incumbent on the therapist to be aware of them. Otherwise he will not fully understand his patients' problems, nor will he be able to assess their behavior and determine what clinical use he can put it to. This is illustrated in the case of Mary (Chapter XIX), the little girl who unconsciously sought erotic gratification from the male therapist. The therapist was aware of the underlying mechanism and knew that it could find only partial gratification on sublimated levels. He therefore handled the situation on the ego level and, through his gentle manner, provided an affectional substitute object for the child.

When a therapist aids a child in comprehending meanings of his play—through which he symbolically expresses his confusion, misunderstandings, and unhappiness—he is relieved of anxiety. The child not only understands better; he now feels that *he is understood*. Because he senses that the therapist appreciates and sympathizes, he becomes motivated to communicate further. This fosters the "transference," and the child's play becomes freer.

In the following episode, a child asks the therapist to watch his play. Such invitations are not unusual after children feel comfortable with the therapist.

John, five years old, was playing with the dollhouse in close proximity to several other children who were in verbal communication with each other, though for the most part each was absorbed in his own play. John called to the therapist, who was seated across the room, "Martha, come watch me play." The therapist rose, and carrying her chair, sat down next to him. John removed the objects from the dollhouse and proceeded to play with them on the floor at the feet of the seated therapist. He did all this without apparently preplanning but with the intention of monopolizing the therapist's attention (confirming the principle that in PGT, as in all forms of analytic group treatment, therapy is primarily of individuals *within* the constellation of the group).

John had several beds and small rubber family dolls in addition to other household items. However, after some initial starts, the theme of his activity centered on one bed. He placed the mother and baby in it and moved the father away. The therapist sat silently for about five minutes. (It is important that a therapist wait until she is able to detect a central theme in a child's play and avoid reacting prematurely. This strategy is equivalent to the process in psychoanalysis of awaiting the flow of meaningfully associative content. Of course, in PGT there will be times when a single, spontaneous play maneuver can be, in itself, revealing and meaningful and can be employed by the therapist for elaboration.)

The therapist asked, "Who is he?" John: "A man." Therapist: "Could it be your father?" John: "No." A second later, "and that's me and mommy in the bed, and he's outside!" Therapist: "You don't like your daddy to sleep with your mother, do you?" The therapist noted at this point that Mike, who took over playing with the dollhouse nearby, had stopped and was listening to the exchange between herself and John. After picking up the thread of conversation, Mike removed himself to another activity elsewhere. (In PGT children's interest and anxiety can be catalyzed through observing the play of others. As has been pointed out, this is one of the major advantages of the group. In this instance, what Mike has seen and heard evidently made him anxious, and he escapes it.)

Meanwhile, the conversation between John and the therapist continued. John: "No, I want to sleep with mommy." Therapist: "I understand. When you were little, you slept with mommy and she held you in her arms. Now you're big and you have your own bed. That's the way it is with all boys." John listened, reflectively.

Then he abruptly shoved the play things aside, jumped up and ran across the room to join Mike.

The therapist was able to give John a rather direct explanation of the meaning of his play—oedipal conflict, rivalry with his father—because on prior occasions her explanations had helped him feel better. John may not exactly have fully appreciated all of the "message" in this exchange, as shown when he abruptly terminated the play, but the enactment and conversation are assimilated, and they have the effect of helping relieve oedipal guilt and fostering repression. In this episode we see that the therapist "desexualizes the interpretation, e.g., "sleep with mommy," choosing her language carefully to point up the meaning at a level of the child's ability to comprehend it.

In another episode we see how one child's play has the effect of catalyzing others who then join in, unlike Mike who, in the previous incident, withdrew because of anxiety. This incident illustrates the enrichment of the treatment process in PGT through the children's own observations of the behavior of fellow group members and the evocation of problem elements common to many emotionally disturbed children.

Joan, Andy, and Bert, ages five to six, were pounding the play dough aimlessly, all three in evident good spirits. Bert rolled his piece and held it up for the others to admire. "Look at my snake." It took only a moment for the others to also fabricate "snakes," which they too held up to view. Andy, almost roguishly, held his "snake" to his crotch, wiggling it about, accompanying it by a "ps-s-s" sound. Bert was scandalized. He looked at the therapist and said to Andy, "You're bad!" Andy laughed and continued to show off his "snake." Joan looked at Andy's gyrating snake and said, "Mine is just as big." This caused Andy to guffaw: "You *can't* have a snake like this. You're a girl." For a moment Joan was nonplussed. Andy elaborated: "Girls don't have wee-wees. That's my wee-wee, not a snake!" By now Marlene and Abel were attracted by the exchange while Andy was having quite a time in his leading role. He turned to Abel saying, "She said girls got wee-wees. That's silly." Marlene volunteered, defensively, "Girls got small ones, but they grow bigger."

At this point, the therapist moved closer to the children and sat down. Some of them glanced toward her; Bert in particular seemed upset by what had been going on. Joan, who had now become fully aware of the implications of the game, said, "My brother calls his 'wee-wee' 'pea-nuts,'" emphasizing the last syllable. The therapist then intervened: "Children call it different names: 'wee-wee,' 'pee-pee,' even 'penis' like grown-ups call it." Again Andy took the dominant role: "But she [Joan] says girls got 'pee...wee-wees.' They don't, do they?" (Andy has on other occasions displayed preoccupations with this subject in his play, and he often manipulated his genitals through the pocket of his trousers.) Therapist: "No, girls are different. They have something different from boys."

Marlene was patently confused, and Bert, while no less anxious than he had been before, was very attentive. The therapist waited several moments and then continued to elaborate with interpolated questions and comments from the children, who were now soberly interested. "People are born that way; they never change. Boys and daddies have penises; girls and mommies have vaginas." "That's it! That's what I got, a 'gina! Mommy told me," Joan exclaimed in sudden, almost prideful remembrance. Marlene now queried the therapist: "What have *you* got?" The therapist replied quietly, looking at Marlene, "The same as you, a vagina." Andy, again: "Is a vagina just as good as a wee-wee?" Therapist: "They are different, but they are just as good." She withdrew a moment later, and the children became involved in another play.

The value of group interaction is obvious, as this incident points up. Andy's play, the presence of the other children, and the calm, informative attitude of the therapist created conditions necessary for relaxed communication. The boys and the girls then became able to verbalize thoughts and related feelings, except for Bert, who was as yet able only to listen. Bert was fearful of the topic under discussion because his parents scolded and beat him for handling his genitals. His fears were further enhanced by exaggerated castration anxiety that inevitably arose from his parents' dealing with his masturbation. Open discussion of such matters and the therapist's objectivity and permissiveness unavoidably exert a corrective influence on children (as well as older persons). However, in Bert's situation, his parents required help to modify their management of the child's indulgence.

The therapist wisely discontinues conversation after conveying what she judged to be sufficient information at the time. At later sessions the children returned to the same topic and its derivatives: conception, pregnancy, birth, neonatal, and other questions about which all children are concerned but about which few are given appropriate information, and most are "afraid to ask" because of parental inhibitions or prohibitions.

Explanations: The Element of Timing

In PGT, as well as in all analytical psychotherapy, a therapist needs to consider the factor of timing of explanations in accordance with both the intellectual and emotional readiness of the patients so that they can assimilate the information and attitudes involved. A situation has to be gauged to see whether it is opportune for discussion of meanings or volunteering information. Because of the still limited vocabulary of the young child, his rudimentary reflective (cognitive, intellectual) capacities and, even more, his emotional unreadiness, the therapist is required to exert great caution in this regard. However, when in his judgment the readiness exists but linguistic limitations prevent formulations of ideas, the therapist can assist the communication process by formulating what the child wishes to say. By supplying an appropriate word or idea for which a child may be groping, by a question or suggestion, or through direct offering of information, the therapist can significantly aid progress in the therapeutic process. Freud (1909) stated in referring to these needs, "A child, on account of the small development of its intellectual systems, requires especially energetic assistance" (p. 104). However, one should not be too energetic. The child must not be overwhelmed with information or explanations beyond his capacities to comprehend, and even if brought within his comprehension, it should not be offered when he is unready and may become emotionally upset.

Two six-year-old boys were sitting on the floor playing next to the easel. Pedro was initially the active protagonist in the play with Peter a silent observer. Pedro had accumulated the small rubber family doll set and, reaching up to the easel which was immediately above, took a brush wet with paint and smeared the father doll. Then, gleefully he had the doll "fly way up in the sky" only to plunge head first into the water in the small pail ordinarily used to hold soiled paintbrushes. Ostensibly he was "cleaning" the doll. However, it was noted that he deliberately held the doll submerged. He then proceeded to apply this assaultive attack on several other members of the "family," with manifest pleasure each time he did so.

Peter, who was at first a rapt observer, was becoming visibly agitated. Finally, when Pedro relinquished one of the dolls, Peter retrieved it, wet and still dripping with paint and water. He wiped it and set it on the floor, repeating this treatment of each doll. Pedro, on the other hand, continued the game with renewed vigor now that he discovered another dimension to the play, namely, that he was able to visit the same fate on the dolls repeatedly. To the therapist it appeared that Pedro seemed almost aware of Peter's distress. Peter finally left Pedro, who soon terminated the game, moving on to another activity.

(Peter was a very timid, frightened child, who had not been able to manifest any aggression in the group and barely spoke to anyone, usually playing quietly by himself. Pedro, on the other hand, was aggressive, verbal, and never seemed overly concerned over his impulsive behavior.)

The therapist observed the episode but chose not to involve herself in it. Her decision was predicated on her assessment of the differential effects that exploration of the meanings of the play would have on the boys, because of their contrasting personalities. Peter, for instance, would not have been able to tolerate inquiries that would expose his severely repressed anger toward his parents. His marked defensive denial of his feelings in this area in the past was such that it would have been unwise to deal with it at the time. However, his shock reaction to Pedro's hostile play suggested to the therapist the need to explore his feelings at some appropriate time in the future. Pedro, on the other hand, could have tolerated the therapist's participation, had circumstances favored her doing so.

There is advantage in giving a patient a correct explanation of his play behavior as early in the treatment as is feasible. When this succeeds in illuminating a feeling or fantasy, and the child comprehends a meaning of which he was previously unaware, it predisposes him toward therapy and the explorative procedures of the treatment process. The child patient feels that the therapist has become an ally.

This occurred with Dora, six years old, after only three sessions. She had painted an apartment-type building such as one she actually lived in. On what appeared to be a fire escape, she had drawn a red streak, leading away from the building. The therapist stopped near her and glanced at the picture on the easel. Dora, a diffident child, looked at him silently. The therapist smiled and said, "It's nice." Dora smiled wanly. Therapist: "It's a big building." Dora nodded. Therapist: "Like yours?" Dora brightened: "We live here," pointing to an upper story. Therapist: "What's that?" indicating the red streak. Dora: "Nothing, just red." Therapist: "Could it be a fire?" Dora, almost explosively, and now excitedly: "Yes, and that's the window, and that's the fire escape, and the people better get out the door or they'll get burned!" She looked up at the therapist, obviously anxious. The therapist reassured her: "Fires can be bad, but the fire escapes and doors help people get safe." Dora's anxiety abated. It was much later in treatment that she revealed the real "fire" — anxiety caused by the libidinal elements of her oedipal strivings, which were being greatly exaggerated and distorted by the neurotic behavior of both parents. Following the therapist's "interpretation" of her painting, Dora became more accessible to treatment.

Accommodating to Children's Vocabulary

Whenever possible the therapist should use the simple language of his patients; attention should not be directed to errors of language or immature speech mannerisms. Sometimes the therapist may offer new words or synonyms for infantile, colloquial terms, not to correct language, but rather to add a dimension of knowledge. This was well demonstrated by the therapist in a preceding incident when she supplied the terms "vagina" and "penis" at the appropriate moments. Note that the therapist introduced the new terms but still accepted Andy's continuing use of "wee-wee." A therapist who didactically corrects inaccuracies of language will only irritate and discourage children from pursuing subjects of importance.

Overinterpretation

Overinterpretation, namely, giving excessive explanations, has little therapeutic or educational effect. Overvaluing "the word" tends to block the progress of meaningful play. If a child is exposed to too extensive explanation or conversation, in general, his play as a form of communication is aborted, stifled, or rendered artificial. He may become overconscious of his play and the uses made of it by the therapist, which will interfere with its associative flow, and consequently with the cathected feelings which are being revealed by it.

Child analysts differ in their views on the questions of interpretation with very young children. It is not really necessary to belabor this matter as far as PGT is concerned. Some elements of behavior and play are undoubtedly more or less neutral in meaning than others, but one thing is certain: if an element of a child's play is truly cathected, it tends to repeat itself, just as a dream or a fantasy of a patient in psychoanalysis that has not been accurately or sufficiently interpreted becomes repetitive. This accounts for the perseverative content of a young patient's play, which generally ceases after the therapist has accurately explained it and the child has had enough opportunity to abreact. A lack of sufficient opportunities for discharging emotional stresses helps perpetuate the rigid content of play.

Reflecting Children's Statements

The technique of reflecting back to patients the content of some of their statements and questions serves several purposes. One child may receive it as an acknowledgment that the therapist is responsive to his needs. By merely reflecting what a child says, the therapist sets the stage, so to speak, for continuing communication from the child, without blocking or redirecting the associated content. This reassures the child so that he becomes able to reveal even more personal feelings. At proper moments the therapist may proceed beyond mere reflection and, using leverage through gentle inquiry or suggestion, may assist the child to reveal feelings in greater depth.

If the method of reflection is overused, it becomes nonproductive. The therapist must necessarily communicate also at other levels to help patients learn more about themselves and to aid them in managing feelings and reality circumstances. Repetitive reflections of what the child patient says can become exceedingly annoying to him, especially when he is actively searching for meaning, which he tends to do more frequently and more than is suspected as treatment progresses. Children have demonstrated irritation with therapists who merely "parrot" their utterances. "I *told* you already!" a child angrily screamed to one therapist who had been repeating word for word what the child had been saying.

Giving Information: The Educational Element

Providing information about subjects important to children is an integral part of treatment, more in child psychotherapy than with older patients. Young children are confused, poorly informed, and misinformed by parents and teachers on matters that their natural curiosity has led them to question. In PGT their real concerns about sexual differences, conception, pregnancy, birth, common fears, and the injurious impacts of social and parental taboos are easily detected by experienced and perceptive therapists in the play and other activities of individuals, of several children together, or of an entire group. It is fascinating to observe how one child's preoccupation in a play form or a simple question directed to the therapist can resonate and immediately coalesce the group's interest. This is an obvious indication of a catalytic stimulus evoking doubts, confusion, and anxieties in matters of common concern.

As children begin to find relief for troubled feelings, they perceive the therapist as an understanding person and a source of what for them constitutes vital information. They welcome helpful intrusions at appropriate moments which serve to correct previously held ideas that evidently never quite satisfied them. Common among these, once again, are the misconceptions and

388

"fairy tales" associated with sexuality and birth provided by embarrassed parents. The troubled young patient is truly hungry for
the truth, which can abate or lay to rest confusion and anxiety
about basic matters affecting his identity, his feelings in general,
and his relationships to significant persons in his life. The
giving of information to patients has already been described in
some of the illustrative material. Perhaps another example will
suffice.

The children in one of the older preschool play groups displayed concern about sexual differences. They had spontaneously
spoken to each other and to the therapist about various topics
revealing castration anxiety, penis envy, misconceptions about
pregnancy and birth, including ideas about oral and anal birth.
Among the supplies in this playroom was a set of dolls, each one
biologically intact, including genitals. While the male genitals
were prominent enough, the vaginas of the female and baby dolls
were poorly defined. Further, there were no anal openings in the
dolls.[2] The boys in the group, in particular, were visibly confused
about the female dolls. In the group's conversations, the therapist
described differences and answered questions. The following session she brought with her some illustrative drawings which more
satisfactorily represented the external anatomical differences
between males and females. In addition there were illustrations
explaining conception, stages of embryonic and fetal development, and birth. The former misconceptions of the children were
readily dissipated; they eagerly participated in viewing the drawings and discussing them.

The therapist may be called on at times for information on
subjects that are much less cathected. Where he is in a position
to satisfy a child's need for information, it is proper for him to do
so, unless, of course, there are therapeutic considerations for
avoiding it. The latter might be the case with a dependent or
demanding child who is trying to monopolize the therapist and is

---

[2] These faults in construction represent technical oversights by a producer of children's
play materials. It is imperative that dolls be anatomically accurate and complete, whether
they are used in the process of therapy, or generally.

389

more concerned with the attention he seeks than with answers to questions which he uses to capture the therapist's interest.

Children sometimes bring up matters requiring the therapist to expand their understanding of anatomy and physiology of meta- bolic, catabolic, and reproductive body functions within the level of comprehension of young children. Children are able to grasp the meanings of body processes such as ingestion, digestion, as- similation, excretion, and reproduction if couched in simple language. It is not difficult for them to appreciate such concepts as:

"Food is good; it helps our bodies grow."

"Some part of food is waste; so it comes out of our bodies."

"Part is solid and comes out of the anus—the backside; another part is liquid, and comes out of the penis or from a little opening in girls and women called the urethra."

"Food helps our bodies move, run, play, talk, and do other things. It's just like when daddy puts gas in the car so the motor runs and moves the car."

Children's "interpolations" during discussions should be looked on as reasonable contributions to content, regardless of the fact that they may be phrased in the idioms of immaturity. Any comments or gestures from children that may be suggestive, "naughty," or provocative are ignored. Once interests become captured by what is really meaningful, such childish reactions cease of their own accord.

Assimilating Information

In communicating to children, adults tend to overstress matters which they, themselves, consider to have important meanings. A therapist should consciously avoid overstatements. It cannot be anticipated that young children will respond with immediate and full understanding. When the therapist makes a statement or points out a meaning, it should not be pursued unnecessarily; it is sufficient to make the statement or explanation and let the child assimilate and integrate whatever he can.

XIX

The Practice of
Play Group Therapy

First Steps

At the initial session the therapist greets each child as he enters the treatment room, and if the therapist has had no prior contact with him, introduces himself by mentioning his name without Mr. or Miss. He tells each child that he may play with the materials at will, after which he seats himself at a side of the room and occupies himself. It is inadvisable to introduce children formally. This serves no purpose, because the children will probably not remember names, and the directness of the approach may increase tension in some of them.

It is advisable that the therapist stay in the treatment room and the children be brought in by a clinical assistant, secretary, or aide, but not by the parent. This avoids the inevitable dramatic separations that occur between parents and young children, ofttimes unconsciously abetted by the former. Furthermore, it prevents the possibility of the therapist's becoming entrapped in mother-child situations and being the cause of the separation. However, because circumstances may not always afford the therapist the optimal procedures of having patients brought to the treatment room, he may have to become directly involved. The therapist should then take the child by his hand and, if need be, carry a resistive child into the treatment room. The tearful and anxious reactions of a frightened child are dissipated as he is attracted by the play equipment and the toys, and the other children who may be present.

When accompanying or carrying a child into the treatment room or in preventing him later from leaving, the therapist should reassure him, for example, "Mommy is in the other room and will stay there while you play. When you finish, you will go to her." The child should not be permitted to leave the room to confirm the therapist's statement, nor should a mother be allowed to come into the room to reassure her child; this will only exacerbate feelings. The therapist should not himself become anxious about such "Draconian" techniques of separation. They may do harm to a child with an actual separation phobia, but this neurosis is rare in young children and, if it exists, the child may require individual play therapy.

Experience has shown that what is identified as separation anxiety is a transient phenomenon in the beginning of PGT and that the gratifications that follow quickly dissolve it. Restoring the children to their parents at the end of a session is best accomplished away from the treatment room, either in a waiting room or, if weather permits, outside the building.

Period of Acclimatization

Despite the sometimes painful episodes associated with separating small children from parents at initial sessions of a group, the children adjust rapidly to the new experience. The amount of time necessary for acclimatization in PGT is much shorter than it is in group treatment of older children. The reason is twofold: first, because the children are younger, their suspicions, distrust, and general defensiveness are not as deeply ingrained; second, because the therapist plays a more active role, the children's interests and motivation are more rapidly mobilized. The therapist's personality, permissiveness, helpfulness, and demonstrated understanding of behavior and needs are additional sources of security of the patients.

Unusual Demands on the Therapist

As indicated elsewhere in this volume, psychotherapy of children requires that a therapist possess special skills and personality attributes.[1] The presence of five or six young children with their

---

[1] See Chapter VII.

individual needs and demands cannot but draw heavily on his physical and emotional strengths as well as tax his tolerance toward acting out. The therapist must remain confident and relaxed in the face of primary process behavior and prevent overdetermined reactions. The capacity to accept the childishness of children, their impulsive and immature behavior, is not common, and only individuals with such a capacity are suitable.

The Therapist's Gender

In keeping with the psychological development and needs of children under six years of age, women are preferable as therapists. Although at this age children have developed perceptions of the differences of male and female roles, the woman (mother) is still prominent as a libidinal object owing to her nurturing and protective functions. At times during treatment the therapist has to respond to the children on levels of physical care and emotional nurture, functions in the realm of a woman and performed more easily and more comfortably by a woman than by a man.

Positioning of the Therapist and His Mobility

The therapist is best seated in a position from which he is able to observe and hear everything that takes place any time, without obstructing the children's activities. Based on his judgment, he must decide whether the content and quality of any child's play or acting out require that he, the therapist, intervene. In this manner he fulfills his role as a *participant-observer*.

In PGT the therapist is a focal person, and because the children soon become aware of his multifarious roles, a sense of expectancy arises on their part. This attitude is generated after their first experiences when the therapist has, through his manner and correct interpretations, demonstrated his understanding of their feelings. They soon begin to anticipate and accept his participation, with the possible exception of the times when they may be acting out aggressively.

Playing with Children

There is no blanket rule as to whether a therapist in PGT should participate in the children's group or individual play activities. To the extent that it is possible to do so, the therapist is most advantageously situated if he can remain a watchful observer, reacting to comments and questions or suitably volunteering a comment, information, or an inquiry. Some children attempt to monopolize the therapist's attention by various means and excuses. One common procedure is to involve the therapist in play, a maneuver that can easily be recognized. The therapist briefly responds to the child's current needs until his securities and strengths will no longer require such support, at which time the therapist may suggest to the child that he can do things on his own.

It is inappropriate for a therapist to abstain completely from the children's activities, as is the practice in AGT and to a degree also in A-IGP. While observing children at individual or group play, there are times when it may further the process of communication if the therapist takes a minor role, especially when requested by a child. A child who is reenacting a family scene with hand puppets, for example, may ask the therapist to hold the father puppet and "be the daddy." Should the child resist the suggestion from the therapist that he play both roles and insist that the latter participate, it is in keeping with his functions to do so. However, the therapist should ask the child to *instruct him* in the performance of his role. It is proper for the therapist to say, "You tell me what to do and say." In this way, the patient's own feelings and attitudes with respect to his parent may come through more readily.

An example of the degree to which a therapist may take part in play without interfering with it took place when a therapist happened to be sitting near several children engaged in building with blocks. The therapist was interested in their conversation, particularly in the reasons for the bickering which occasionally arose. One of the children, rather matter-of-factly, asked the therapist to hand him blocks from the box situated near where he sat. This the therapist did without comment, easily transferring single blocks from the box to the thrust-out hands of first one and then another child. At no point was there interruption in the play, nor did it interfere with the therapist's observations. He was helpful, and the children seemed to have expected this of him.

What is more significant is the fact that the therapist was able to talk with them about their occasional quarreling while still passing blocks.

MANAGING CHILDREN'S AFFECTIONAL BEHAVIOR

Young children rapidly establish emotional ties with the therapist. Feelings and patterns of behavior which are related to parents become readily displaced in this relationship and favor reenactment of cathected material. In order for therapy to be effective, there must be affectional feeling on the part of the child toward the adult. This clinical fact was recognized by both Melanie Klein and Anna Freud, even though there was substantial divergence between them as to the young child's ability to form an actual transference—Anna Freud asserting that what does occur is that the child forms a *substitute* relationship with the therapist.[2]

While children's spontaneous demonstrations of positive feelings toward the therapist are tolerated, the therapist should not encourage them unnecessarily, which can sometimes happen as a result of positive countertransference. The therapist should be as concerned with a child's affectional expression toward him as he would be toward the same child's negative behavior, such as provocation and anger. There will be times when the child will abreact hostile, even hateful feelings, using the therapist as a substitute for parents.

The degree and the manner in which a therapist may respond to a child's affectional or libidinal behavior, or how he allows himself to be used as the recipient of such behavior, will depend on what the child is seeking, the motivation for which may be conscious or unconscious. For specific reasons children may solicit from the therapist various types of indulgences, including unconscious erotic gratification, open demonstrations of approval and love, comforting, or mild reassurance. The following example will illustrate and amplify this point.

---

[2] This has also been expressed by one of the authors (Slavson, 1952, pp. 168-174).
  A transference neurosis is conceivable *after* latency, and mostly in early adolescence with its attendant unresolved and conflictual elements. It is therefore a part of treatment in analytic forms of therapy with persons much beyond the oedipal stage.

Mary, five years old, moved toward the seated therapist, a man, and said, "I want to sit there," indicating his lap. Instead of permitting her to do so, the therapist reached for a small chair and placed it directly in front of himself. He looked at Mary, and said, "Come sit down." Mary, petulantly, "I wanna sit on your lap." Therapist: "Yes, I know, but you're a big girl now. I do like you. You can sit here and we can talk," pointing to the chair. Mary sat down.

In this case the therapist's decision was predicated on his comprehensive knowledge of Mary's problem, including the fact that she always acted in a seductive manner. Her request for physical contact had a strong erotic tinge; it was not exclusively psychological, and had the therapist allowed it, it might have increased her anxiety. At other times, Mary has been observed playing with the inflated Bop-Bag by lying on it and rubbing against it with her body. Eventually, when opportune, some of this behavior would have to be a subject of discussion.[3]

Under other circumstances, with a different "Mary" and a female therapist, the therapist could conceivably allow the child to sit in her lap, even holding her to provide momentary comfort, then place her in a standing position. This would be appropriate if the child sought such reassurance for reasons arising from a feeling of loneliness or hurt caused by some incident in the group. On the other hand, the same female therapist might have to be more circumspect if a boy of five sought to sit in her lap. To carry this a step further in order to demonstrate the sensitivity, knowledge, and skill demanded of a therapist in PGT, a female therapist may be less constrained in physical contact with a four-year-old boy. The possibility of sexual fantasy in a child of this age is considerably less than if he were five or six.

Physical contact with children in PGT, by both male and female therapists, regardless of the sex of the children, should be kept to a minimum. This will prevent the possibility of exaggerated affect and decrease the risk of generating jealousy in other members of the group.

[3] This is not meant to imply that inquiry and interpretation would necessarily expose the meanings of the behavior at its primitive level.

It is conceivable that a child may experience a degree of rejection if his request for "mothering" receives only a moderate amount of gratification or is perhaps altogether avoided by the therapist, as in the case of Mary. This, however, is *therapeutic rejection*. The child's libidinal needs may not be satisfied at the moment, but intensification of the problem is avoided. The main purpose of psychotherapy with children is not to gratify their libidinal needs, which could arouse emotions *oppositional* to the therapeutic process but rather to resolve the problems which arose originally because the children's libidinal urges were altogether thwarted or overstimulated by parents.

INTERVENTION

Whereas parents often intervene to block and deny children's expressive needs, intervention by the generally permissive therapist is always determined by psychological considerations, and in the interest of the patient. In the home young children become accustomed to having their activities limited, and they anticipate the "Don't," "Stop it," "No," "I told you not to" of parents. In PGT they have to learn to adapt to freedom. On the other hand, the therapist should be mindful of the extent to which young patients are capable of using freedom constructively in ways that foster improved behavior and personality.

Situational restraints deliberately built into the playroom setting still allow the children a good deal of freedom, obviating the need for imposing limits by the therapist. However, intervention is required whenever a child's act or conduct is countertherapeutic or there is a possibility of physical or psychic injury to himself or to others in the group. Young children lack practical experience, which makes them unaware of the consequences of some play activities. Thus, their limited ability to anticipate the inherent possibilities of danger in such acts as throwing hard objects or jumping carelessly requires vigilance on the part of the therapist. He needs also to be on the alert for group contagion, through which other children may be drawn into an undesirable activity. An example of this is when an agitated child is permitted to run in and out of the treatment room, which should be prohibited, or when several children begin to throw objects around in the room.

When direct intervention is necessary, it is still essential that it be employed in a manner that does not offend or shock the children. Psychotherapy does not eschew the experiencing of guilt, frustration and even a modicum of anxiety and emotional pain. Intervention is also called for when a child is subjected to excessive frustration. In the following episode the therapist failed to gauge the child's ability to tolerate rejection.

Rose, four years old, sat in the corner silently weeping; she had been excluded from their play by two other girls. After a while she stopped crying and began to play alone with the doll and carriage. However, when Eloise snatched the doll from her hand, Rose could not contain her tears. She now lay on the floor and cried bitterly. The therapist did not become involved; she felt that Rose had to learn to cope with situations such as these, and since there was no actual fight or a danger of one developing, she decided that it was not necessary for her to take an active part. However, she should have comforted Rose, for it was known that she had experienced much rejection in her brief lifetime and was easily hurt. The therapist should have picked her up from the floor, dried her face, and engaged her in another play activity; or she could have spoken with Eloise about her unjust act and had the doll restored to Rose.

Treating Children's Aggression

When children are aggressive toward each other, the therapist may allow a moment or two to assess its intent and intensity. If the decision is made to intervene, the immediate purpose is to create a break in the action. This is followed by procedures that convert the acting out to verbalization *about* the conflict and is further pursued by the therapist, who may, if necessary, suggest alternatives. Very young children often need assistance in learning how to displace and sublimate aggressive feelings and settle disputes.

Victor and Pedro were fighting angrily and with seeming intent to hurt each other. The therapist interceded at once, separated the combatants, and held them apart. "What's the matter?" he inquired. Both boys responded with a spate of words, the therapist barely making out the content. However, despite the fact that the cause of the conflict was unknown to him, one thing was certain: Victor and Pedro could not be permitted to continue their fight. They were both angry, impulsive children who tended to hit out when they felt frustrated. The therapist again spoke: "I see you are both angry. *What shall I do? I don't like you to get hurt.* I know. Here, hit Joe Palooka." The therapist placed the large, inflated, plastic image of a man between the boys, calling upon each separately to punch it. Victor and Pedro did so with a vengeance. It appeared obvious that they still harbored strong feelings of anger and would probably have preferred whacking at each other instead of the figure; however, their anger dissipated, and a few moments later they were laughing aloud as they continued their game.

The therapist acted wisely. This situation was obviously not suitable for exploring meanings of the boys' feelings, which were really based in rivalry with their siblings. At other times, when there was less possibility of physical hurt, the therapist could be in a more advantageous position to explore the antecedent sibling rivalries. Meanwhile, the therapist succeeded in helping the children discharge anger, without harm to either one, a valid channel for sublimation.

In PGT play materials are provided to enable hostile and aggressive feelings to be discharged without danger. An inflated vinyl figure and a wooden pegboard with a mallet are items that help displace and sublimate anger and drain off aggressive feelings. Children display their anger also by playing with items such as dolls, blocks, and puppets, but anger is not as easily inflicted even on symbolic baby or parent dolls without generating anxiety and guilt which can be frightening to a child caught up in the momentum of fury.

Mario, Frank, and John were having a good time punching the Joe Palooka. They argued and competed vociferously. Frank and John wandered away; Mario was evidently being too "tough" for them. Mario continued alone, this time pummeling and kicking the figure. (He did not appear discomfited by the nearness of the

therapist, who had wandered over to observe.)[4] Mario, now venting his anger in a fixed and almost violent manner, grabbed a
small watering can lying nearby and struck the figure with it. At
this, the therapist extended her hand, saying, "Give me the pail."
Mario stood a moment, apparently resistive to the quietly stated
request, then relinquished the can, resuming punching and kicking the figure.

Therapist: "See, the can would make it break. Punching is
all right, but kicking will also break it." Again, Mario hesitated,
then assaulted the rebounding figure, this time with his fists only.
Therapist: "That's a real hard sock!" Mario turned, now with a
slight smile, in acknowledgment of the therapist's comment.
Therapist: "Who is it?" pointing to the figure. Mario: "I hate
him. I'll kill him!" Therapist: "Hate him?" Mario didn't reply.
Therapist: "He's a man?" Mario (now explosively): "He hits my
mama. I hate him." Therapist: "You get frightened, and angry.
I know how you feel." Mario stopped, walked toward the therapist, took her arm and leaned against her, tears streaming from
his eyes. The therapist comforted him, wiped his face, and then
drew him into another activity.

In this episode, the therapist allows Mario to act out the anger
he feels toward his father, who does treat his wife and children
cruelly. However, she also prevents Mario from unconsciously
acting out the equivalent of homicidal intent. This would be
fraught with extraordinary fear and guilt and intolerable for the
child. Mario can relieve a good deal of the anger he feels toward
his father in his play with the figure and also by verbalizing his
feelings in conversation. There was no point in the therapist's
attempting further exploration and interpretation, or even commenting unnecessarily about his anger toward his father. Mario
can get relief from stress and emotional sustenance through the
transference. Only modification of circumstances in the family,
by treating both parents, can eliminate the traumatizing effects
upon the boy.

[4]The therapist's knowledge of Mario's capacity for losing control of himself moved her
toward the boy as a restraining strategy and a possible means for exploring the significance of his act.

Block play is another activity for sublimating aggression. Not only are children fascinated by the creative uses to which blocks lend themselves, they are also gratified by the discharge of aggression through destroying what they build. Since representational objects such as dolls, household furniture, small automobiles, and boats are included in block play, such destruction thinly conceals aggressive, hostile intentions. The therapist may use this play to explore feelings and to uncover underlying meanings. The following episode points up how one child acted out his aggression and, at the same time, catalyzed similar behavior in other children in the group.

Irene, Mellita, and Joel were building with blocks near each other—Joel alone, but the other two sharing. Joel had fabricated a high tower with smaller units at its base. He had placed mother and father dolls in what were obviously intentional positions of danger. The girls were attracted to Joel's play by his excited comments: "Watch out! Here they go!" Sure enough, the building teetered and collapsed with a resounding crash. Joel plumped himself down in the wreckage and gleefully kicked the blocks and figures helter-skelter. Mellita must have thought this good fun or perhaps she was made anxious by some of the implications of Joel's play, because she shoved over part of her own building. Irene remonstrated briefly, but then she too actively joined Mellita in finishing the job of destruction.

The therapist had been standing nearby during the latter part of this episode. "What happened?" she inquired. "Joel busted all the buildings," Mellita volunteered, seemingly only too happy to attribute the events to him. Joel: "You did too!" Therapist: "What happened to everything?" Joel: "The people fell down." (He could have said "buildings.") Therapist: "I see. And the people . . .?" Irene: "They're all right!" Joel: "No. They got hurt, killed." Irene rebutted, "You don't *have* to get killed." Joel insisted that it was so. Therapist: "What made it fall?" Joel replied, "Me." Therapist: "Perhaps you were angry." Joel: "Yeah, I wanted them to hurt." Therapist: "Them?" Joel would not elaborate. Therapist: "Could they be your mother and father?" Joel peered up from the floor, studied the therapist deliberately,

401

then spoke: "Yes. I hate them and my sisters too." The therapist then continued to elicit from Joel a good deal of his strong ambivalence toward his parents, and even stronger feelings toward two older sisters. In this colloquy the therapist conveyed her appreciation for his anger, much of which was justified, and his sense of impotence in being unable to express it directly. All during this time, Mellita and Irene listened attentively, occasionally interjecting comments, expressing their sympathy for Joel.

Block play as used by another child revealed a different problem and also helped discharge anger.

Enrico, four years old, played by himself with blocks and other objects. The therapist observed him build something, destroy it, and then restructure it. He took a vantage position to follow the child's play. Enrico built a simple enclosure, using only a small number of blocks. He roofed it over with several thin planks so that there was no opening in the building. To put objects in or to remove them he would shift one of the planks. Enrico put small furniture items in the "building," and then silently played at moving the rubber dolls in and out. The parent dolls were often brought into the open, and Enrico made them "walk" away from the house. Sometimes the baby doll was brought out and set down on the roof.

Enrico once aggressively flung the parent dolls away, first walking them a short distance from his building. Then he placed the baby doll in the building and covered the roof. At this point the therapist interjected, "That's a big building, Enrico. What's inside?" Enrico lifted one plank to reveal the contents. The baby had been placed on a bed. "He's alone?" questioned the therapist. "They all went away," replied Enrico. He removed the baby doll and then, shoving his legs back and forth in a kicking motion, demolished the building. Therapist: "It's all broken." Enrico: "I don't care." Therapist: "The little boy is all alone." Enrico: "Yeah. He's angry with the house [home] because he's alone." Therapist: "The house?" Enrico did not respond to this reflection. Therapist: "Who are the people over there?" pointing to the discarded dolls. Enrico: "Daddy and mommy." Therapist: "The boy is angry with his daddy and mommy?" Enrico, venting more anger: "He always takes my mommy away!" Therapist: "And you would like your mommy for yourself, like when you were little?" Enrico nodded his head, dejected. Therapist: "But they always come back to the house, just like you made them do. And they will never leave you all alone. You are big now so they can leave you with somebody when they go shopping." Enrico responded that he wanted his "mommy to stay." The therapist acknowledged his displeasure, interpreted the infantile claim for the mother, and again assured Enrico that he was "growing up" and that "daddies and mommies sometimes spend time alone."

Physical Attack on the Therapist

A child's aggressive behavior toward the therapist must be dealt with immediately in PGT. To ignore such aggression on the part of a child at this age may increase his anxiety in some instances and, what is even more important, may encourage and support his own acting out and that of others who may join him in the fracas.

There are permissible ways through which aggressive feelings toward the therapist can be discharged by young patients. It may occur through play materials, but sometimes it takes more direct paths, such as provocations, teasing, or defiance. Since it is necessary in treatment for children to abreact to hostile feelings by displacement, a reasonable amount of such symbolic aggressive acting out may be allowed. However, physical *attacks* upon the person of the therapist cannot be tolerated, and should an angry child attempt to strike him, direct restraint applied firmly but calmly is necessary.

Jack, a four-and-a-half-year-old, was brought for treatment because of hyperactivity, hyperaggression, and low frustration tolerance. His behavior in the play therapy group reflected these characteristics, making it necessary for the therapist to intervene from time to time to moderate it. Jack liked his male therapist and at times displayed warmth toward him.

During one session, Jack was particularly aggressive and provocative. He pounded away at the large inflated, plastic figure with both hands, carried it across the room, and deliberately plumped it down next to the seated therapist. Fully conscious of what he was doing, as revealed by the gleam in his eyes, Jack socked the figure, causing it to hit the therapist. He repeated this "game," looking gleefully at the therapist, who was now preventing the figure from rebounding against him by placing his hand against its side.

This protective gesture annoyed Jack, and he proceeded to pull the therapist's hand away from the inflated figure. The therapist offered mild resistance to Jack's tugging at his arm and hand. The boy's expression changed from glee to frustration, then to anger. The therapist said, "You want it to hit me." Jack did not respond but continued to tug at his hand. The therapist calmly removed Jack's hand and shifted his chair several feet away. Jack, undaunted, again picked up the figure and placed it near the therapist. However, before he could strike it, the therapist picked it up and, followed by Jack, carried it some distance across the room and set it down. Jack looked at him angrily. The therapist said, "I know you sometimes feel angry with big people and you want to hit them. It's all right for you to hit the Bo-Bo," which was exactly what Jack proceeded to do, even more vigorously than before.

The therapist acted correctly in limiting the boy's thinly disguised assault. Acknowledging Jack's need to ventilate the anger he felt, he supplied him with an acceptable object for canalizing it. Jack accepted the limits imposed by the therapist because of his underlying positive feelings toward him. The therapist also interpreted the source of the child's anger by implication, without identifying the real focus of anger, the parents. Further interpretation was not indicated at the time.

A child's aggressive behavior in PGT, even when it has abreactive value, needs to be at all times monitored by the therapist and controlled when indicated. Negative forms of behavior in PGT— as in all psychotherapy with children—should be fleeting, impermanent. It behooves the therapist to accept it, understanding its meanings, and deal with it with little delay.

REGRESSIVE, CATHARTIC ACTIVITY

Some emotionally disturbed children between the ages of four and six need to work through pregenital preoccupations. For this reason liquid and plastic media are made available. These substances and accessory equipment such as pails, brushes, and paper lend themselves to regressive as well as cathartic play.

One has only to observe young children using these media to sense the primitive, infantile mechanisms at work. They are much preoccupied in exploring sensorially, tasting, smelling, touching, and squishing. Furthermore, they often unconsciously pass flatus and belch, which are usually associated with aggression on oral and anal levels.

Such regressive play cannot be subjected to analytic interpretation by the therapist. The therapeutic delivery in this type of play stems from two factors: (1) cathartic release of an abnormal amount of cathexis which was fixated through defective child-rearing practices; (2) providing gratification for sensory needs, which has not been met during earlier years of life.

Since this kind of play is essential and is encouraged by the clinical design, it behooves the therapist to be mindful of his own attitudes and responses in dealing with it. Forewarned is forearmed, for there are strong countertransferential tendencies on the part of therapists during the inevitable smeary phase. The therapist's intolerance may lead to unnecessary or premature intervention on his part, replicating, although in milder degree perhaps, the unreasonable and punitive restrictions of parents.

The therapist who accepts children's cathartic play and, at the same time, takes practical measures for their physical care, is actually helping remove their fears and exaggerated reaction formations. Verbalization about cathartic play activities is seldom necessary, for ministration to the needs of children is preemptive. Occasionally, at this age, a child may need reassurance, especially when beginning experimentation in such play evokes anxiety. Reassurance can be sufficiently conveyed by an approving glance, an offer of assistance, and if need be, a word of encouragement. Thus, in the case of Carmen, who was distressed because wet sand got on her arms and in her hair, the therapist proceeded to brush it out, saying in a reassuring way, "Don't worry; I'll fix it."

Another common accompaniment to regressive play is the use of infantile words associated with body excrements and eliminative functions. Children may first test the therapist's permissiveness, but then speak to each other freely. Of course, different children evince various types of reactions to "bad" language, ranging from surprised "Oohs" to "Did you hear what *he* said?" To all such remarks the therapist remains noncommittal.

Substances of liquid or plastic consistency not only promote regressive play but tend to proliferate acting out. When substances like water, sand, clay, and finger paints are used aggressively by one child against another or against the physical setting, the therapist's intervention is indicated.

Leo, Mary and Joan were playing at the sandbox. For some reason unobserved by the therapist, Leo and Joan started to pull at each other. Joan pulled Leo's hair. He yelled and retaliated by throwing a fistful of sand directly into her face. Joan began to cry. Therapist: "What happened?" Leo, angrily: "She took my pail and she hurt my head!" Joan, sobbing: "My eyes hurt." The therapist took wet toweling, wiped Joan's face and tearing eyes, brushing sand from her hair. The therapist spoke in neutral manner: "You're both angry. You can share the pail; you decide how. But it is better not to throw sand." With that, the therapist left the vicinity of the sandbox so as to avoid further comment from either child.

Intervention may also be necessary when a child preoccupied with smearing begins to smear himself excessively. In such a case the therapist should use reasonable and judicious techniques to circumscribe the activity without, at the same time, implying disapproval.

Five-year-old Rafael was messing with finger paints. After some aimless smearing, he suddenly began to cover his hands and forearms with black paint. Then he wiped a good deal of it on his face. The therapist was made aware of this by the chortling of another child who said, "Hey, look at Rafael's face!" The attention of the entire group was drawn to Rafael as all clustered about, laughing and commenting. The therapist walked over and proceeded to wipe the paint from Rafael's face, to the accompaniment of the excited chattering of the others. Rafael was far from displeased by the attention he was getting from the group and the therapist. She commented as she wiped his face, "Painting is fun, but I don't want you to get it in your eyes."

Rafael's mother had left her husband, taking him with her. A white woman, she was now living with a black man (which may explain the attempted coloring on Rafael's body and face). Rafael was confused and upset, first by the loss of his father and second, because of the color difference between his mother, himself, and his "stepfather." Later in therapy he began to verbalize this, and the theme of black and white dominated his communications.

When a therapy group continues to be too much involved in acting out with materials of low resistivity that too easily lend themselves to regressive play, the therapist can help abate it by indirect methods of situational restraint and thus avoid appearing as a prohibitor. Thus, a sandbox may temporarily be out of "fresh" sand or altogether missing for one or more weeks while "it is being fixed." Likewise, finger paints may be unavailable until replenished. These procedures provide enough intervening time for a temporary, hyperactive pattern to dissipate.

It is essential that the therapist be wary of the degree of regression that may be permitted in a group. Were he to overindulge cathartic acting out of a highly immature quality beyond a reasonable amount of relief of hypercathected feelings, he would increase the young patients' emotional burdens. The therapist needs to be aware of the fact that it is his responsibility to help his patient attain self-control by properly abetting mechanisms of repression, suppression, and especially sublimation.

At proper moments the therapist must become concerned with sponsoring in his young patients healthier forms of coping, adjusting to, and compromising. Because the young child's superego is unformed, the therapist must represent and act as a benign superego through his behavior and understanding, gently and in consonance with the tolerances of each child. This personality integrative role represents not only an essential attribute of the therapist, it must, in addition, become consciously and functionally delineated. An example illustrating the application of this principle follows.

Sonia is five years of age. She has been in PGT for about eight months. Originally she was extremely shy, constricted in manner, and avoided other children. Now, however, she is much freer and she has been able to tolerate contact, even at times seeking it. With the therapist, she is relaxed and not at all suspicious, which was not the case at the beginning of treatment. Sonia is able to use the play materials, which she was unable to do earlier — another sign of the disappearance of her former constriction. For almost two months she has been preoccupied with playing with water and sand, using the shovel, pail, the watering can, and various other small toy items which she occasionally incorporated in her play. Her play, however, was very messy, and the surroundings, including Sonia, would become soiled. The therapist gave her much latitude in this, since it was obviously important to provide her gratifications of anal and urethral interests. These had been earlier and severely dealt with by parental mismanagement.

For the past two sessions Sonia has been playing with poster colors (water paint in small jars). Starting with brushes, she proceeded to use first her fingers and then her hand in spreading paint on paper, her arms, and her dress. When she became aware of having soiled her dress with bright, colored paint, Sonia appeared to have misgivings, but only momentarily. As if she had entirely dismissed it from her mind, she began to mess the paper aimfully, using both hands rather vigorously.

The therapist walked toward Sonia, carrying a smock and several paper towels with which she began to wipe some of the paint from Sonia's hands, arms, and dress. Sonia, a little petulantly, made as if to withdraw the therapist's hands, but the therapist persisted in repairing the child's appearance to some extent, and then she put the smock on Sonia. Sonia looked down at it, then up to the therapist, who was now beginning to clean the table. The therapist said, "Painting is fun. This is a big girl's smock. It will keep your dress clean. And here is another paper and a brush," handing them to her. Sonia picked up the paintbrush, made tentative lines with it on the paper, and then became preoccupied with experimenting in drawing closed figures. She was genuinely interested in her new "discovery."

The therapist's intervention was based on her judgment that Sonia had already gained much relief through smearing, and that continued regressive use of paint, or other such media, would offer no further advantage. Therefore, by cleaning Sonia and through implicit suggestion and providing fresh drawing paper and brush, the therapist acts as an agent of sublimation. In this case, Sonia's therapist, who also saw the mother on a regular basis, was not unmindful of the fact that the mother was adamant in her strict intolerance of the child's messing.

Ego Reinforcement Through Physical Activities

Children eventually take to climbing on tables, chairs, and shelves. Since this can have ego-strengthening values, there is merit in permitting it, but within limits of safety. If the therapist is concerned about it in particular instances, he can stand nearby in case a child should need help. A good item for "acrobatics" is a "teeter-type" board set which contains several hardwood planks and blocks that can be arranged to make different combinations for adventuresome contrivances: seesaw, bridge walks, etc. A timid, anxious child can overcome his fears, grow more secure, and gain confidence when he succeeds in some special activity of which he was formerly incapable, which also includes human relationships.

This was dramatically demonstrated by Hank, five years old, with autistic qualities. Initially isolated from others in the group, Hank was now occasionally able to join his group mates in play. At one session, two boys made a large "boat" out of long hollow blocks, several chairs, and other items. They made a cockpit type of setup, contrived by placing several of the blocks one atop the other, surmounted by a "captain's chair." Both boys took turns carefully and gleefully climbing to the seat to "drive the boat." Hank watched apprehensively but, to judge from his expression, enviously. Once, when the boys were preoccupied with other arrangements, Hank slowly approached and gingerly climbed on the lower block, about a foot off the floor. At the first sign of the return of the other two boys, Hank withdrew. This brave new venture was attempted several times thereafter by Hank, the success of each attempt apparently registering on him with an impact of having accomplished a most daring exploit. When he finally did make it to the top, he gingerly sat on the chair, holding an imaginary wheel as he had observed the others do. An almost beatific expression came over his face. He caught the eye of the therapist and glowed. The therapist, from a distance, smiled broadly, nodding her head in congratulatory manner. When Hank descended, in compliance with the demands of the "owners" of the structure, it was with assurance and an obvious expression of mastery.

A single episode for such a disturbed child has considerable ego-strengthening effects and can be considered a critical event in therapy.

Taking Materials Home

It is not unusual for children to want to take things away from the treatment room, which is often caused by their need to test the therapist. Sometimes it may be merely a desire to possess an attractive toy. Because young children and, in particular, those who are emotionally disturbed, tend to perceive love in terms of whether adults (parents) give them things, it would be unwise to establish immutable rules against taking objects home. A better procedure would be to deal with situations as they arise.

For example, a child may take a small toy with him and return it the following session. Something has been gained in this transaction: confidence in the therapist. On the other hand, the same child may not return the item and, instead, may try to take another object the following week. Only consideration of the particular child in terms of his basic problem and his motivation for taking objects should determine the therapist's response. He may tell the child, "I know you like to borrow the toys to play with at home. But we need them here when children come. So, it's all right to borrow them, but you must bring them back next week." Children's taking objects from the treatment room may represent an incident, a trend, or a pattern,[5] and the therapist's management of the behavior will in each instance have to be

---

[5] The student should note that this procedure varies in basic approach from that employed in AGT.

governed by the underlying meanings.

If all children in a play group take things home, the therapist has to assemble them and talk with them as a unit. He should explain that the toys are necessary to their play in their room and that the "office" will not have money to replace (get) them again. Then the therapist should suggest that the children talk about it. Parents may also be enlisted to prompt their children to return borrowed items. A therapist will probably encounter fewer management problems in this area through judicious and relaxed intervention than were he to attempt to apply rules rigidly.

Young Children Do Not Steal

A word should be said about stealing. The student will have noted that the taking of objects from the treatment room has not been characterized in such a context even with our older children. Nor can it be. The taking of things, especially by young children, cannot be considered stealing. At this age they do not have a sense of ownership; they just take things they covet. The idea of ownership is alien to their psyches.

Serving Food

As in other forms of group treatment of children, and for similar reasons, food is served at the end of the session. However, if a group meets in mid-morning or mid-afternoon, food may be served before play activities begin. The repast should be a simple one — milk and crackers — in which the therapist performs all the work, such as setting the table, serving, and washing up. Young children readily become involved in acting out with food, and this can quickly take on a hyperactive quality. For this reason, cooking or heating food and great food varieties should be avoided. With children in the lower age brackets the therapist should not indulge acting out at the table. If a child spills liquids or drops crackers, it is proper for him to clean the child, the table, or the floor immediately without comment.

Clean-up Chores

Children in PGT should not be expected to clean up any mess or disorder caused by them during the session. The only time a therapist does not remedy damage or disorder is when a child *deliberately* causes it. The therapist may later and unobtrusively set in order the physical condition caused by the young patient. During the session the therapist, however, may clear away encumbrances like blocks, tools, and other objects that obstruct movement or cause stumbling.

Should any child voluntarily choose to help the therapist, the latter acknowledges it by an appreciative remark. In fact, in time children even in a play group may volunteer to assist the therapist in setting the table and replacing materials. However, whatever learnings accrue with respect to orderliness and cleanliness should come about without verbalization.

Therapist's Attire

The attire of therapists should consist of ordinary, everyday clothing so as not to set them off from persons in the children's milieu. Both male and female therapists should be sensibly attired; the male may remove his jacket during the session. Special attire such as smocks, white jackets, or uniform dresses has the effect of making the therapist appear formal and more distant. "Hippy" clothes particularly should be shunned.

Length of Treatment Sessions

Because young children have short attention spans, treatment sessions in PGT should not extend beyond one hour and a quarter in duration. Beyond that period young children grow either desultory or hyperactive. Termination of sessions should follow immediately after the brief repast and before the therapist cleans up and straightens the room. Early in the life of the group, children may test him by playfully hiding or running to a corner away from the exit door. The therapist patiently waits, reiterating that it is time to leave. In agency practice it is helpful to have an aide or a secretary escort the children to parents who are kept waiting for them in a room at a distance from the treatment room. Parents may call for their children, but it is advisable that they do not bring them into the treatment or playroom before the sessions start.

412

TERMINATION

Because of the pliability of young children, they respond rapidly to PGT and the period of treatment is, therefore, briefer than in experiential forms of treatment such as AGT. Here, too, the matter of termination is predicated on the individual patient's personality and his overall adjustment. For children who are to continue, treatment arrangements are made and the decisions discussed with their parents. Treatment is usually interrupted during long holidays and the summer months. Termination of play therapy should be planned for a time of a natural seasonal break for the children and their families such as before summer vacation.

It is recommended that each child for whom therapy is being terminated be so informed by his parent in the fall, in the event a child asks about the group or the therapist. The parent can then explain with words to this effect: "You don't have to go any more, Janet, because you are getting along much better. Even Miss Smith [the therapist] feels the way I do, and she told me how glad she was that you are doing so well."

XX

The Treatment Room, Furnishings and Equipment

THE TREATMENT ROOM

Dimension and Physical Properties

A treatment room for the practice of PGT is relatively small compared with that which is used in AGT or A-IGP. The optimal dimensions of the room for a group of five or possibly six children is 15 feet long by 13 feet in width. This will provide sufficient space for mobility and also will allow a reasonable opportunity for individual play. At the same time, the size of the room will prevent the children from spreading apart too much from each other. It will also enable the therapist to observe and hear all that goes on and respond readily.

Toilet Facilities, Furnishings

To prevent the children from becoming separated from the group and probably being lost, and to avoid having the therapist leave the playroom to accompany a child to the toilet, this facility should be attached to the room. Where this is not feasible, an assistant seated *outside* the entrance door may conduct children to and from the toilet. It should be impossible to lock the door leading into the toilet.

The furniture in a PGT room (the tables, chairs, shelves, etc.) and if possible, the toilet fixtures should be of a size suitable for small children. It would be helpful to have the floor of the playroom covered with linoleum, or rubber or cork tiles that can be cleaned easily and, in addition, provides a safety factor should a child fall. As for reducing other potential hazards due to structural features, the same precautions can be used here as were detailed with respect to the setting for AGT.[1]

A table, preferably round, 3 feet in diameter and 22 inches high, is all that is needed. This serves to draw children into proximity. Young children tend also to use the floor as a work surface. The same table can be used for refreshments. The chairs must be of appropriate size and height, with one large chair for the therapist. Only enough chairs should be provided for the number of children in the group. All furnishings must be simple, sturdy, practical, inviting use, without having to be concerned as to soiling or damaging them.

Sandbox

A basic item is a medium-sized sandbox. A circular or elliptical one is preferred but not essential. The box can be located out of the way, in a corner of the room. Sand and water have atavistic appeal to children while relating as well to genetically derived anal and urethral preoccupations.

Items needed to supplement sand and water play are toy pails and shovels and objects that float, such as small boats and even small sticks. The children should not be discouraged from using other items from the available play materials in their water and sand play, which may include such things as rubber or plastic doll figures, wood blocks, and short rubber hose. Water and sand play reveal children's feelings. One child on several occasions had members of his doll "family" fall off a boat into the water and "drown."

Sink

A double sink is advisable, though a single sink proves adequate in cleaning chores and for children's water play. It should be attached low enough to accommodate the children. A stopper is needed for it so that the sink can be partially filled for play.

---

[1] See Chapter IV.

416

Storage Shelves

Play materials should be exposed to view at times when groups meet, which is best achieved by open shelves attached to or built on the walls. However, when this is not possible, detached closets can be substituted. A tier of three wooden shelves, appropriate in height and about 6 feet in length, usually suffices.

Storing sheets of paper for sketching and painting is usually a bothersome problem. It can be simplified by building a narrow, vertical compartment alongside the open shelves, or, better still, close by the easel. Some painting easels have a brace shelf attached to the legs. This can be used to hold large sheets of paper in lieu of a vertical storage compartment. One child's small painting easel is usually sufficient for a group. Provision must be made for drying and displaying finished paintings on the walls.

Kitchen Facilities

Since the preparation and serving of refreshments in PGT is not an elaborate procedure, a simple small cabinet or a wall shelf out of the way is satisfactory for storing the items of cutlery, cups, saucers, and other paraphernalia to be used in serving food.

Positioning of Equipment

Attention has been given to the setting and its basic furnishings, but in addition, the matter of utilization of space is important. Some of the principles that apply here are similar to those in AGT. During the existence of a group, the setting should not be altered to a considerable degree by removal or addition of basic furnishings.

Cleaning Implements

Implements for cleaning are important, as the therapist has to remedy conditions caused by spillage of water, paints, and sand. Therefore, a broom and dustpan, a sponge, a floor mop, rags, old newspapers, a refuse pail, cleaning powder, and soap should be provided. While the therapist should strive to maintain order and cleanliness, he should avoid becoming overly preoccupied with restoring the room to a pristine condition while the children occupy it. More thorough housekeeping is reserved for the children's departure. Protective materials such as smocks and aprons should be available to prevent concern about spoiling clothing. During a group's regressive play it is well for all concerned not to be hampered by the need to protect clothing or the environment.

PLAY EQUIPMENT

Differential Valence of Play Materials

The play materials supplied in PGT are to varying degrees libido-activating. They are selected for their relevance to children's growth needs and their peripheral and nuclear psychological problems, usually arising from family relations, anal, urethral, and natal preoccupations. This quality determines the degree of valence of a given material or object, namely, its potential for evoking significant psychological content differentially in each child (Schiffer, 1969, p. 72). Some play materials are directly representational, e.g., hand puppets and dolls depicting family members and other persons. Other items such as an inflated vinyl figure (Bo-Bo), while not exactly representational of a psychologically significant person, lend themselves easily to identification as familial and nonfamilial persons. In addition are play items which are associated with realistic daily activities in the lives of children and which can be used in play to reenact conflict situations they experience, e.g., toy house furniture.

Sexed Dolls

A set of sexed dolls is invaluable in that it helps children to speak of matters related to sexual differences, pregnancy, and birth, and reveals anxieties and misconceptions in these matters.[2] The children discover the unique difference of such a set of dolls when they change the doll's clothes. Some children are at first shocked by the discovery and may for a time avoid the dolls from anxiety and embarrassment. However, these reactions do not

---

[2] These dolls were mentioned earlier with particular reference to the fact that those presently available are physiologically incomplete. Alterations can be made with oil paint or by adding perforations (anus and vagina) to correct the omissions.

persist, especially when other children, less constrained, openly examine the dolls and speak about them.

It has been our experience that children in treatment, with few exceptions, reveal curiosity in varying degrees about human anatomy and welcome suitably formulated enlightenment about body structure and functions, particularly as related to sexuality. In PGT, children, whose understanding of such matters was originally obfuscated by the parents' ambivalence and negative reactions, become assured by correct information. This experience in itself has immense value, inasmuch as matters related to sexuality become so prominently involved in the etiology of emotional disturbances.

The children's first discovery that talking about body differences and body functions is permissible may lead to a degree of acting out. Having found freedom in an area where constricting forces formerly predominated, some children, more often boys, reveal their anxiety through blatant and exaggerated behavior which serves to release tension and, when the therapist deals with these matters suitably, stops of itself.

Graphic Materials

Graphic materials used in PGT are paints, poster colors, finger paints, crayons, pastel chalk, pencils, drawing paper, and implements necessary in the use of such materials. It is not necessary for all recommended varieties of these materials to be available at all times. The therapist adds or removes certain items from time to time as circumstances may require.

It was described earlier how these materials are sometimes used in acting-out play, but it is important to add that children find other uses for them. Regardless of their problems, children initially explore materials to learn their nature, their consistency, color, color changes by blending, odor, and taste. The therapist should not be unduly concerned with the effects of such explorations and experiments, including the tentative tasting of foreign substances, except in the cases of children who are known to eat pica.[3] In such instances, the therapist should intervene.

[3] The term pica refers to a condition in which children compulsively place objects in their mouths, such as paints and crayons, which they sometimes swallow.

Once the children have familiarized themselves with the media, they use them appropriately. They may at first make what appear to be random designs, blobs, irregular shapes, figures resembling people or animals. The therapist should avoid asking questions based on the assumption that a child is trying to "depict something." This is a common error, which entraps parents and teachers. Children do not invariably express feelings through their random scribbles and drawings. However, at times even nonspecific productions can provide emotional release and convey special meanings. Thus, broad brush lines, drawn with gross muscular freedom, can represent aggression, as can similar action in painting a wooden block or the leg of a chair.

On the other hand, timid children discover new and safe outlets to release feelings heretofore blocked by fear. Because the objectification of feelings, conflicts, and fears through graphic media is so often amorphous in context, questions from the therapist such as, "What is that?" will fall on deaf ears. Or should the child feel constrained to reply to a therapist because he likes or is afraid of him, he may contrive an artificial answer. The therapist in PGT should consider children's use of graphic media as a means for exploration, regression, release of aggression, and other feelings, and for discharging anxiety as well as for desultory play.

When children draw their artwork to the attention of the therapist, or should the therapist volunteer a remark on it, it is best to make comments of a neutral nature. However, in cases where there is an unmistakable attempt at representation of a real feeling with manifest meaning in the light of what is known about the child's difficulties, the therapist may probe for the latent content. In one instance this was done by a therapist who noted that a child had drawn all the members of his family except his siblings.

LIST OF PLAY MATERIALS

The following materials are recommended for PGT in addition to the equipment such as sandbox and easel which have been listed. Some items may be added or removed from time to time, because of transient problems involving one or more children. A

420

case in point might be the temporary removal of finger paints to inhibit excessive smearing by a particular child and the substitution of another graphic medium for sublimation; or on the other hand, finger paints may be added to help an inhibited child.

Blocks

One full set of multiple unit wood blocks, Caroline Pratt type, stored in a separate one-shelf cabinet placed alongside the general supply shelves which hold the other play items; six wood planks; six large hollow wood blocks, or large styroform blocks; one large packing crate or carton (if wood, check for possible splinters).

Representational Items

One family hand puppet set, including grandparents, rubber or plastic; one doctor hand puppet; one policeman hand puppet; one molded rubber family doll set—the adult figures approximately six inches tall; one family set of sexed dolls, with three children: a boy, a girl, and a baby doll—all with removable garments; also, play equipment accommodated to the doll's size— carriage, crib, small nursing bottle, etc.; two inflatable, vinyl plastic figures—one large (adultlike), the second smaller than the patients.

Play Household Items

One complete set of house furniture, hardwood; a hardwood doll house to accommodate this is optional.

Transportation Items

One hardwood train set, small, to supplement block play; several hardwood vehicles: small trucks, autos; several hardwood or plastic boats that float.

For Sandbox

Screened, dried sand, 100-pound bags (for replenishing when it becomes malodorous); two small pails and shovels (if metal, with rolled edges to prevent cuts).

421

Water Play

Either in combination sand-water box or in sink trough, one plastic funnel; one small plant watering can; sink outlet stopper; rubber suction bulb to draw water and squeeze it out; several plastic containers or jugs for filling and emptying; large sponges, toy mop, large mop, cloth and paper towels.

Clay

Plasticine (only of good quality; otherwise it becomes too hard for use by young children).

Play Dough

Several clay boards. Note that one type of clay is sufficient at any one time. Regular clay is messy.

Graphic Materials

One box of pastel chalk sticks; one box of large crayons; several drawing pencils; poster color water paints; black, white, red, green, yellow, blue; artist's brushes (various widths); plastic smocks or aprons; finger paint, assorted colors; large sheets of drawing paper; several plastic sheets, useful for various purposes.

Miscellaneous

First-aid kit; one toy stethoscope; plastic baby nursing bottles; a supply of disposable plastic bottle nipples.

Note that no play items in the treatment room — toys, materials, containers — should be made of glass. Metal toys should be examined for sharp edges. The abundance of variety of play supplies listed above is not mandatory. The best practice is to begin with a limited number in the most commonly used categories and add others that, in the judgment of the therapist, may advance the therapeutic process of some or all of the children.

Other, additional materials may be used. The essential criterion is that they be of a nature to further the processes of child analytic therapy. Care should be taken to avoid an oversupply of materials. An excessive number of items tends to clutter the treatment room, overstimulate and confuse the children, and block interaction.

PART IV

THERAPEUTIC PLAY GROUPS
IN ELEMENTARY SCHOOLS

XXI

Therapeutic Play Groups
in Elementary Schools

Children spend more time in schools than anywhere else except the home. For better or worse, the school represents a large part of their daily lives. The school is not only advantageously situated with respect to the identification of developmental problems in young children, but it also has potentials for carrying on preventive and rehabilitative programs. The children are in a position to experience the effects of corrective measures in the very setting which, in most cases, was instrumental in exposing their personality disabilities.

EARLY SCHOOL LIFE AND CHILD DEVELOPMENT

Children's schooling during the early years is a critical part of their developmental life experiences that permanently shape personality and character. The effects of schools on character formation have recently become even greater as children of three and a half and four years of age join nursery and Head Start programs. The separation from the family coincides with the beginnings of autonomous feelings in the emerging personality of the child. A good school program can reinforce and encourage fruition of individual potentials and healthy autonomy. When the separation from the home presents unusual difficulties, they betray personality malformation requiring special attention.

Early schooling is psychologically significant also because it occurs when conduct and habit patterns that influence alloplastic development are being inculcated and habituated. In school, adjustment to the requirements of group living should further the development of object awareness and subordination of atavistic urges. However, in wholesome educational practice, alterations in children's immature behavior and attitudes are achieved in keeping with the graded demands of childhood, not at the sacrifice of individuality or because of a fear of punishment which is at present the case.[1]

EARLY DETECTION AND CORRECTION OF EMOTIONAL PROBLEMS

For young children school can be considered a "proving ground," a measure of their state of psychological development. Since it is the first societal setting beyond the immediate family, it puts adaptive capabilities to the test as well as contributing to social development. As a child's emotional "equipment" is exposed to new demands, his intrinsically healthy resources may become operative or his weaknesses may be exposed more obviously. Consequently, some parents may observe qualities of behavior in their children of which they have been altogether oblivious.

The atypical behavior manifested by some children in schools may be a superficial reaction reflecting temporary anxiety caused by the new adjustment requirements; it need not always be the excrescence of emotional disturbances. Deviant reactions to situations yield to appropriate handling by teachers resulting in normal adjustment. Close cooperation between teachers and clinicians, the latter acting in a consultative capacity, is always helpful in distinguishing between emotional problems and transient reactions to stress. It is precisely at this point that clinical observations and suitable corrective decisions have to be made by parents, teachers, and mental health specialists.

Although it has always been common practice to ensure that children receive inoculations for preventable physical diseases, at no time have efforts been made to survey child populations of communities for signs of treatable emotional problems. Recent efforts in this direction, as desultory as they are, portend a

[1]The authors define "education" as the promotion of growth on *all* levels, intellectual, emotional, and social.

promise for universal corrective secondary prevention[2] of emotional disorders. Given a younger school population, improved methods of detection, more suitable educational practices, and communication with parents, mental health can become a social reality.

CHILDREN IN DISADVANTAGED COMMUNITIES

In the degrading social and economic conditions in urban disadvantaged communities the incidences of individual disturbances and social pathology are particularly high. Much of it is attributable to the large numbers of "broken" families and their abject poverty.

Since children in these areas are entering schools earlier than in the past, school-based treatment programs are beginning to be strategically situated to help them and their families. It is unlikely that existing child guidance facilities — family agencies, hospital clinics, or other community resources — can do more than scratch the surface. One fact is no longer debatable: *in such communities mental health services for troubled young children must be brought to them within the geographical setting with immediate and easy access for both the children and their families, namely the public elementary school.*

Schools are more accessible geographically than the aforementioned agencies, which are considered "foreign" resources by most foreign and even native parents. On the other hand, their perception of schools is undergoing modification and there is a growing proprietary interest in schools. They have become more familiar, and resistances to counseling, guidance, or psychotherapy can be thus more easily dealt with.

Gordon and Meers (1971)[3] studied a group of young black children classified by school officials of an urban ghetto as intellectually retarded and worked with them for three years. Their

[2] By "secondary prevention" is meant preventing and arresting emotional disorders in children by corrective treatment procedures immediately upon detection of early signs of emotional atypicality. Primary prevention would be involvement of parents in pre and postnatal psychologic care of babies and children.

[3] Paper presented at the Twenty-seventh Congress of the International Psychoanalytic Association, Vienna.

findings revealed that the children were not, in fact, intellectually retarded. Rather, their seeming deficiencies in abstract thinking were found to be the result of prolonged and persistent violence to which they had been subjected. The children reacted in the only ways their limited coping abilities allowed — by incorporating it into the unconscious in fantasies. These had arrested their development. The extraordinary passivity that characterized some of the children studied turned later into violent behavior as their suppressed aggressions came to the fore. It seemed that the treatment they had been receiving drained their psychic energies and left little for academic learning. Survival needs being preemptive, their energies were wasted, with the result that the boys appeared mentally retarded. Such developmental anomalies can be corrected to a considerable degree through proper corrective programs within schools. Without such programs, most emotionally disturbed children will not receive any help whatsoever.

Historically, schools have been unsuitable for children of all ages because they have been, and still are, inflexible, restrictive, confining, unable to individualize education and meet emotional needs. Traditionalism built up a ponderous self-perpetuating inertia. Another factor is economic: our culture even at this late date still fails to value its children sufficiently to expend the necessary funds for improved education, which is also the case with other human services. Schools still fail to provide the supportive and enriching environment essential for growth, true learning, and personality expansion.

Increasingly, schools are being recognized in some quarters as a primary force for promoting social improvement, and the popular historic concepts of the school and curricula are undergoing, in spots, revolutionary modifications. Parents are being more involved in schools, and as a result their defensive barriers, their traditions and self-isolation are crumbling. The growing utilization of parents in some areas as para-professionals has greatly contributed toward welding schools closer to communities. In addition to innovative educational programs, ancillary services to entire families are gradually becoming a part of a larger community-serving school function, i.e., broader health services, Head Start classes, nurseries, cultural and recreational programs for all age groups.

PSYCHOTHERAPY AS A PART OF SCHOOL SERVICES

The authors believe that psychotherapy for emotionally atypical children between the ages of four and eight years should be made an integral part of the total educational and child care curricula of every public elementary school. This recommendation is not extraordinary or unrealistic; medical services have for some time been part of school programs. In the past the emphasis has been primarily on detection and treatment of common physical illnesses and dental care. Emotional problems of pupils received tangential, if any, attention and at that only in cases of pronounced pathology. In the light of our knowledge, we can no longer consider emotional and physical well-being as disparate entities, and there is no reason for such an anomalous situation to be perpetuated.

There is also an unfortunate tendency to view emotional problems of children in ghetto schools as unconnected to the depressive features of the community milieu. This dichotomy prevents objective diagnostic procedures and inevitably leads to errors in the assessment of problems, treatment planning, and methodology. Another impediment to aiding mental health and school achievement is the fact that the disturbed child of the ghetto is lost sight of as an individual and is pessimistically labeled as inaccessible to treatment. It is as if the community is viewed as the target of treatment (which is correct on a socioeconomic level) and the child perceived as a symbol of the whole.

In the preceding chapters an effort has been made to detail reasons for employing group treatment methods in clinical settings and private practice of a variety of behavioral problems. These reasons hold also for group therapy in schools. The procedures outlined can be employed also in schools, though some minor adjustments may be necessary because of the special programs, physical settings, and personnel.

SPECIAL PROBLEMS IN SCHOOLS

One of the authors has spent more than 20 years in integrating a type of play group therapy for young children in the schools in New York City. In his experience with several hundred such groups, he found conditions there that, while not altering the psychological principles and technical procedures of group therapy, nevertheless do affect the *management* of groups. In addition to the practical considerations such as location of treatment rooms (which must be located as far as possible from the regular activities), the scheduling of group sessions (so as not to interfere with children's schedules), and similar problems, there are also attitudinal factors related to the defensiveness and resistance of teachers and administrators that can affect a group project.

Staff Resistance

Problems related to physical conditions can usually be resolved without great difficulty, but the resistance of teachers, administrators, and custodial staff requires special handling. Unless clinicians work toward helping teachers understand child development and behavior and the underlying meanings of deviant conduct, they are bound to find their missions difficult and often impossible. A teacher's nonsupport or opposition causes him to blame the therapy group for his own failure in dealing with an intransigent group member in the classroom. Not understanding the enormity of the intrapsychic problems of a pupil and defending his ineptness to deal with it, the teacher confronts the therapist with the angry accusation, "You have been seeing him for months, and he's just the same—or worse!"

In one instance, a teacher strenuously objected to having a child in her class continue in a therapeutic play group which he had attended an entire preceding school year. Her reason was, "No child of mine needs guidance!" In this instance the more enlightened school principal transferred the child to another more sympathetic teacher. However, in another school, under identical circumstances, the principal refused to assist, thus openly sacrificing the child's interests to the hostility of an inflexible teacher. The cooperation of the school principal is crucial to success and survival of a treatment program; should the principal prove undependable when put to test, it would be inadvisable to continue work in such a school.

CHARACTERISTICS OF THE THERAPEUTIC PLAY GROUP

Starting first as an experiment in two elementary schools in

1951, during the next two decades therapeutic play groups were conducted in many public elementary schools of New York City. As already noted, during this period several hundred such groups proved successful in treating a large number of disturbed young children, most of whom were started in the first grade at ages five and six, remaining in groups a minimum of one school year, most continuing several years and some as long as four years. Almost all the schools involved were in ghetto areas where existing community clinical resources were limited and already utilized beyond capacity.

Little actual psychotherapy was being provided centrally or locally by the schools themselves. Whatever services were available were primarily committed to referrals of the most seriously *disturbing* children who had been suspended for uncontrollable behavior and for examinations of children for brain damage or intellectual retardation. The therapeutic play group method was employed to aid children who were not pathological or considered "emergency" cases but who, nevertheless, required help which was not available elsewhere in the community.

With a few rare exceptions, however, it is not possible, in public schools, to provide a setting for AGT or A-IGP for latency-age children that would allow for the unrestricted freedom and acting out. In order to meet the psychological needs in public elementary schools, it was necessary to devise a group method that would suit the needs of the problem pupils and at the same time also retain their unique physical and human settings. We have, therefore, a form of group therapy which we term the Therapeutic Play Group (TPG).

An extraordinary number of patients referred by teachers and guidance workers came from ghetto areas. Most suffered from the absence of physical and emotional nurture by parents or "substitute parents," and had been exposed to rather severe violent treatment. We felt that long-term supportive relationships with humane, tolerant, and understanding paraprofessional *group workers* would undo some of the personality and character malformations in these children. Basically, the therapeutic groups offered corrective reexperiences by counteracting the distortive effects of prolonged deprivation and abuse.

Reality testing being an essential element in the treatment of children, classrooms supplied ready transition from the TPG to them. Thus, a child who improved through TPG felt more secure, resulting in more satisfactory classroom participation. The contiguity of the TPG and regular school activities also makes feasible prompt observation and evaluation by adults of changes in behavior and overall adjustment of group members. Since many of the children came from broken homes, they were placed, whenever possible, in a therapeutic group with a male and female worker team to simulate the family.

The scope of the groups had to be accommodated also to the level of knowledge and the initial lack of therapeutic skills of the guidance counselors who were recruited to serve as "group workers." Except in a few instances, clinically trained personnel was not available to conduct groups, and the present author, who served as trainer and consultant, interested mostly women counselors as "para-therapists." All of them had teaching experience and graduate training in counseling that included the study of basic psychology, child development, and counseling methods, but no foundation in clinical methodology or the practices of therapy. Because they lacked the professional skills necessary for analytically oriented therapy, training of counselor-group workers was focused on the principles and methodology of experiential, activity-type groups. They received intensive preparation via seminars and observation of ongoing groups through one-way mirrors. Those of the candidates who proved suitable were assigned to conduct groups. They were then *continuously supervised,* beginners weekly for at least one year.

In the early stages of a group, play is the principal activity of the children for which appropriate materials are made available. In-depth interpretations of children's behavior and group interactions are not given the workers during the individual supervisory sessions. Rather, the worker's attitudes of permissiveness, acceptance, and helpfulness are emphasized, which creates a therapeutic climate much like that in AGT.

Because the play materials tend to be libido-evoking, a good deal of regressive play takes place, enabling the children to gain relief through catharsis. If a particular child or the group becomes too excited, the group worker uses varying intervention methods to modulate acting out (1) through muting its intensity by marginal participation; (2) by introducing another acceptable activity such as reading a story or playing a game.

Children five to eight years old cannot utilize unconditional permissiveness allowed older children. Their acting out needs monitoring to hold it down to their tolerance levels. Suitable intervention by the group worker is therapeutically a pivotal factor. Negatively catalyzing stimulation, such as some impulsive children are capable of, can rapidly induce maniclike behavior, often involving an entire group, which may not always abate by itself.

CRITERIA FOR SELECTION

Because one of the main aims of therapeutic play groups in schools is to provide corrective experiences as promptly as possible, children five and six years of age were considered the primary patients, although some groups were started with slightly older boys and girls. As indicated earlier, many children continued in treatment for several years. These groups, which started initially with play as the principal activity, became more like AGT.

The children who are referred by teachers present problems ranging from moderate to severe. Those with serious behavioral and pathological problems, for whom a permissive noninterpretive group method would be either counterindicated or of insufficient depth, should be rejected for their own protection and for the other members of the groups, as well as to prevent overwhelming the marginally trained para-therapists. Extreme care needs to be exercised in selecting and grouping children to attain psychological group balance. Despite these precautions, some children have to be removed from a group because of unanticipated behavior and referred for disposition by the appropriate member of the school staff, who may be a psychiatrist, guidance counselor, social worker, or administrator.

LEARNING DIFFICULTIES AND THE EFFECTS OF TREATMENT

Learning difficulties commonly associated with emotional problems are usually manifested as soon as children begin to receive instruction in the fundamentals of reading and writing. Intellectual potentials are aborted by tension, anxiety, and unhappiness, and unless emotional conflicts are dissolved or attenuated through treatment, academic learning continues to suffer. Without alleviating these emotional blocks to learning, educational remediation to correct learning deficiencies usually fails.

It has been observed that motivation for learning increases and achievement improves in many children who have been treated in therapeutic groups. As In Jerry's case,[4] ego energies that were absorbed in coping with emotional stresses become available for cognitive and intellectual processes, and children who formerly remained unmoved by parents' and teachers' pressures and unaffected by remediation now seemed to want to learn. School becomes a happier place. Improvements in reading, writing, and other subjects have occurred in many children who have had play group treatment without remedial teaching.

THE TREATMENT SETTING — THE PLAYROOM

The physical requirements and furnishings of a playroom are basically the same as those described in Chapter XIX.[5] Its location in a school, however, is an important consideration, because the regular school activities may not be interfered with by noises that inevitably emanate from a therapeutic playroom. The best location is a corner or wing of a school building as remote as possible from classrooms, offices, and hallway traffic. Some likely places within schools that the author has found suitable are: an office adjoining a gymnasium; a dressing room of the auditorium; a storeroom (with windows); an unused teachers' rest room; a locker room stripped of lockers; sometimes a vacant classroom if it is sufficiently removed from other classrooms and is not too spacious for five or six children.

The playroom should be modified in appearance from other parts of the school to facilitate children's psychological accommodation to the therapeutic climate as they move from the structured settings of classrooms. Built-in fixtures such as blackboards, clothes

---

[4] Described in this chapter.

[5] The play materials used are types similar to those listed in Chapter XIX, though smaller in quantities and of less variation.

lockers, and storage closets can be changed in appearance with colored burlap and eventually covered by the children's paintings and drawings. Furniture, tables, and chairs should be different from types used in classrooms, but if this is not feasible, the table surfaces may be permanently covered with bright-colored plastic. These procedures are designed to foster the children's perceptions of the playroom as a setting different from classrooms.

PLAY MATERIALS AND GAMES

Play equipment and other supplies used in a TPG (see footnote 5) are chosen to free conflicted feelings stemming from noxious experiences and to favor more positive experiences and relationships. Depending on the ages of children and the nature of their presenting problems, items which foster excessively regressive play (finger paints, sandboxes) may have to be omitted and more mature materials and equipment supplied instead. Thus, for children who require extended therapy we add tools, play, and game media, and materials for crafts appropriate to their ages, e.g., small hand looms, precut leather forms for lacing, sewing, crocheting, and bead work for girls, some lumber and tools for boys.

The nature of the activities changes by virtue of these additions because of changing interests and changes in the children themselves. Where several therapeutic groups use the same room, it is necessary that some items be removed from sight to make the setting suitable for groups of younger children who may follow. Similarly, the early childhood appurtenances for play such as baby carriage, crib, and dolls are locked in closets during sessions when older children use the room. The principle of fixity[6] of the setting, the furnishings, and equipment applies in the TPG as it does in other modalities of group treatment.

Refreshments are also served and the children always look forward to them. On special occasions, as when a session occurs during Halloween, Thanksgiving, Christmas, or Easter holidays, the group worker adds special foods and little gifts. In the eyes of children who are deprived of the holiday remembrances (which are taken for granted in many homes), the perception of the

[6] See Chapter IV.

group worker as a caring and giving person is very important in strengthening human bonds.

CHILDREN'S REACTIONS TO PSYCHOTHERAPY IN SCHOOL

Children, including the youngest, quickly learn that school is a place where orderly routines are considered important, even though some troubled among them do not accept this. Those who are placed in treatment with group workers who conduct themselves differently from teachers and in a setting different from classrooms may be confused initially. However, as the relationship with the group worker becomes meaningful, confusion disappears, and their negative feelings toward school and teachers are diluted through the positive experiences in the therapeutic play groups.

ADMINISTRATIVE CONSIDERATIONS

Frequency, Duration and Timing of TPG Sessions

Group sessions are usually held during school hours on a once-a-week basis, although departures may be made under special circumstances. One such circumstance is the extended school day, no longer a novel practice now that some schools have late afternoon recreational and cultural programs, making it possible to hold group sessions after school dismissal. No hard and fast rules can be laid down with respect to the time play groups meet, because much depends on the ages of children, the frequency and duration of group sessions, the possibility that some children may be unavailable at times other than when they are in school, and realistic school administrative problems having to do with the physical plant, the availability of a treatment room during regular school hours, and other such practical matters.

Attention should also be given to scheduling group sessions at times that will not interrupt the children's regular classroom activities, particularly the instructional periods. Experience has shown that children can be separated from classrooms once or twice a week at times that do not conflict with ongoing learning activities. A factor to bear in mind is that teachers tend to resist interference with their habituated teaching practices.

It is recommended that for children from prekindergarten to

the third or fourth grades group sessions be scheduled during regular school hours. This makes matters less complicated for parents, who would otherwise have to bring them back to the school building later in the day. Older children, however, may be scheduled after school hours where the school has an extended day program. A group session requires one hour. Young children's interaction tolerance span is such that sessions lasting more than an hour lead to purposeless, fragmented behavior. Should one hourly session a week be deemed insufficient for a particular group, a second session may be considered rather than extending the time.

Ending Sessions

If held during the regular school day, it is recommended that sessions be scheduled for the hour ending either just before twelve noon or before three o'clock, the customary dismissal times. This practice facilitates orderly transition back to regular classrooms; it also minimizes the possible carry-over of activated behavior from playroom to the classroom as at times children leave a group session ebullient and excited. Although these heightened states are usually quickly suppressed by the authoritative classroom setting, it is best for the project that they do not draw upon themselves criticism and scoldings from teachers and other adults.

Use of Monitors

The practice of having two upper-grade children escort the young pupils to and from the playroom proved very helpful. Experience has shown this to have several values: (1) the use of the same monitors for a period of time builds up an affinity between them and the younger children, while the older children exert a fraternal, moderating effect on their charges; (2) the group worker's essential neutrality and permissiveness are not jeopardized, as they well might be if he were to fetch the children from and return them to their classrooms. In instances where group workers have done this, some teachers have made gratuitous, damaging remarks. In one incident, a teacher, in the child's presence, said to the worker, "Take him. Keep him *all* day. I can't stand him any more!" Such developments can be prevented

439

if the group worker bears in mind the principle that the children ought not perceive him in a professional relationship with teachers and school administrators.

Terminating a TPG

The matter of termination of therapy, the need to consider each child's readiness for it, and other matters relating to dissolution of groups have been dealt with previously in this volume. The same psychological considerations apply to treatment groups conducted in schools, but there is one element which community agencies do not have to contend with here: most of the children continue attending the same school after treatment ceases. Exceptions to this are few, occurring in some cases when a family moves from the neighborhood at a time coincident with termination of treatment of a child.

If a play group is to be discontinued, the group worker so informs the children. The children are given sufficient time to work through feelings of rejection and anxiety that may be induced by the announcement, made about a month before the final group session. During sessions following the announcement, there may be some acting out of a mild fashion and behaving immaturely, almost as if "demonstrating" their unreadiness to end the group. The group worker, at appropriate times, reassures them, even to the extent of elucidating some of their separation feelings. The true test of the therapeutic program will be whether the children do, in fact, cope with this terminal reality without extraordinary consequences. Other plans may have to be implemented for some children who require additional treatment or other support after a TPG is discontinued.

The fact that children remain in school after termination of a play group, plus their inclination to attempt to perpetuate a relationship with the adult who has been a source of much gratification and who is still "within reach," leads them to seek him out occasionally in his office to say "hello" and to maintain contact in other ways. The group worker must accept this, while at the same time continuing psychological weaning. In almost all instances these brief, friendly, episodic visitations have proved sufficient to support children as the threads of dependence wither.

A problem that seems indigenous to schools, in particular, sometimes arises with the unanticipated transfer or reassignment of a group worker to a different school by administrative fiat of supervisors who may be insensitive to the special needs of children with whom the group worker is involved. Such a drastic event leads to premature closure of a TPG, since there may be no replacement for the group worker, or if there is, he usually does not have the required training to carry on the group. The group worker has to salvage as much as he can from this precipitous, unplanned event to spare the feelings of the children.

A method which has been used successfully is for the group worker to mail a personal letter to each child with a small gift as a memento. A sample follows:

Dear Mary,

The Board of Education has sent me to another school to do a different kind of work. I did not know this was going to happen, and I am sorry I had to leave. I hope you like the gift. Perhaps some day if I am near the school I shall come to visit.

Yours truly,
Mary Smith

The group worker must ensure that these letters and gifts will be received by the children, because in urban, ghetto communities, mail (especially addressed to children) easily goes astray. A safe way to guarantee that the children will receive their mailed packages, including the letters, is to address them in care of their respective teachers, to the school's address.

FOLLOW-UP

One unique advantage in school-based group programs is the relative ease with which follow-up studies of children are done during and after treatment. The group worker is most advantageously situated to determine the later adjustment of the children through the classroom teachers and occasionally also through circumspect direct observation.

The Matter of Confidentiality

The confidentiality pertaining to children and families observed in child guidance practices applies also to schools and has to be observed by all persons concerned, including teachers, and all the other school staffs. No entries should be made in school cards revealing information of children in treatment and no facts released even to school personnel without the consent of parents. However, much is to be gained in some cases from sharing information with teachers and some others of the school's staff who are in any way involved with the child, and parents have to be reassured that no information will be broadcast. It is advisable that parents be so informed from the beginning, including the fact that no entries will be made on children's school records.

In conferences, information should be judiciously conveyed to teachers that will help them understand a child's behavior, his emotions and needs. Methods can be tactfully suggested by the group worker which teachers can employ in handling the child in the classroom, but at no time should the members of groups get the feeling that they are being "reported on."

Case Illustrations of Two Children

Instead of presenting a full protocol of a group session to illustrate the dynamics that prevail in a school therapeutic play group, we narrate condensed treatment histories of two children from two different groups. The illustrations have been culled from protocols of actual group sessions, and the interactions are more or less typical of a TPG. They also record the improvement in the two pupils and point up some of the special situations that arise in schools where groups meet.

It is altogether unlikely, for reasons which will become more apparent presently, that these children, both of whom presented serious problems, would ever have received therapy in the community.[7] In addition, the nature of the problems would have required comprehensive programs involving also parents, had

---

[7]Except for Jerry, who would probably have run afoul of the law for truancy or another form of delinquent behavior.

there been cooperation from them.[8] Nonetheless, significant changes in overt behavior have been brought about in both children, and in one, penetrating modifications in character were achieved.

SANTA

Because of the large number of fatherless families in economically deprived areas, it is not uncommon to find many children with problems attributable to the traumatic effects of this separation. For such children a TPG conducted by a worker team, a man and a woman, is indicated, though not always attainable or absolutely necessary. The presence of surrogate parents facilitates deeper "transference," and the group becomes a psychological analog of the good family.

This was the case with Santa, six years of age, who lived in a slum area. She was a member of a TPG composed of six boys and girls, all from the first grade. This group was specially designed for children who, like Santa, had suffered the loss of one or both parents. The worker team consisted of a male psychologist and a female guidance counselor, until session 45, at which time the counselor left the school, and the group then continued meeting with only the male worker.

Santa was a sturdily built, active child who was quite pretty when she smiled, but when angry her face became grim and sparks kindled her eyes. Santa preferred wearing dungarees and blouses. She could easily have been taken for a boy, because her muscular coordination and mobility were more masculine than feminine.

Santa lived with a woman who claimed to be her maternal grandmother, although there was a real question as to the accuracy of this relationship. Several younger "cousins" lived in the same apartment. Only an incomplete picture of Santa's development could be obtained from the grandmother and other sources. It was known that she had been born in Puerto Rico and at the

[8] The factor of parent resistance is common in disadvantaged communities. When complete child guidance and family agency services become part of the school's curriculum, it will be easier to get parents to cooperate. Unfortunately, this was not the situation when our project was conducted, nor is it now.

age of two was "given" to her grandmother to rear. It was questionable whether she had ever known her father. Santa's mother, who had remarried, lived in another state and had no contact with her daughter. Santa called her grandmother "mother," despite the fact that her surname was different.

The grandmother was able to give information about Santa from the age of two, at which time she was speaking and walking, though not fully toilet-trained. Santa was enuretic, for which she was regularly punished by whippings on the legs with a strap. She sucked her thumb when upset and also during sleep, which was restless, sometimes with crying or talking. Santa would isolate herself from her "cousins," get angry and throw things if the grandmother compared her unfavorably with any of them. Despite these difficulties, the grandmother disavowed real problems with Santa. If she thought Santa disobedient, she beat her, but in marked contrast to this severe handling she would sometimes spoon feed her when she refused food. One thing which really concerned the grandmother was Santa's recklessness when she played in the street after school, unmindful of the danger of automobiles, and because of this, the grandmother sometimes forced her to remain in the house.

Santa's teacher described her as "aggressive and bullying, disliked by children because she tried to dominate them in games. She was quite capable of holding her own in boy's groups and was known to fight with them. Santa liked her teacher and could respond to limits, but her interest in learning was minimal and her work was poor." Her former kindergarten teacher remembered Santa as quarrelsome and dominating, which was also confirmed by other teachers who knew her. In kindergarten Santa had been excessively demanding and constantly sought attention. It was felt that she was "starved for attention."

Extracts from TPG Sessions

During the first session of the group, Santa exhibited the behavior described by the several teachers. She needed no "warm-up" to the new experience. The other two girls in the group isolated themselves, but Santa insisted on joining the boys' activities. When she was rebuffed several times by them, she sat down at a table and looked alternately sad and angry. At one point, after she had persistently but vainly tried to play with the boys, one of them, Walter, said laughingly, "You're a boy!" Santa was no less insistent when Paul told her that "only boys" were permitted to play their game.

Santa's aggression increased at the second session when she quickly demonstrated her superiority over the girls by taking away games and other materials from them with impunity. When she took clay from Carmen and began to fabricate it, Santa announced, "I'll make a giant man." It also became evident that Santa seemed more interested in the male than in the female worker, although she made easy contact with both. Once, because she could not open a jar of paint for Santa, she said critically that the worker "had no muscles" and had sent her to the male worker for help.[9]

Despite the differences in Santa's attitudes toward the workers, she demonstrated an inability to share either one with the other children. She seemed to need physical contact with both workers. During an early session Santa left the table, ran to Walter and teased him. He chased her playfully. Santa would repeatedly run to both workers, hugging each one in turn as she tried to escape Walter.

During session 5 Santa continued her active play with Walter, provoking him into chasing her and laughing loudly when he did so. Santa hopped on and off the ottoman as it was being pushed about by Walter. She then jumped on and off the easy chair and screamed in a high-pitched voice. She rolled on the floor once, Walter on top of her. She called to the female worker, "Help me," but then laughed aloud, indicating that she was in no danger. Walter said, "You're my horsey." Following this activity Santa asked permission to go to the bathroom. Later in this same session, she revealed her preoccupation with matters concerning identity. During refreshments she spilled milk on a napkin in which she had wrapped her piece of cake. Walter suggested she

---

[9]It is important to note, as a point of technique, that the female worker could have opened the paint jar. Instead, she professed an inability to do so and sent the child to the male worker. At all times when worker teams conduct play groups, it is important for the maintenance of their proper functional roles that each perform tasks that are traditionally and psychologically identifiable as male and female.

use a paper towel. Santa punched the paper and said, "Look. It's got no muscles!" Later she gave the male worker a piece of candy.

By session 8, the psychodynamic pattern was clearly delineated: the workers represented parent figures and the other children siblings. Also, in this short time there were clear cut differentiations in her libidinal relationship to the workers; she continued to seek out the male worker in particular, hugging him and involving him in her work and play. Rivalry with the other children was apparent, but it was most pronounced with the boys. When the group first started, Santa had insisted on participating with the boys as equals, but now this began to assume a provocative quality. The following extracts from session 8 illustrate this.

Walter built a wall of blocks and used it to jump over. He continued to increase its height and once asked the male worker how high he thought it was. The worker replied that it looked like "championship" height. Walter was pleased, saying that his father was state champion high jumper who could jump seven feet.[10] Santa yelled at Walter to stop making so much noise when he failed to clear the wall once and knocked the blocks over. Walter rebuilt the wall and asked the male worker whether he thought that he (Walter) could do it. The worker replied in the affirmative, and Walter did jump it successfully this time. Santa said, "I can do it." but she did not get up from the table where she was working. When the male worker complimented Walter by saying, "Atta boy," Santa mimicked him. Walter said quietly, "It's better than being a girl."

Later during this session, Santa momentarily put her arms around the male worker and her head on his chest. She then giggled. It was also during this session that she showed how readily her anxiety about separation could be invoked. She remarked that Sam—another child in the group—no longer came (he had moved). She repeated this at still another session.

In an evaluative report Santa's teacher indicated that since the

---

[10]Walter was an only child of elderly parents. His father did not work because of some obscure ailment. Instead, he cleaned house, shopped, and cooked, while his wife earned the livelihood. It was this role reversal of the parents that had damaged Walter's development and was the primary reason for including him in this TPG. Walter's evident need to "masculinize" his father was shown in this remark.

girl had joined the group she became "friendlier" and that "her demands for attention had lessened." She was being accepted more readily by other children and played less aggressively in games. She still had no close friends and tended to relate more to boys. She was provocative and impulsive but less so than before.

When the play group resumed its regular sessions following the summer vacation, Santa became even more involved with both workers. Also, the episodes of rivalry with the other children became more frequent and even more intense. She began to use both poster and finger paints in regressive smearing and would "dirty herself, despite the use of a smock." During session 18 she unconsciously expressed herself in such a way as to again reveal her basic problem. She told the female worker at great length of a movie in which a girl wanted to wear a uniform "like a boy" in the army. It seemed that the girl's father was in the army; she did not have a mother. Toward the end of this same session she called the female worker, "mother," seemingly unaware of her error. A few weeks later Santa showed interest in dolls and the play furniture and played "house." She refused Walter's invitations to join him in his games.

During session 24, some interesting interplay took place between Santa and Walter. The interaction between these two children had particular interest and therapeutic value because of the similarity of their underlying problems. Walter wrote a note to Santa which read: "From Walter to Santa. I have a girl friend." He showed it to her and she pretended to read it, although she undoubtedly could not read all of it. Walter then became quarrelsome; he tried to push her and then pulled her hair. Santa actually cried and said she did not want to play with him. She rushed to the male worker who was seated on the couch at the time, reading to Carmen, and threw herself into his lap, whining like a baby. Later Walter pulled a doll away from Santa, who then pursued him trying to recover it. She accused him, "You're a girl."[11]

Santa regressed further; she sought out the male worker openly, whining and behaving in an infantile way. Periodically, probably

[11] Children seem to be intuitive "diagnosticians!" Each child in the group by now had correctly verbalized the faulty psychosexual development of the other.

in response to oedipal anxiety, she made contact with the female worker and spent time with her. One of the newer additions to the play group equipment was a large, inflated plastic figure, about four feet tall. Several times Santa lay quietly on the floor with this figure, her arms around it, in close body contact with it. Further, Santa began to sit in the small play crib, cramping her body so as to fit into it.

When she painted at the easel, her favorite subject was a clown. She varied its composition from time to time, but the content and style remained essentially the same. The clown, a false image of reality, might have unconsciously personified her own identity, now in the throes of change. For the first time, during session 27, she painted the clown as a distinctly feminine figure. In the following session she appropriated the female worker's smock and said, in mock anger, "It's mine!" Her attitude toward the male worker was now becoming ambivalent. She vacillated between infantile dependence and coquettishness. During session 31 Santa climbed on a small filing cabinet in the corner of the playroom, next to the sofa. When the male worker walked close to her because she was almost four feet above the floor, Santa called him by name and unexpectedly leaped into his arms. This was repeated several times. It took much effort on his part to cradle this psychological "baby," who was now a husky seven-year-old child! At another time she teasingly touched his hand with a paintbrush and threatened to "paint him all up."

Both workers began to note distinct changes in Santa's physical appearance, her carriage and voice. She wore skirts and dresses more frequently; [12] her hair was braided; she walked and spoke in a more feminine manner. During session 34 Santa made direct inquiries about the real relationship between the workers. She had been fooling around with a sponge, with which she pretended to clean the faces of both workers. She asked first whether they were sister and brother; then whether they were father and daughter; finally, whether they were cousins. Santa was quite self-conscious as she posed these questions. She was told that the workers were friends. When the table was being set later for refreshments, Santa directed the workers to sit one on either side

[12] The first time she did so, she also wore dungarees underneath her dress.

of her. She persisted in seeking gratification on an infantile level during the next several sessions.

Another time Santa climbed on the filing cabinet. Neither worker prevented her or commented on it. After a short time she called the male worker and jumped into his arms. He then carried her across the room. She made noises like a baby while in his arms. She asked to be let down in a different manner from other times, speaking gently instead of with her usual roughness. Later she went to the crib, picked up the doll, and cuddled it. She became embarrassed when she happened to catch the eye of the male worker.[13] She then climbed into the crib. The male worker pushed the crib around the room with Santa in it. Later, when Carmen sat on the sofa next to the male worker, Santa said jealously to them: "The two babies can go to sleep!"

In session 36, the female worker was absent. Santa inquired about her with evident anxiety. She had to know where she was and when she would return. She walked around aimlessly and several times said, "Mommy, mommy." When she said this she looked at the male worker and smiled. (The temporary "loss" of the female worker was reminiscent of earlier separation experiences in Santa's life.) At the next session she questioned the female worker carefully about her absence. Of much interest is an episode that took place when the female worker was putting smocks on Santa and another child, preparing them for painting at the easel. These smocks had been made from discarded men's shirts. Santa refused hers and insisted on a "lady's" smock. This was given to her. When she wanted help later in removing it she went to the male worker and said, "Papa, take it off."

Understandably, Santa's relationships with the workers generated much rivalry from the other children. At times[14] the workers were hard put to it to meet the needs of all the children. The demands of children on the workers fluctuated, as one or the other worker became momentarily needful to a child. Santa competed with all the others, but her relationship with Walter still seemed most meaningful to her. With Walter she flirted, teased,

[13] The reader will recall the warning against watching children's activities directly. Therapists must learn to see without appearing to.

[14] The rivalry patterns in this group were also much more complex than those which are encountered in play groups conducted by one worker.

often argued. He, in turn, was very much influenced by this behavior, because it helped fortify his masculinity.

Inevitably, interactions in the group modified the extent of individual rivalries as the demands of separate children, including Santa's, became temporized by the weight of group decisions. This is a maturational force; the group eventually demands equal sharing; and the group is able to mediate, limit, and frustrate.

A second evaluation on Santa's progress was done after two years, just before the summer vacation:

Group Workers. Santa seems more interested in her appearance. Her hair is neater, and she wears ribbons in it. She no longer wears trousers and she no longer acts like a "toughie"; her mannerisms are more feminine.

Teacher. Santa did not attend a dance festival in which she had shown much interest, because she did not have a "fluffy" dress as did the other girls.

Grandmother. Santa is more interested in dresses; she insists on wearing ribbons. She wants to go to camp and wants to take all her dresses with her. Santa talks constantly of the group and her happy experiences there. She no longer remains away from home for long intervals as she periodically did in the past. She now kisses her grandmother when she leaves for school, which is a new development.[15]

When school reopened in the fall, the female worker was unexpectedly transferred to another school.[16] It was decided to continue the play group with the male worker alone. The children, of course, inquired about her absence and were told that the "Board of Education" had sent her to another school; that *she wanted to remain* with the group but had no choice in the matter. The children demonstrated anxiety by remaining physically closer to the male worker throughout the session. A short

[15] This development is a tangible illustration of the dynamic of *transference in reverse* discovered through AGT. This dynamic occurs when negative feelings are transformed into positive toward a parent as a result of patients' (of all ages) first experiencing warm feelings toward the person of the therapist, i.e., instead of the customary transferring of feelings from parents onto the therapist, the reverse occurs—the patient transfers feelings generated toward the therapist onto parents or their substitutes.

[16] This unplanned occurrence, which was certainly counterindicated as far as the TPG was concerned, would never have happened had the counselor been under the administrative supervision of a child guidance unit, which was not the case at the time.

time later, Santa herself moved from the neighborhood. However, by special arrangements made by the principals of the new school and of the original one, and with the consent of the grandmother, Santa was permitted to return to her original school once a week to attend the play group.

During session 55 a fascinating episode took place, demonstrating the child's growing consciousness of the alterations in her personality and behavior. The therapist reported that when Santa asked the worker for help, Carmen came over to where he was standing with Santa carrying a book to show him something. The picture she showed was of a family of turtles. Santa laughed, saying it was Carmen's "family." Carmen asked the worker to read to her, and they both sat down on the sofa where Mary was also seated. Mary snuggled close to the worker as he read to Carmen. Santa was now talking aloud about the new school she attended. She said that she liked it because the boys did not hit her. She then called Carmen a "tomboy" and added, "That's why boys hit you!" She spoke a few moments about tomboys and the fact that Carmen acted like one. Santa then added that *she* played with girls and was not a tomboy.

During session 59, Santa shyly gave the male worker a small photograph of herself and asked him whether he ever saw the female worker. He replied that he could get in touch with her. Santa then gave him another copy to give to her.

Santa became involved with Mary, who had recently been making demands on the worker. Santa teased her and said Mary was the worker's "baby." During session 63, Santa expressed disappointment because the school had only six grades and she, therefore, could not continue in the play group beyond that grade.

At about that time, the male worker reported that he met Santa on the street during lunch recess. When he walked away after chatting a few moments with her, he said, "Good-bye." Santa asked, in a teasing way, "You're not going to take me with you?" The worker replied that he would see her at the next group session. Santa's remark, and the worker's, were prophetic: session 63 was the last she attended. Again she had moved and was transferred to still another school, at a considerable distance. Her participation in the play group terminated. The worker sent her a farewell note.

Summary Evaluation

When Santa was referred at the age of six, the confusion in sexual identification was already advanced. This was observed in her dress and behavior, in her speech, her preference for the companionship of boys and participation in their activities. This distortion in character had been caused by early separation from her real parents and the subsequent absence of male persons during the formative years when she was being raised by her grandmother. It could be theorized that Santa "restored" the image of the father she had not known by unconsciously incorporating the pattern of masculinity in herself. In the TPG, under the penetrating influence of the reconstituted, libidinal transferences with the male and female workers, sexual libido could be externalized and fixed onto appropriate objects. For this to take place it was necessary for Santa to gratify early nurture needs, which she was enabled to do in the relationship with the workers.

The sustained and intensive experience within the TPG produced healthful modifications in Santa's identification. In the security of the relationships with the workers, regression took place and, over a considerable period of time, Santa was able to satisfy some of the emotional cravings which in her earlier life had been aborted. Of fundamental importance was the fact that in the transference relationships Santa was able to experience elements of the oedipal conflict. This could not completely substitute for the oedipal phase which had been lacking because of dislocations in her actual life experience, but it was sufficient to effect important alterations both in Santa's character structure and in her behavior. Later, the group eventually blocked Santa's continuing dependence on the workers, and this acted as a maturational influence, helping her sublimate and integrate the new growth experiences.

This case is not unusual in disadvantaged communities. Unless meaningful therapeutic programs are integrated within schools, children like Santa will probably not have the opportunities for corrective treatment at the time when such treatment is crucial.

JERRY

Jerry, a delinquent boy, was in the second grade when referred by his teacher. At the age of seven and a half, he presented a serious attendance problem. Truancy was a major difficulty also with his four older brothers, all of whom were eventually brought to children's court. An older sister, a narcotics addict, died from an overdose of drugs. The father, an alcoholic, died when Jerry was six years old. His behavior toward everyone had been severely punitive. Jerry's mother was confused, helpless, and disorganized. Her attempts at management were pitifully inadequate, and her distraught behavior added fuel to the disintegrative conditions in the family. The family, maintained by the welfare department, occupied an adequate apartment in a low-cost city housing project.

This type of family, with its many problems, has been depicted in clinical literature and family agency practice as "hard-core, multiproblem." In such families the children commonly acted out in delinquent patterns, and rehabilitation through therapy and casework is most often ineffectual because of the complex ramifications extending beyond the symptoms and behavior manifested by individual members of the family. One factor, which acts as a constant exacerbation of the overall family problem, is the failure of the children to make adequate adjustments in school, which usually leads to unremitting pressures from school authorities.

By the time he reached the second grade, Jerry had already cultivated the swagger, language, and conduct of his older siblings. His youth, and in addition, a pronounced, infantile speech defect did not support the image of the practiced delinquent but rather gave his behavior an incongruous quality. He was uninterested in schoolwork because "tough guys" were not supposed to be scholars; he lacked basic learning skills and could not manage even simple material. Jerry bullied his classmates. The teacher could control him, but this required her frequent intercession, disrupting the classwork. Jerry was suspicious of all adults and defensive against them and ambivalent toward persons who were kind with him. At times he could be momentarily responsive, but then would quickly retreat, his face mirroring overt suspicion. When first referred, he was exhibiting mood swings: sometimes he was withdrawn and impassive, at other times impulsive and angry.

This child's variant behavior reflected the confusion and stress to which he had been exposed from birth. Instead of contributing to his emotional growth, the parents had been tragically deficient in their relationship with Jerry, as they had been also with each other and with the other children. The father's behavior created fear and feelings of rejection, and the mother's weak and inconsistent attempts to maintain the integrity of the family prior to his death added more impetus to the delinquencies of the boys. Jerry could not accept kindness (love) from his teachers, because during his developmental years his relationships with his parents had been frustrating and inconsistent. His mood swings at the time of joining the play group were reactive depression resulting from frustration and anger.

It was felt that this child needed a long-term experience with an adult who would accept him regardless of his behavior and consistently support him, which would eventually enable him to form a positive relationship. Given this relationship, it would be possible for Jerry to modify his acting-out, delinquent, hostile ways. Jerry was placed in a TPG with four other boys of the same age and grade level.

Except for several months when he was removed temporarily from the group, *Jerry attended almost all of the 92 group sessions during a period of three years.* He acted aggressively toward the others from the very beginning. His manner was bullying, even against boys who had also been referred for their aggressiveness. Jerry, being the tallest, was able to maintain his dominant position in the group. When at times he joined in games, he would alter the rules to suit his whims and advantage. Jerry behaved toward the group worker as if she[17] were nonexistent; he avoided looking at her, but was fully conscious of her presence. At times he seemed almost aware of the arbitrary quality of his behavior, but did nothing to modify it. In response to the permissiveness of the worker, he would appropriate whatever toys or materials he wished from the shelves, where they were readily available, and from

---

[17] The guidance counselor assigned to the school, a woman, achieved excellent results with this boy and the others in the group, but a male worker is better indicated for boys of this age.

other children. Within minutes after entering the playroom he would grab a paintbrush from one boy, push another out of a chair, or poke someone. If the worker tried to limit some of this behavior by indirect methods, such as sitting closer when he was acting out or by trying to initiate a game, Jerry would either ignore her completely or shrug his shoulders negatively. Some children complained aloud about Jerry, but the worker did not intervene because she felt that this behavior was well within the tolerance of the group. Unpredictably, Jerry sometimes stopped provoking others and withdrew to a corner of the room. Only rarely did he speak to the worker.

A preliminary evaluation was done after Jerry had been in the group several months. It was felt that his acting out was a continuation of the behavior for which he had been referred, but with one new element—the need to test the worker. It was concluded that the fact that the worker tolerated his aggression confused Jerry and prompted him to act out even more. His demeanor toward her, almost scornful at times, was due to uncertainty and distrust. It would take much time before Jerry could establish a positive attitude toward the worker; meanwhile she must continue to be as permissive as possible. Further, because of Jerry's defensiveness, the worker should continue to avoid initiating contact with him, but was to respond if he sought her out. It was also felt that Jerry needed a *saturation experience* with an accepting adult before he could dare relax. This therapeutic plan was predicated on the assumption that the older children could continue to sustain Jerry without deficit to their own needs.

During 14 group sessions, Jerry continued to be aggressive, demanding, manipulative, but at times, also isolative. He rarely came into direct contact with the worker. Almost abruptly, during session 15, beginnings of positive change in Jerry became evident. It was as if the proverbial walls of Jericho came tumbling down in response to the gentle, persuasive, and persistent impacts of tolerance and understanding.

From the record: Jerry and Harry came into the playroom. Both were laughing. Harry greeted the worker. Jerry went to hang up his coat; then he and Harry ran to the plastic "bop" bag and began to punch it. They argued over it, laughed, and then both rolled with it on the floor. Norman entered and said,

"That's not the way you're supposed to play with it!" He threw his books on the table and joined them. A moment later Norman came to the worker to protest, "He [Jerry] doesn't own that, does he? He won't let me play with it!" Jerry, who was lying on the plastic figure said, "I had it first." Again Norman appealed to the worker, who replied mildly, "It's for everyone." Harry and Jerry laughed and told Norman to hang up his coat. He did so, joined them, and now all three boys rolled on the floor with the "bop" bag. At refreshment time Harry asked, "Miss R., didn't I always know we get milk?" Norman interrupted before she could reply, "Yeah, I was here before you!" Harry added defensively, "Miss R., didn't we always come here?" At this point Jerry, who was still painting at the easel, said, "Yeah, we were here from the second grade." Norman persisted, "I was here more times than you." Harry denied this. Jerry said, "I came here a long time ago. I was the *first one ever* to come here!" During refreshments, Jerry drank milk but did not eat the cake. He left the table before the others and began to punch the "bop" bag. Harry came over and brought Jerry's cake to him. Jerry said he could have it. As the worker was clearing the table, Jerry made a paper airplane, which he painted and sailed across the room while still wet. Some of the paint got on Mike. The worker suggested that Jerry wait until it dried. He laughed.

During the seventeenth session Jerry's contacts with the worker increased. It was Halloween, and the worker had set the refreshment table in party fashion before the boys arrived. When the children entered the room, they were very pleased with the unexpected surprise. Jerry approached the worker and asked, "Is today the last day?" The worker said, "No." Harry asked, "Tomorrow is the last day?" The worker again replied in the negative. The party appearance of the playroom must have made them anxious about termination, because the worker had also arranged a party at the last meeting of the play group in June, preceding the summer vacation.

Harry asked if he could pour the milk. The worker nodded. Jerry came over in an instant: "I wanna do it!" Harry: "I asked first." Jerry: "You do two and I'll do two." The children talked aloud about the small gifts each had found in the bags next to their plates, and about past Halloween experiences. For the first time since he had been in the group, Jerry ate and drank in a relaxed manner. When he finished he painted at the easel and made a very nice picture of a pumpkin. He complained to the worker that the green paint was too watery. She agreed. Later during the session he came to show her still another painting. She admired it and helped him hang it on the wall. He pointed to it and then to other paintings and said, "This is mine . . . This is mine . . . This is mine . . . This is mine!" When it was time to leave, he asked the worker for a larger bag to hold his candy, the presents, and the things he had made. The worker gave him one.

Now, with increasing momentum, Jerry became dependent on the worker and his rivalry with the other children more pronounced. Whenever he was momentarily frustrated, he became petulant, like the child he really was. He spoke frequently to the worker, sat close to her during refreshments, and continued to vie with others for her attention. From time to time he would revert to testing the worker, but he was now able to tolerate limits if the worker found it necessary to invoke them. The worker described Jerry at this time as being "infinitely more responsive" in his relationship with her. He began to come to the worker's office door early on the day the group was to meet to remind her to send for him. He also began to make short, unannounced visits to her office at other times during the week.

In one session, Jerry became involved in an argument with Norman. Again they argued about "who came first." Jerry insisted, "I was the first. I saw her in the office. The truant officer brought me!" The intensity of his rivalry with others mounted and became evidenced again and again through increasing aggression. When it became evident that the group was no longer able to withstand his angry attacks and that the worker would have to use direct restraints, which would vitiate her role not only with Jerry but with the other children, it was decided that he should be removed from the play group and be seen by her individually.

Thus, in the third year, after 76 group sessions, Jerry was removed from the TPG. The explanation for the change was tactfully presented to him by the worker, who stressed that she sometimes saw children in groups and sometimes individually, and that it might be "better" for Jerry if he came alone, since he had been so "excited" during recent sessions. At first Jerry seemed to like the idea, but after an absence of six sessions from the group during which time he was seen alone, he said he preferred to be in the group. Before returning him, the worker discussed with Jerry the situation which had made it necessary to see him individually and the implications of his rejoining the group. Jerry said that he thought he could manage differently now.[18] The children accepted him back, but with obvious reservations.

At the first session the worker entered the playroom to find the boys already present. It was obvious from the mischievous expressions on their faces that something contrived was going on. They told her that there was a "dummy" in the closet. This proved to be Jerry, who was hiding in the wardrobe. All the children laughed at the joke. The pattern of Jerry's rivalry continued, but diminished in intensity, and the others had less difficulty in coping with him. Jerry responded well to the worker's support and praise. During the last 16 sessions of the play group there were marked changes in the boy. He participated in conversations, cooperated during games, and shared materials. More importantly, he was better able to share the worker's attention.

It had earlier been noted, during the latter part of the second year of the play group's existence and continuing into the third year, that Jerry's school attendance improved. Truancy was much less frequent. He also responded better in class, and began to show an interest in learning. He was given monitorial responsibilities which he really enjoyed. Several teachers and others who had known Jerry during his difficult years commented favorably about the changes in his attitudes and behavior. Jerry continued to "drop in" on the worker after the play group was terminated. His manner was friendly, more mature.

Evaluation

Jerry had suffered highly traumatic experiences in a family which seemed altogether bereft of health-producing elements. As early as at the age of seven, he manifested characteristics of a

---

[18]While not completely so, Jerry's response is an illustration of the dynamic discovered in AGT of *derivative insight*, i.e., insights and understanding not derived through open discussion with a therapist or a group, but out of experience and either emotional reactions or reflection. It is conceivable that Jerry cogitated on his group experiences, came to an awareness that he could now manage his behavior, and asked to be reinstated.

delinquent, perhaps the beginning of a sociopathic character, an inevitable consequence of his psychologically pathogenic family.

The initial therapeutic plan was easily formulated; its implementation was another matter. In essence, the worker had to build up elemental trust in the boy to overcome intensive distrust of adults, generalized negativism, and open defiance of ordinary rules and regulations. Jerry needed to evolve his own design and "timetable" if there was to be any change, and the worker succeeded in bridging his distrust through her consistent accepting role even when intervention became unavoidable to limit the boy's severe aggressions in several episodes. Finally, Jerry was able to form a positive attitude toward the worker, an essential first step.

In Jerry's case, the play group could have psychological viability as a behavior modifier only at a point when the worker assumed primary object identity. This became manifest when Jerry's diffuse antisocial aggression changed to sibling rivalry, which was dramatically demonstrated in his arguments with the other group members as to whom the worker had known "first." The intensity of this rivalry was the factor that led to his temporary removal from the group, as the boys could no longer withstand his aggressive domination.

Spending time alone with the worker was the critical event in this boy's treatment, for it placed him in a "preferred child" status. Having experienced this gratification, he was emotionally ready and sought to return to the group within a short time. The group had now assumed the quality of a new family in his psychic economy. The measures of Jerry's improvement were his successful reentry into the group, his new-found ability to adjust to group demands (reality), and the positive acceptance by the other children. Evidences of basic changes in Jerry's character were his improvement in school and the teacher's acceptance of him, which he would have perforce originally suspected and resisted but now felt comfortable with.

Jerry, a seven-year-old youngster who was rapidly moving toward full delinquency, was successfully treated in a therapeutic play group, but it took three years to achieve it. If they are to be helped, the plethora of children in urban ghettos with problems such as Jerry's must be identified early in their school careers and placed as soon as possible in suitable treatment *within schools*.

References

Erikson, E. H. (1940), Studies in the interpretation of play. *Genet. Psychol. Monogr.,* 22: 557-671.

Freud, S. (1907), Creative writers and day-dreaming. *Standard Edition,* 9:141-153. London: Hogarth Press, 1959.

—— (1909), Analysis of a phobia in a five-year-old boy. *Standard Edition,* 10: 3-149. London: Hogarth Press, 1955.

—— (1920), Beyond the pleasure principle. *Standard Edition,* 18: 3-64. London: Hogarth Press, 1955.

—— (1931), Female sexuality. *Standard Edition,* 21: 223-243. London: Hogarth Press, 1961.

—— (1932), New introductory lectures on psychoanalysis. *Standard Edition,* 22: 3-157. London: Hogarth Press, 1964.

Glueck, B. (1928), The significance of parental attitudes for destiny of the individual. *Ment. Hyg.,* 12: 722-741.

Isaacs, S. (1933), *Social Development in Young Children.* London: Routledge.

Klein, M. (1932), *The Psychoanalysis of Children.* New York: Norton.

Piaget, J. & Inhelder, B. (1969), *The Psychology of the Child.* New York: Basic Books.

Schiffer, M. (1969), *The Therapeutic Play Group.* New York: Grune & Stratton.

Slavson, S. R. (1934), *Science in the New Education.* New York: Prentice-Hall.

—— (1937), *Creative Group Education.* New York: Association Press.

—— (1939), *Character Education in a Democracy.* New York: Association Press.

—— (1945), *An Introduction to Group Therapy.* New York: International Universities Press.

—— (1946), *Recreation and the Total Personality.* New York: Association Press.

—— (1947), Contraindications of group therapy for patients with psychopathic personalities. In: *The Practice of Group Therapy.* New York: International Universities Press, pp. 95-106.

—— (1948), *Recreation and the Total Personality.* New York: Association Press.

—— (1952), *Child Psychotherapy*. New York: Columbia University Press.

—— (1954), *Re-educating the Delinquent through Group and Community Participation*. New York: Harper.

—— (1958), *Child-Centered Group Guidance of Parents*. New York: International Universities Press.

—— (1959), A Bio-quantum theory of the ego and its applications to group psychotherapy. *Internat. J. Group Psychother.*, 9: 5-30.

—— (1964), *A Textbook in Analytic Group Psychotherapy*. New York: International Universities Press.

—— (1965), *Reclaiming the Delinquent through Para-Analytic Group Psychotherapy and the Inversion Technique*. New York: Free Press.

—— (1972), Group psychotherapy and the transference neurosis. *Internat. J. Group Psychother.*, 22: 433-443.

Spitz, R.A. (1945), Hospitalism. An Inquiry into the genesis of psychiatric conditions in early childhood. *The Psychoanalytic Study of the Child*, 1: 53-74. New York: International Universities Press.

—— (1946), Hospitalism: A follow-up report. *The Psychoanalytic Study of the Child*, 2: 113-117. New York: International Universities Press.

Spotnitz, H. (1961), *The Couch and the Circle*. New York: Knopf.

Van Ophuijsen, J.H.W. (1945), Primary conduct disturbances, their diagnosis and treatment. In: *Modern Trends in Child Psychiatry*, ed. N.D.C. Lewis and B. Pacella. New York: International Universities Press, pp. 35-42.

Glossary

ACTION COMMUNICATION: Natural in children; actions and behavior stemming from conscious or unconscious feelings and intent (contra verbal communication).

ACTION INTERPRETATION: A therapist's helpful or restraining acts conveying his understanding of the patient's need or intent (contra verbal interpretation).

ACTIVITY GROUP THERAPY (AGT): A method of group treatment of specially selected latency children where the corrective modality is experiential, flowing from significant activities and interactions in a group (contra analytic group psychotherapy).

ACTIVITY-INTERVIEW GROUP PSYCHOTHERAPY (A-IGP): A treatment method derived from AGT with latency children presenting neurotic features or traits, that includes individual and group interviews based on patients' play, manual activities, and verbalizations.

ANTECEDENT EXPERIENCES: Episodes affecting a patient at home or school, or contact with fellow patients immediately preceding a therapy session, that set his moods and determine his behavior.

ANTINODAL BEHAVIOR: Periods of quiescence and group equilibrium, following periods of hyperaction (see NODAL PERIOD); a phenomenon characteristic of all groups.

AUXILIARY (INDIGENOUS) THERAPIST: In analytic therapy (A-IGP and PGT), the spontaneous assessment by a child of an underlying meaning of another's act, emotional display, or verbalized communication.

CHILD-ORIENTED: A therapeutic setting and/or attitude of therapist suited to and emphasizing the needs of children.

CONJOINT THERAPY: Concurrent treatment in a group and in individual therapy, with two different therapists, also called COOPERATIVE THERAPY.

CONDITIONED ENVIRONMENT: An environment designed to activate patients to reveal or express conscious and unconscious urges supplying inner release, confrontation, and interaction with fellow patients (contra CONTROLLED ENVIRONMENT).

CORRECTIVE EXPERIENCES: Experiences which dissolve or counter the pathogenic experiences and relations of a person's past.

CRITICAL EVENT: A manifestation by a patient by an act, verbal communication, or emotion indicating the beginnings of the resolution of his NUCLEAR PROBLEM.

DERIVATIVE INSIGHT: The spontaneous formulation of insight by a patient as a result of self-initiated reflection or a sudden awareness of his problems or meanings of his behavior (contra interpretative insight).

DIVIDED THERAPY: Therapy in which one or both parents are concurrently in treatment with different therapists.

DYNAMIC EQUILIBRIUM: The condition of a group continuing in equilibrium despite basic tensions and interpersonal hostilities held in suppression.

EMOTIONAL CONTAGION: The spread of an emotion, usually regressive, from one group member to others; actuated by FOCI OF INFECTION.

EXCLUSIVE CASE: A patient treated solely in a group (contra CONJOINT THERAPY).

EXCURSIONS: Trips to places of interest in the community, additional to or substi-

463

tuting for regular AGT sessions; designed to extend children's experiential horizons, increase feelings of competency and autonomy, and provide broader fields for reality testing.

Foci of infection: Negative instigators who persistently activate destructive acts or disturbances on a group; *pseudo focus of infection* — one who by his manner and attitudes activates one or more of his fellow group members who *appear* to be foci of infection (contra true focus of infection).

Function relatedness: In an activity room, the arrangement of furnishings, equipment, supplies and utilities according to their use; *see also* visual stimulation.

Group: A complex of three or more persons in which intellectual and/or emotional interaction occurs among individuals in their relations with one another. A married couple, for example, in a dyadic relation, become members of a group when one or more children are born to them because they and the others have to deal not only with each other but also with the network of relations among all of them.

Group balance: The composition of a therapy group, particularly an activity therapy group, where the characterological and behavior patterns will not be reinforced to the detriment of the group, where instigators, neuters, and neutralizers are balanced.

Group ego: The hypothetical resultant of the vectors of the egos of group members which they give up to the group in order to invest power in it, which serves the interests of group synergy, coherence, and integration; also a process essential in socialization of individuals.

Group interview: The verbal interchange in analytic group therapies (A-IGP and PGT) between the therapist and one, a number, or all the group members leadto discharge and/or clarification of emotions.

Heterogeneous grouping: Refers to (a) therapy groups composed of members of both genders, (b) the proper selection for all modalities of group treatment of patients of varying temperaments, behavioral patterns, and diagnoses to insure the psychological balance of the group and its therapeutic effectiveness.

Homogeneous grouping: Refers to groups composed of patients that are alike with respect to one or more criteria, such as age, sex, culture or ethnicity. For therapeutic purposes, groups may be homogeneous in these regards, but best results are obtained in groups where the patients are characterologically heterogeneous. Experience, however, indicates that all persons seeking psychotherapy have problems in two areas: hostility to parents and siblings, and sexual difficulties. The question of homogeneity and heterogeneity is not as important in grouping children as in grouping adults.

Hyper proximity: The effects of a too-small room for a group that gives rise to discomfort, irritability, and conflict, especially among children.

Individual interview: In analytic group therapies (A-IGP and PGT), the personal discussion held by the therapist with an individual child during a group session.

Infectiousness: A spontaneous tendency whereby moods and behavior of stronger members spread to the less autonomous and to the group as a whole.

INSTIGATORS: Patients who stimulate positive or negative activity and/or interactions in a therapy group; positive instigators exert psychologically beneficial effects; negative instigators promote disharmony; *see also* NEUTERS, NEUTRALIZERS.

INTERSTIMULATION: The catalyzing effect of individuals who mutually stimulate one another resulting in intensification of behavior of all involved; the basis of group process.

ISOLATE TABLE: In AGT, a small table in a minimally used area, but not altogether removed from the group's activity; used to accommodate, at the initial stages, insecure and withdrawn children.

"KNOWABLE" NATURE OF A GROUP: In AGT, the constancy of all the elements in the physical setting, the functions of the therapist, and the total therapeutic climate that enhances a sense of security by eliminating the strain or shock of unpredictable changes requiring readjustments.

LIBIDO ACTIVATING: The intrinsic potential of some play materials used in analytic therapies (A-IGP and PGT) to elicit feelings and thoughts on conscious and unconscious levels, especially involving oral, sexual, and elimination fantasies.

LIBIDO BINDING: Craft tools and materials used in AGT that lead to aim-directed handiwork but do not activate children's unconscious; *see also* VISUAL STIMULATION.

LOW RESISTIVITY MATERIALS: Materials employed in AGT that easily yield to manipulation, such as plasticine, crayons, paint, materials for weaving, leather, etc.; *contra* RESISTIVE MATERIALS.

MIMICRY PLAY: An early form of children's play in which pretense and role playing are prominent; a level of communication by the young child in play therapy.

NEUTERS: Patients with weak identities, who succumb to influences of stronger personalities in a therapy group; *see also* INSTIGATORS, NEUTRALIZERS.

NEUTRAL: In AGT, a quality of the therapist's role and demeanor.

NEUTRALIZERS: Patients who have the effect on the group of diminishing or terminating hyperactivity and/or aggression through personal influence rather than force or bullying; *see also* INSTIGATORS, NEUTERS.

NODAL BEHAVIOR: In AGT, transitional periods of hyperactivity and group disequilibrium; a phenomenon in all types of groups and of all ages.

NUCLEAR PROBLEM: The focal element (or elements) constituting the central problem of a patient from which his distress and unadaptive behavior flow, such as oedipal conflict, incestuous wishes, specific frustrations, failure in sibling rivalry, traumata, etc.

PERIOD OF ACCLIMATIZATION: The beginning period in therapy groups required by patients to adapt to the therapeutic climate and the new relationships.

PLAY GROUP THERAPY (PGT): A group treatment method for prelatency children where various types of age-appropriate play materials are supplied and where the therapist may speak with individual children and/or the group, at opportune times, explaining and interpreting their feelings and behavior on their level of understanding; includes also dyadic, triadic, and total group interactions and attitudes.

465

PRIMARY GROUP CODE: A fundamental principle of all therapy groups—the basic code of conduct and procedures which preferably should arise from the therapeutic climate and emerging transactions. The statement by a therapist to an adult or adolescent group, "Here we say anything that comes to our minds," is an example of a primary group code. In children's groups a tacit code arises from the group climate set by the therapist.

REACTIVE BEHAVIOR: The behavior of a child (also of adults) generated by pathogenic conditions or less so by intrapsychic states. All child patients' behavior has elements of reactive behavior. There are, however, children whose problems are predominantly or totally of this order.

RE-EDUCATIONAL PROCESS: A corrective therapeutic characteristic in children's therapy derived from the corrective patterns in the conduct of a group in which the therapist's total demeanor plays a critical role.

REPRESENTATIONAL PLAY: An early form of play, involving imitation and identification, in which a child uses toys to duplicate objects and situations in his environment.

REPRODUCTIONAL PLAY: An advanced form of play through drawing and painting; may disclose valuable content in play therapy.

RESISTIVE MATERIALS: Lumber, metal and similar hard materials used in AGT.

RESONANT EMPATHY: Characteristic of young children in therapy groups—the spontaneous mirroring of a charged emotional manifestation of another child.

ROLE CONSISTENCY: The constancy of the therapist's role, especially in AGT, which yields security in children and begets positive transference.

SITUATIONAL RESTRAINT: Planful room setting in AGT that prevents injurious outcomes of unrestricted children's free acting out, obviates the therapist's having to set limits or exert restraints.

SITUATIONAL THERAPY: A therapeutic modality in which the setting and relationships are the sole or the major instrumentalities, as in AGT; contra ANALYTIC THERAPIES.

SLOUGHING OFF: The automatic disappearance of symptoms as a result of ego strengthening and improved self-image without the ministration of catharsis and insight; a phenomenon occurring in children due to their psychologic plasticity.

SOCIAL FIXITY: The structure of ordinary groups where the status and behavior are defined and limited by the authority of a person or a group.

SOCIAL HUNGER: The instinctive affective need for human association.

SOCIAL MOBILITY: The climate of all therapy groups that allows freedom of action, association, and status achievement according to each member's powers and potentials.

STATIC EQUILIBRIUM: An unvarying condition of fixity in a group without opportunities for changes in activities, moods or relationships; devoid of nodal behavior, unsuitable for therapy.

SUPERNODAL BEHAVIOR: Hyperactivity involving an entire group, exceeding the group's capacity for tolerance or self-regulation; if persistent, indicates faulty grouping.

SUPPORTIVE EGO: A symbiotic or anaclitic relation between two persons in which one is the dependent subject; usually short-lived, dissolved as the latter's ego is strengthened and his personal security established.

THERAPEUTIC CLIMATE: The physical and emotional conditions conducive to the particular therapeutic modality. The chief elements are (1) suitable physical setting; (2) predominantly relaxed climate; (3) unconditional acceptance of the patients by the therapist, akin to love; (4) correct treatment choice and combination of patients.

THERAPY IN THE GROUP: Characteristic of analytically oriented groups in which a patient is temporarily the center of the group's attention and is discussed by the group or the therapist.

THERAPY THROUGH THE GROUP: Where the dynamic interactions of the group as a gestalt serve as the primary therapeutic force as in AGT.

THREAT AREA: Emotional and ego limits, invasion beyond which renders the individual uncomfortable, "hurt," or demeaned. The threat areas of "sensitive" people, for example, are much wider than those of the tough, who are not easily hurt.

TRANSFERENCE IN REVERSE: The transforming of a patient's negative feelings toward parents and other important persons in his life into positive feelings as a result of the positive transference toward the therapist.

UNCONDITIONAL ACCEPTANCE: The therapist's consistent and unqualified acceptance of a patient's *personality.*

VALENCE: The differential degree of intrinsic value to a patient (or group of patients) of experiences and/or materials in the course of treatment.

VISUAL STIMULATION: The effect of display of toys, play materials, tools, and other equipment employed in a specific treatment modality to activate patients' therapeutic involvement; *see* FUNCTION RELATEDNESS.

Index

Abreaction, 38, 307
  in play, 363; *see also* Acting out
Acclimatization, 46, 88
  in activity group therapy, example
    of, 14, 242
  in play group therapy, 391
  see also Glossary
Acting out, in activity-interview group
  psychotherapy, 307
Action communication, 31; *see also*
  Glossary
Action interpretation, 92, 105, 125,
  147, 152; *see also Glossary*
Activity(ies)
  and ego reinforcement, 409
  manual, in activity group therapy, 40
  nature and scope of, 28-31
  play and, 361
  in treatment, activity group therapy,
    40
  types of, 38
Activity group therapy (AGT)
  acclimatization in, period of, 89
  administration of, 257
  application of, 2
  and basic characteristics of thera-
    pists, 136
  beginnings of, 2
  character modification through, 57
  cooperative cases in, 265
  critical event in, 103
  dynamic equilibrium in, 111
  equipment and supplies for, 81-85
  eschews interpretation, 3, 133
  as exclusive method of therapy, 2,
    266
  excursions in, 100
  fire play in, 98
  five basic elements of, 211
  incident, trend and pattern in, 102
  instigators in, 49
  lending money in, 102
  length of session in, 259
  and letters to clients, 257

  motoricity as communication in,
    31
  neutralizers in, 49
  and praise, 155
  outlines of reports of, 269, 271, 273,
    275, 276, 293
  protocols of group sessions in, 9,
    173, 183
  recording sessions in, 260
  and relationship to psychoanalysis, 3
  reeducation as process in, 51
  reporting outlines in administration
    of, 260
  in residential treatment, 223
  scapegoating in, 117
  selection and grouping in, 107
  setting for, 55
  shock effect in, 87
  socialization effects of, 104
  supportive ego in, 116
  termination of, 215
  therapist's strategies in, 144-165
  and therapy through the group, 52
  training for practice of, 126
  and traveling expenses, 259
  see also Transitional groups
Activity-interview group psychotherapy
  (A-IGP)
  basic assumptions of, 297
  catharsis in, 313
  discussions in, 304
  equipment used in, 304, 312
  flexibility of, 349
  and group composition, 312
  group protocol of, 315
  interviews in, 308
  levels of interpretation in, 303, 306
  and resistance, 306
  therapist's role in, 302
  transference in, 141
  see also Glossary
Adaptation in development, 56
Adjustment, 56
Aggression, 398; *see also* Acting out

469

470

471

therapy "in" and "by" the, 347, 377, 381
transitional, 215
see also Catalysis, Dynamics, Inter-stimulation, Therapeutic play group, Glossary
Group balance, 112; see also Glossary
Group ego, 179; see also Glossary
Group interview, 308; see also Glossary
Groupism, 179, 244
Guidance counselor, as group worker in schools, 434

Habit disorder, 33; see also Primary behavior disorder
Heterogeneous grouping, 112; see also Glossary
Homogeneous grouping, 112; see also Glossary
Hospitalism, 356
Hyperproximity, see Glossary

Identification
in groups, levels of, 45
and therapist as model for, 137
Incident in behavior, 102; see also Trend and Pattern
Individual interviews, 308; see also Glossary
Infection
in groups, true and pseudo foci of, 39, 114
Infectiousness, 49, see also Glossary
Inhibition of play, 362
Inhelder, B., 356
Initial responses, in activity group therapy, 39
Insight, 299
nature of, in children, 303; see also Derivative insight
Instigator, 49, 50, 113, 178; see also Neutralizers, Neuters, Glossary
Interaction, group, 383; see also Group, Dynamics, Catalysis, Inter-stimulation
Internalization
in character formation, 56
of experiences by children, 27

Interpretation
levels of, 306, 380, 382, 386, 404
and limited vocabulary of children, 387
and overinterpretation, 370, 387
quality of in activity-interview group psychotherapy, 303
Interstimulation, 49, 370, 373; see also Glossary
Intervention, 397, 403, 406
through situational restraints, 407
in therapeutic play group, 435, 457
see also Permissiveness
Interviews, 308, 309
Isaacs, S., 359
Isolate
table, 70
in activity group therapy, 45
see also Withdrawn child, Glossary

Klein, M., 361, 395
"Knowable" nature of the setting in activity group therapy, 79, 437; see also Glossary

Lability of children's emotions, 27
Language, its use in treatment of children, 125
Latent meanings of behavior, 133
Letters to children, in activity group therapy, 257
Liaison in child guidance agencies, 268
Libido-activating materials, 40, 305
in activity-interview group psychotherapy, 304
in play group therapy, 355, 418
see also Glossary
Libido-binding materials, 40, 88, 304; see also Glossary
Low resistivity materials, 78; see also Glossary

Malleability, children's psychic, 312
Masturbation, 383
Mimicry play, 357; see also Glossary
Model, object
for sublimation, 301
therapist as, 407

Money, expenses for traveling to group
sessions, 259
Motoricity
as form of communication of children, 31
effects of frustration on, 128
and play, 356

Neurosis, 375; see also Diagnosis
Neurotic trait, 33
sloughing off of, 297, 374
Neuter, 113; see also Instigator, Neutralizer, Glossary
Neutral
and children's perception of quality
in therapist, 142
and figures depicting it, 139, 140
quality of the therapist in activity
group therapy, 38
Neutralizer, 49, 113; see also Instigator, Neuter, Glossary
Nodal behavior, 46-49
in activity group therapy, examples
of, 14, 20
figure-depicting, 47
see also antinodal behavior, Supernodal behavior, Dynamic equilibrium, Glossary
Nuclear problem, 103; see also Glossary
Nurture, 127

Oedipal conflict, 375
and defense mechanisms, 380
see also Diagnosis

"Pablum" therapy, 168
Parents of children in treatment, 379
Pattern
in behavior, 102
see also Incident, Trend
Permissiveness, of therapist in activity
group therapy, 95
Perseveration in play enactments, 387
Physiology
children's interest in, 389
and emotional development, 127
Piaget, J., 356

Play
abreaction in, 363
associative process of, 364
and catharsis, 305, 366
and curiosity, 358
as ego "defense," 360
fantasy in, 361
and identity, 358
inhibition of, 362
interpretation of, 366
mimicry, 357
nature of, 355
origins of, 356
and passivity, 360
patterns of, 356
in psychotherapy, 360
reality and unreality in, 360
representational, 357, 362
reproductional, 357
symbolism in, 356, 362
and verbalization, 370
Play group therapy (PGT)
acclimatization, period of, 391
and affectional displays, 395
aggression in, 398
and "borrowing" equipment from
the treatment setting, 410
changing patients in, 378
educational process in, 388
ego reinforcement in, 409
furnishings and equipment for, 416
group balance in, 376
and group chores, 412
interpretations, nature of in, 380
intervention in, 397
and length of session, 412
and physical attacks upon therapist,
403
practice of, 391
and rate of improvement of children,
365
and refreshments, 411
and regression, 405
selection and group composition in,
375
and sibling rivalry situations, 376
and social development in group, 373
and "stealing," 411
and termination of treatment, 413

473

and child development, 427
early detection of problems in, 428
psychotherapy in, 431-432
and socialization, 428
relationships of teachers and clinicians in, 428
as therapeutic milieu, 4, 427, 429
Selection of patients
for activity group therapy, 109-110
for activity-interview group psychotherapy, 278
for play group therapy, 375
for therapeutic play groups in schools, 435
Secondary behavior disorder, 33; see also Primary behavior disorder
Sensory deprivation, 356
Setting, treatment
for activity group therapy, 55; at Children's Village, 231; design for a treatment room, 65; and function relatedness in the, 59; inappropriate, 60; "knowable" nature of, 79; equipment and supplies for, 81-85; physical details of, 63-76
for activity-interview group psychotherapy, 312
for play group therapy, 415
for the therapeutic play group in schools, 436
Shock effect, in activity group therapy, 87
Sibling rivalry, treatment of in groups, 376
Situational restraints
contra direct restraints, 61-62
and regressive play, 407
in the treatment setting, 31, 397
see also Glossary
Situational therapy, see Glossary
Slavson, S.R., 2, 28, 35, 107, 109, 165, 220, 225, 226, 251, 255, 349, 359, 379
Sloughing off, 305
contra working through, 35, 303; see also Glossary
Social fixity, 41, 43, 44; see also Glossary

Glossary
Social hunger, 46, 107; see also Glossary
Socialization through activities, 104
Social mobility, 41, 43
contra social fixity,
figure of, 44
see also Glossary
Spitz, R., 356
Static equilibrium, 112; see also Glossary
"Stealing," 96, 164, 234, 245, 411
Strategies, therapist's, in activity group therapy
answering personal questions, 154
avoiding parents, 150
avoiding preferential treatment of children, 167
blocking fights, 146
borrowing money, 163
dealing with denial, 154
dealing with obduracy, 147
handling discarded clothing, 153
handling cheating, 153
helping with projects, 151
handling "stealing," 164
lateness or absence of therapist, 160
locked-out children, 163
managing overdependent children, 147
meeting challenges from children, 157
playing games with children, 159
preventing injuries, 161
preventing vandalism, 162
removing a group member, 148
seeing without looking, 144
scrambling residence numbers, 154
special requests from children, 165
supporting a weak child, 152
testing frustration tolerance of the group, 150
on the use of "thank you," 156
withdrawal from a child, 152
Sublimation
of aggression, 400
capacities of children, 302
models for, 301

apy, 125, 142
see also Substitution, *Glossary*
Transitional groups, 215
Trend in behavior, 102; *see also* Incident, Pattern
Trips (excursions), 100, 194

Unconditional acceptance in activity group therapy
example of, 199
quality of, 143
by the therapist, 38, 105
see also Glossary

Valence of· play materials, 428; *see also Glossary*
Van Ophuijsen, J.H.W., 33
Visual stimulation
in the treatment setting, 59, 69
see also Function relatedness, *Glossary*
Vocabulary, primitive, children's use of, 406

Withdrawn child, 92